Everyman, I will go with thee, and be thy guide,
In thy most need to go by thy side.

This is No. 940 of Everyman's Library. A list of authors and their works in this series will be found at the end of this volume. The publishers will be pleased to send freely to all applicants a separate, annotated list of the Library.

J. M. DENT & SONS LIMITED
10–13 BEDFORD STREET LONDON W.C.2

E. P. DUTTON & CO. INC.
286–302 FOURTH AVENUE
NEW YORK

EVERYMAN'S LIBRARY
EDITED BY ERNEST RHYS

ESSAYS & BELLES-LETTRES

STORIES, ESSAYS AND POEMS
BY WALTER DE LA MARE · WITH
AN INTRODUCTION BY THE AUTHOR

WALTER DE LA MARE, born 25th April 1873 at Charlton in Kent. Educated at St Paul's Cathedral Choir School. Entered the City office of the Anglo-American Oil Company at the age of sixteen. Wrote in his spare time, contributing poems and tales to the Press and publishing two volumes of verse and one novel, until he adopted literature as his sole profession in 1908.

STORIES, ESSAYS AND POEMS

WALTER DE LA MARE

LONDON: J. M. DENT & SONS LTD.

CONTENTS

STORIES

POEMS

CONTENTS

INTRODUCTION

ONLY two things were needed in the preparation of this volume. First, to choose what was to be included in it; and next, to add a few words of introduction and explanation. But how often what at first sight seems simple enough, proves in the event quite the reverse. Why should there be any difficulty? An author cannot but be familiar with his own books, nor need this familiarity breed positively nothing but contempt. And although distance is exceedingly unlikely to add enchantment to his literary past, Time's optic glasses should at least bring it into better focus.

Indeed, whatever its final defects and deficiencies may be, every writer who takes pains with his work—and authorities so diverse as Rousseau and Cardinal Newman are agreed that pains indeed they are—has been his own persistent and implacable critic. In the very act of writing he ranges to and fro over the field of his consciousness, like an owl quartering a cornfield in the twilight. He is perpetually harking back, rejecting, rearranging, revising, deleting. He is as industrious, and as much in the air, as Keats's spider; he is as silently engrossed as a grub in its cocoon, except that instead of spinning his vital silk, he is, rather, unwinding and rewinding it. He may detest and rebel against these absurd necessities, but he cannot evade them.

There are, it is true, fortunate pens as 'ready' as the Psalmist's; but the readiness came of long practice. And a glance at most manuscripts, few of which are likely to be first drafts, is evidence enough of the general rule. Even a writer's 'final' proofs—bitter scorn though these may be of the practical publisher—will at least hint at his last desperate efforts to find straw to eke out his clay. The Egyptian whom Moses interred in the sands of the desert was mildness itself by comparison.

Not that this ludicrous and inordinate care and trouble need be easily detectable in his work when, however faulty, it is finished. If it have any art, then Art will have so far concealed it. Nor in itself need all this contriving be of any moment even to those who may approve of its outcome. We may be interested and amused to hear that Balzac was the *bête noire* of his printers, and was accustomed to write by candlelight far into the small hours—attired in a dressing-gown, and fortified by quarts of black coffee; that the anatomist of melancholy loved to sit on the green banks of the Isis and listen to the bargees exchanging oaths; that Wordsworth could and did 'compose in the rain, stockstill under an umbrella, in the middle of a field, and on the day after his wedding'; and that Christina Rossetti was never observed by her brother William to compose at all—since she wrote on any scrap of paper that came handy, her bedroom wash-stand for desk.

The spectacle, on the other hand, of Gustave Flaubert, enslaved day after day in the elusive pursuit of the one just word is, for most of us, far less attractive. How many even of his closest readers would have 'noticed' if, here and there, he had put up with the next best? And although we might agree that our delight in a book depends largely upon its technique; nevertheless, so long as a thing has been done to our liking, why trouble about *how* it has been done? Since, too, every artist is something of a medicine-man, he himself is apt to prefer to keep silent concerning that *how* (and preferably even concerning the why, the when, and the where). I know of one punctilious craftsman who blots out his rejected words with India ink. Flora herself, indeed, her lovely day's work done, has never, alas, been known to leave her brushes and paint-box behind her. Henry James, on the other hand, intensely reticent concerning 'the private affairs of his work,' was, in this, exceptional. And fortunately for his fellow-craftsmen, since his introductions are of singular interest.

This inclination to secrecy seems to be a sort of instinct. Young children are capable of it. Many years ago a priceless small boy I knew took it into his head and heart to enter an open competition devoted to the manufacture of a Good Plain Cake. Until his smoking-hot masterpiece was safely out of the oven, he kept locked the kitchen door. The seed, that is, conceals the flower; the artist begins early. And *he* won the second prize.

Not that a writer who is a diligent and drastic critic of his own work is necessarily its best critic. He may have endeavoured to know himself; and therefore his qualities—good, bad, and indifferent. But is he, any more than the rest of us,

capable of knowing his complete self? His style, however
defective it may be, cannot but truly mirror him, and *his*
defects. But is it within his power to see clearly and fully his
own face—as others see it—in that small glass? It would be
amusing to see him trying. However that may be, the selection of prose and verse that follows, taken from an unconscionable number of books, has been made, at my earnest suggestion,
by Miss Mildred Bozman. She, too, has originated its arrangement. And I am most grateful to her for so difficult, unusual,
and generous a kindness. So much for my first little difficulty.
The other involves the reader.

> Who is Sylvia? What is she?
>   That all our swains commend her?
> Holy, fair, and wise is she;
>   The heaven such grace did lend her. . . .

That—for writer and reader—is the accepted situation. But
who, indeed, *is* this Sylvia? Most writers (and I speak from a
prolonged personal experience) must be content with comparatively few of her. Others enjoy a host. Mrs Henry
Wood, to look back a little, decoyed, with her *East Lynn*,
literally millions into her net. Even poets, and poets so dis-
similar as Martin Tupper and Coventry Patmore, let alone
Byron and Scott, romped, as they say, into six figures. Yet
of Ellis, Currer, and Acton Bell's *Poems* only three or four
copies were sold within a year of publication. Still, they too
enjoyed *that* fraction of a 'public'—and one which has since
been considerably augmented!

Every public, too, whatever its dimensions, consists of in-
dividuals—of privates. What, then, is the link between any
writer, great or minor, popular or esoteric, and his privates?
To what degree and in what fashion does the nebulous presence
in his mind of this phantom company influence and affect his
work, either in kind or in quality? I can recall no comprehensive reply to this question. Isaac Disraeli wrote at large
on the amenities and curiosities of literature, on the Literary
and Moral Character and on the calamities, quarrels, and
eccentricities of authors—a fruitful field. But of this missing
link he says, I fancy, very little. Yet the word 'publicity'
was in circulation in his day, and the 'fan mail' must have
preceded even Rowland Hill.

The vanity of authors is proverbial—and frequently peeps

out of a mask of modesty. But even the most modest and by no means the least gifted of them all, Mr Anon., addresses the equally anonymous. When the 'reader' *is* invoked, it has long been customary to apostrophize him, or her, as dear, gentle, diligent, courteous, or 'well-affected.' A winning approach; but how often is it fully justified? Does it imply that the writer himself has never sighed, yawned, jeered, or even imprecated his way through some rival wilderness of print which, so far as he himself was concerned, flatly refused to blossom like the rose? Surely the tepid, the heedless, the indifferent, the bored, the critical, the censorious, the destructive, the utterly unsympathetic and hostile reader must be common enough. Those, too, who nibble but refuse to bite; those who, of malice aforethought, come to curse, and would be dissuaded from doing so neither by indignant ass nor minatory angel. It cannot be that a resolute, active, trenchant, pitiless attitude to books is confined solely to reviewers. Surely not. Even the most well-affected of readers usually resembles bee or butterfly. He recognizes his favourite flower by instinct, and will approve of nothing but his chosen nectar. Indeed, it may be of far greater service to an author to have his book judiciously damned by one discriminating reader, than idly flattered by another. None the less, to keep either of them anxiously in mind when in the act of composing his next might well be for him a shocking calamity.

'The Printer' of Donne's *Songs and Sonets* thus addressed his wished-for 'Understanders': 'For this time I must speake only to you: at another, *Readers* may perchance serve my turne; and I thinke this a way very free from exception, in hope that very few will have a minde to confesse themselves ignorant. . . .' Way free from exception this may or may not be; it is, at any rate, an exceptional way; and it keeps the reader in his place. And Henry Vaughan's, 'To all Ingenious Lovers of Poesie. Gentlemen. . . .': that is another way, and irresistible. Yet another was that of Shakespeare's boon companions and fellow-actors, Heminge and Condell. They addressed the *Plays* as follows: 'To the great Variety of Readers. From the most able, to him that can but spell: There you are number'd. We had rather you were weighd. Especially, when the fate of all Bookes depends upon your capacities: and not of your heads alone, but of your purses. Well! It is now publique, & you will stand for your priviledges wee know: to read, and censure. Do so, but buy it first. . . .' And it proved—head and purse—an excellent investment.

Every reader, of course, can be relied upon to stand for his 'privileges'; and no writer need be much in doubt of the mere 'numbering.' Concerning that, his publisher will soon enlighten him. The 'weighing' of them is another matter. Whether they are few or many, they are likely to agree no more than 'the clocks in London.' On the other hand, the winning over of one reader of genius might richly compensate him for the heathen and heartless neglect of—well, quite a number of others. And although, as Mr Max Beerbohm whispers, 'artists, be they never so agoraphobious, do want praise,' every artist, whatever his gifts and aspirations may be, is limited for blessed company to his own kith and kind.

But what, again, is the positive effect of this nebulous influence on a writer's work? How far will he trim his sails towards what he supposes are the Fortunate Isles; how far follow some will-o'-the-wisp or attempt to circumvent it? Does he fix his gaze on this ignis fatuus, or glance at it only now and then? Does he endeavour to placate and beguile, make things easy, 'charm,' or challenge and defy? If propaganda (and the value of that depends on the source of its inspiration) is his intention; or edification, or mockery, or destruction, or the airing of his opinions; then, of course, a certain target must be clearly in his mind's eye. So, too, if perhaps, greatly daring, he has only children in view. If, again, his paramount desire is solely to cajole, amuse, shock, impress, or delight, then he shoots his arrow, if not wholly at large, at any rate into the air—and in Longfellow he will find his consolation. But tastes change; and what may shock the shockable to-day (of all times) may fail even to titillate them to-morrow.

Needless to say, there are other incentives. A craving for renown, for example—the last infirmity to be ejected from that very rare thing, a noble mind. But no goddess is less patient of pursuit, and it is usually a ghost that overtakes her. Nobody, again, but a fool, said Dr Johnson, would write for anything but money. So much here, however, depends on the precise meaning of the word 'for'; and folly, of course, is the prerogative neither of the illiterate, nor of those who read but never write. It is a thorny question; money is an insidious and covetable bait. It implies a market; and a market implies purchasers—a public. But that Milton would have struck out a comma or altered the spelling of a single word in his *Paradise Lost* solely with a view to converting into guineas the £10 he was to be 'paid' for it, is at least improbable. And when William and Dorothy Wordsworth set out with Coleridge on their walk to Porlock and Culbone, having determined that a poem, as yet unwritten, should provide them with the necessary £5 for their expenses, is it conceivable that 'the clumsiest attempt at German sublimity I ever saw,' as Southey described *The Ancient Mariner*, was made one syllable less clumsy in order to prevent the £5 from shrinking into £4 19s. 6d.? Would Coleridge have written the poem twice as well for double the emolument? Would he have destroyed it for any 'consideration'—unless, perhaps, Wordsworth's? The man of genius starves in his attic. Why?—because he cannot write, or because he refuses to attempt to write, 'for' money? Because, heedless of the baker at the area bell, he listens to the wind in the spectral laurels, or for the voice that says, *Cry !* ? Even the most professional of writers, if he is worth his salt, is also in vital respects something of an amateur. And a labour of love has qualities that not even Croesus could ensure. The labour done, the labourer is worthy of his hire; and that preferably ample.

Fame and payment apart, literature, it is generally agreed, is a means of communication, of communication with others. That is certainly one of its main intentions. But is it the most intrinsic of them, the very fountain of desire and delight, the secret incitement, the spell? True, if even the most incorrigible and imaginative of writers were marooned on one of the desert islands to be mentioned later—together—with another goose (for the sake of its quills), a hogshead of ink, and reams of hand-made paper—he would probably refrain from authorship. He might even decide to roast the goose gipsy-fashion. But would he not continue, if only by mere force of impulse and habit, to 'make up,' to daydream, to commune, and even communicate, as have other castaways, with himself? And this with no one and nothing remotely in the shape of a public in his mind, except the seals and sea-birds and *perhaps* an Ariel—for juvenile lead to his own ageing Prospero.

Indeed, are we not nearly all of us constantly engaged not only in this self-communion, and often at an acute extremity, but also in what might to some frigid and practical Martian

seem the most inane of make-believe, fancy, fantasy, and speculation? All of which, while abjectly rudimentary perhaps, is
still our own. Writing frees this, explores it, gives it shape and
a richer meaning. Unlike Samuel Pepys, sole occupant of *his*
privy island, we may refrain from confiding the merest morsel
of this tongueless colloquy to pen and ink. We may seldom
so much as mention it, let alone discourse upon it, to our
fellow-creatures. Still, it is there. And although in this
inward commerce we too may conceive of unseen witnesses,
they are emphatically *not* in the nature of a 'public.'

Examine any anthology of English verse, or scrutinize any
piece of fiction which is not solely a copy, sketch, or caricature
of life but directly and closely involves its originator, and what
is likely to astonish us is the fact that here, challenging the
interest or contempt of the world at large, are statements of so
private and personal a character that they could hardly have
been deliberately shared with any other fellow-creature. Not
that these secrets are necessarily revealed to all who read them.
Poetry has a language of its own; wearing one's heart upon one's
sleeve is not the same thing as endeavouring to put it into
words; and daws are not the only fowls that fly in heaven. Nor
is any human being a simple unity. Feelings as well as
thoughts may be expressed in symbols; and every 'character'
in a story is not only a 'chink,' a peep-hole in the dark cottage
from which his maker looks out upon the world, but is also in
some degree representative of himself, if a self in disguise.

How can so intimate a revelation be explained and justified?
Keats has his own answer to this question in his Letters. Is
it not because any particular writer so concerned was, as precisely and fully, lucidly and faithfully as his human speech was
capable of, talking to himself?—an inky self, no doubt, but to
the man also 'that he is when he has not got his pen at work.'
Within—far within, perhaps—was *this* self, this 'secret
sharer,' no more consciously aware of any conceivable public
—whether few, or fifty thousand feeding like one—than is a
child chattering to himself in bed on the brink of sleep.
'Who's *talking* up there?' inquires a voice from the foot of
the stairs. 'Me's talking to I, mother, nobody nelse.' That
being so, then it is only to a similar inward self, to a secret
sharer in others, that what the poets have written has any
hope of going home. Why, however pleasant the venture
may otherwise prove, is it notoriously precarious to meet in

the flesh the writer of any book really after one's own heart? Not because either the writer himself, or one's own self, is absent from the meeting. But simply because in the usual give and take of life, even when two human beings in complete sympathy are face to face, the spirit within cannot but remain, except perhaps in glimpses, only dimly perceptible, and, in much that most matters, mute.

If there is any truth in this conclusion, then it applies in relative scope no less to the 'poet Bunn' who, as Mr Arthur Symons tells us, 'was born at the end of the eighteenth century and died in 1860, endeared to posterity by his nickname,' than to Sophocles and Shelley. As soon as an Idea—however unworthy of the initial capital it may be—as soon as the Imagination really gets into a man's mind, then most things else fly out of the window. The 'poet Bunn,' then, in hospitable memory, I trust that the gentle, judicious, courteous, and well-affected Reader will be merciful, if not indulgent, to what follows, having first looked in the 'Almanack' to 'find out moonshine.'

W. DE LA M.

1938.

EDITORIAL NOTE

Everyman's Library is a practical attempt to make great writings available to Everyman, so that there are sound reasons, both critical and realistic, for a restricted presentation of the works of living authors. Walter de la Mare's very individual imaginative genius is expressed in poetry, in the novel, in the short story, and in such hardly classifiable prose works as *Desert Islands* and *Early One Morning*, and therefore it has been thought better to represent him in the series not by any single volume of prose or verse, but by a miscellany. All his work bears very clearly the impress of his genius and personality as an artist, for he is a highly individual writer and if his writings were to appear unsigned there would be few 'doubtful attributions' either to-day or in time to come. Yet each work, the recurrence of certain characteristic themes, types, and images notwithstanding, has strong individuality of its own, and seems to resist representation in the miscellany by 'something else of that kind.' The work of selection has been made difficult by wealth and variety of material.

In compiling the present volume it has been decided to make no excerpts from the novels: a time will probably come when one or more of these will stand complete in *Everyman's Library*. Work directly for children (though in a writer of this calibre there is no very definite frontier)—nursery poems, sheer nonsense verse, such delightful and delighted child-seen pictures as *Soo-eep*, such child-speculations as *Miss T.*, and all the prose tales with the exception of *Sambo and the Snow Mountains*—has also been omitted. There remains a selection from the short stories, from the very unusual critical prose (which is usually rather creative and meditative than strictly critical) and from the main body of verse.

Walter de la Mare is first of all a poet. His prose works, even when furthest removed from 'poetic prose' (and his style varies considerably) have always something of poetry—its intensiveness, its recondite, highly-organized central nervous system. Even his two long novels, *The Return* and *The*

Memoirs of a Midget, with their passages of realistic detail and
expansiveness, shape to the memory as 'poems,' for the idea
which gives them being, the fire which forges them, are of the
imaginative order which we call poetic.   When we think of
Walter de la Mare's work we think of the words 'beautiful,'
'sinister,' 'dreamlike,' but behind these of the master-word
'Imagination,' and of a writer who has explored and extended
its realm for us in a measure which, so far as it is ever calcu-
lable, cannot be calculated within this generation.   We do
not think of 'Realism,' although after a moment's reflection
we remember that his works both in verse and prose *contain* a
good deal of this in a curious, an attentive, an accurate, a
piercing observation of the colour, the texture, the movements
which the senses report of Nature and of human mind.   This
observation finds expression at times in verse almost—never
quite—for its own sake; and always it gives actuality even to
those poems which soar highest above, or burrow furthest
below, the actual.   In the stories and novels one aspect of this
realism is a strong though usually uninsistent grasp of the
domestic, the economic, the hum-drum, the suburban frame-
work in which so many lives are lived that lends a compelling
intensity to those adventures of the soul 'trespassing so close
upon the confines of existence' which are Walter de la Mare's
chief concern, forcing the reader to ask 'Is it I?'   In psycho-
logical subtlety de la Mare has a kinship with Henry James
which appears, for instance, in the story of *The Almond Tree*:
but Henry James would hardly have handled the subject
treated in that masterpiece of story-telling, *Missing*.

Walter de la Mare's imagination has a wide gamut, from
sheer (though very seldom *mere*) fancy and whimsy, through
beautiful and terrible dreaming up to that visionary power by
which man lays hold of reality in the sensual and supersensual
worlds.   But to what realities, to what worlds beyond the
sensual, does he guide us?   He has not much to say of the
world of schematized perfection, of the full circle, in which
the philosophic intellect finds appeasement, although he is far
from unaware of it, and draws near to it in that strange story,
The Vats.   He leads us up to the confines of time and space,
and very near to 'death's door' (a phrase which may almost
be said to gain a new significance from his work!), but though
many of his finest poems approach they never quite enter the
heaven of justice and of love in which man's heart and soul

seek triumph and sanctuary and into which Vaughan and Blake enter with the familiarity of sons. To the ultimate questions his imagination offers variable answers, or answers 'in a tongue no man can understand.' Sometimes we gaze with him into the unutterable void—

> where human pathways end
> And the dark enemy spreads his maddening net

—the nemesis of the adventurous imagination. But far more often he comes to us almost as a revenant, or in the guise of one of those real, lovable, yet frightening little boys of his tales, trailing so strangely both airs from heaven and blasts from hell, to show us convincing, almost *reminiscent* glimpses of Hereafters and Beyonds, as various, as intractable, as lovely and as dangerous as the mysterious Here and Now of everyday consciousness.

The stories in this volume have been chosen as far as possible to represent certain types of Walter de la Mare's tales, the poems have been grouped to suggest certain aspects of his verse. The representation, the suggestion, are necessarily incomplete: each work is more than worth having for its own sake. The appreciation of Walter de la Mare's spirit given here is also incomplete, the technical aspect of his work has not been touched on. Both aspects are admirably studied by Mr Forrest Reid in *Walter de la Mare : A Critical Study* (Faber and Faber, 1929).

M. M. BOZMAN.

The following is a list of Walter de la Mare's chief works:

Henry Brocken, 1904; *Songs of Childhood*, 1907; *The Return*, 1910; *The Three Mulla Mulgars*, 1911; *The Listeners and other poems*; *Peacock Pie*, 1913; *Motley and other poems*; *Rupert Brook and the Intellectual Imagination*, 1919; *Collected Poems 1901–1918*, 1920; *The Veil and other Poems*; *Crossings, A Fairy Play*; *Memoirs of a Midget*, 1921; *Down-adown-Derry*, 1922; *Come Hither*; *The Riddle and other stories*, 1923; *Ding Dong Bell*; *Lewis Caroll*, 1924; *The Connoisseur and other stories*, 1926; *Stuff and Nonsense*, 1927; *Desert Islands and Robinson Crusoe; On the Edge: Short Stories*, 1930; *The Fleeting and other poems; Stories from the Bible; The Lord Fish and other tales*, 1933; *Early One Morning; Collected Poems 1919–1934*, 1935; *The Wind Blows Over*, 1936; *This Year, Next Year*, 1937.

ACKNOWLEDGMENTS

PERMISSION has kindly been granted by Messrs Constable for the inclusion of the majority of the poems; Messrs Faber & Faber for the extract from *Desert Islands,* and several of the stories; *The Times* for 'A Book of Words,' which appeared in the Literary Supplement of 1st June 1922; and the Golden Cockerel Press for Mr de la Mare's Introduction to *The Cricket on the Hearth,* which was specially written for the Limited Editions Club's edition.

STORIES

THE ALMOND TREE

MY old friend, 'the Count' as we used to call him, made very strange acquaintances at times. Let but a man have plausibility, a point of view, a crotchet, an enthusiasm, he would find in him an eager and exhilarating listener. And though he was often deceived and disappointed in his finds, the Count had a heart proof against lasting disillusionment. I confess, however, that these planetary cronies of his were rather disconcerting at times. And I own that meeting him one afternoon in the busy High Street, with a companion on his arm even more than usually voluble and odd—I own I crossed the road to avoid meeting the pair.

But the Count's eyes had been too sharp for me. He twitted me unmercifully with my snobbishness. 'I am afraid we must have appeared to avoid you to-day,' he said; and received my protestations with contemptuous indifference.

But the next afternoon we took a walk together over the heath; and perhaps the sunshine, something in the first freshness of the May weather, reminded him of bygone days.

'You remember that rather out-of-the-world friend of mine yesterday that so shocked your spruce proprieties, Richard? Well, I'll tell you a story.'

As closely as I can recall this story of the Count's childhood I have here related it. I wish, though, I had my old friend's gift for such things; then, perhaps, his story might retain something of the charm in the reading which he gave to it in the telling. Perhaps that charm lies wholly in the memory of his voice, his companionship, his friendship. To revive these, what task would be a burden? . . .

'The house of my first remembrance, the house that to my last hour on earth will seem home to me, stood in a small green hollow on the verge of a wide heath. Its five upper windows faced far eastwards towards the weather-cocked tower of a village which rambled down the steep inclination of a hill. And, walking in its green old garden—ah, Richard, the crocuses, the wallflowers, the violets!—you could see in the evening the

3

standing fields of corn, and the dark furrows where the evening star was stationed; and a little to the south, upon a crest, a rambling wood of fir-trees and bracken.

'The house, the garden, the deep quiet orchard, all had been a wedding gift to my mother from a great-aunt, a very old lady in a kind of turban, whose shrewd eyes used to watch me out of her picture sitting in my high chair at meal-times—with not a little keenness; sometimes, I fancied, with a faint derision. Here passed by, to the singing of the lark, and the lamentation of autumn wind and rain, the first long nine of all these heaped-up inextricable years. Even now, my heart leaps up with longing to see again with those untutored eyes the lofty clouds of evening; to hear again as then I heard it the two small notes of the yellow-hammer piping from his green spray. I remember every room of the old house, the steep stairs, the cool apple-scented pantry; I remember the cobbles by the scullery, the well, my old dead raven, the bleak and whistling elms; but best of all I remember the unmeasured splendour of the heath, with its gorse, and its deep canopy of sunny air, the haven of every wild bird of the morning.

'Martha Rodd was a mere prim snippet of a maid then, pale and grave, with large contemplative, Puritan eyes. Mrs Ryder, in her stiff blue martial print and twisted gold brooch, was cook. And besides these, there was only old Thomas the gardener (as out-of-doors, and as distantly seen a creature as a dryad); my mother; and that busy-minded little boy, agog in wits and stomach and spirit—myself. For my father seemed but a familiar guest in the house, a guest ever eagerly desired and welcome, but none too eager to remain. He was a dark man with grey eyes and a long chin; a face unusually impassive, unusually mobile. Just as his capricious mood suggested, our little household was dejected or wildly gay. I never shall forget the spirit of delight he could conjure up at a whim, when my mother would go singing up and down stairs, and in her tiny parlour; and Martha in perfect content would prattle endlessly on to the cook, basting the twirling sirloin, while I watched in the firelight. And the long summer evenings too, when my father would find a secret, a magic, a mystery in everything; and we would sit together in the orchard while he told me tales, with the small green apples overhead, and beyond contorted branches, the first golden twilight of the moon.

'It's an old picture now, Richard, but true to the time.

'My father's will, his word, his caprice, his frown, these were the tables of the law in that small household. To my mother he was the very meaning of her life. Only that little boy was in some wise independent, busy, inquisitive, docile, sedate; though urged to a bitterness of secret rebellion at times. In his childhood he experienced such hours of distress as the years do not in mercy bring again to a heart that may analyse as well as remember. Yet there also sank to rest the fountain of life's happiness. In among the gorse bushes were the green mansions of the fairies; along the furrows before his adventurous eyes stumbled crooked gnomes, hopped bewitched robins. Ariel trebled in the sunbeams and glanced from the dewdrops; and he heard the echo of distant and magic waters in the falling of the rain.

'But my father was never long at peace in the house. Nothing satisfied him; he must needs be at an extreme. And if he was compelled to conceal his discontent, there was something so bitter and imperious in his silence, so scornful a sarcasm in his speech, that we could scarcely bear it. And the knowledge of the influence he had over us served only at such times to sharpen his contempt.

'I remember one summer's evening we had been gathering strawberries. I carried a little wicker basket, and went rummaging under the aromatic leaves, calling ever and again my mother to see the "tremenjous" berry I had found. Martha was busy beside me, vexed that her two hands could not serve her master quick enough. And in a wild race with my mother my father helped us pick. At every ripest one he took her in his arms to force it between her lips; and of all those pecked by the birds he made a rhymed offering to Pan. And when the sun had descended behind the hill, and the clamour of the rooks had begun to wane in the elm-tops, he took my mother on his arm, and we trooped all together up the long straggling path, and across the grass, carrying our spoil of fruit into the cool dusky corridor. As we passed into the gloaming I saw my mother stoop impulsively and kiss his arm. He brushed off her hand impatiently, and went into his study. I heard the door shut. A moment afterwards he called for candles. And, looking on those two other faces in the twilight, I knew with the intuition of childhood that he was suddenly sick to death of us all; and I knew that my mother shared my intuition. She sat down, and I beside her, in her little parlour, and took up her sewing. But her face had lost again all its girlishness as she bent her head over the white linen.

'I think she was happier when my father was away; for then, free from anxiety to be for ever pleasing his variable moods, she could entertain herself with hopes and preparations for his return. There was a little green summer-house, or arbour, in the garden, where she would sit alone, while the swallows coursed in the evening air. Sometimes, too, she would take me for a long walk, listening distantly to my chatter, only, I think, that she might entertain the pleasure of supposing that my father might have returned home unforeseen, and be even now waiting to greet us. But these fancies would forsake her. She would speak harshly and coldly to me, and scold Martha for her owlishness, and find nothing but vanity and mockery in all that but a little while since had been her daydream.

'I think she rarely knew where my father stayed in his long absences from home. He would remain with us for a week, and neglect us for a month. She was too proud, and when he was himself, too happy and hopeful to question him, and he seemed to delight in keeping his affairs secret from her. Indeed, he sometimes appeared to pretend a mystery where none was, and to endeavour in all things to make his character and conduct appear quixotic and inexplicable.

'So time went on. Yet, it seemed, as each month passed by, the house was not so merry and happy as before; something was fading and vanishing that would not return; estrangement had pierced a little deeper. I think care at last put out of my mother's mind even the semblance of her former gaiety. She sealed up her heart lest love should break forth anew into the bleakness.

'On Guy Fawkes' Day Martha told me at bedtime that a new household had moved into the village on the other side of the heath. After that my father stayed away from us but seldom.

'At first my mother showed her pleasure in a thousand ways, with dainties of her own fancy and cooking, with ribbons in her dark hair, with new songs (though she had but a small thin voice). She read to please him; and tired my legs out in useless errands in his service. And a word of praise sufficed her for many hours of difficulty. But by and by, when evening after evening was spent by my father away from home, she began to be uneasy and depressed and though she made no complaint, her anxious face, the incessant interrogation of her eyes, vexed and irritated him beyond measure.

' "Where does my father go after dinner?" I asked Martha one night, when my mother was in my bedroom, folding my clothes.

' "How dare you ask such a question?" said my mother, "and how dare you talk to the child about your master's comings and goings?"

' "But where does he?" I repeated to Martha, when my mother was gone out of the room.

' "Ssh now, Master Nicholas," she answered, "didn't you hear what your mamma said? She's vexed, poor lady, at master's never spending a whole day at home, but nothing but them cards, cards, cards, every night at Mr Grey's. Why, often it's twelve and one in the morning when I've heard his foot on the gravel beneath the window. But there, I'll be bound, she doesn't *mean* to speak unkindly. It's a terrible scourge is jealousy, Master Nicholas; and not generous or manly to give it cause. Mrs Ryder was kept a widow all along of jealousy, and but a week before her wedding with her second."

' "But why is mother jealous of my father playing cards?"

'Martha slipped my night-gown over my head. "Ssh, Master Nicholas, little boys mustn't ask so many questions. And I hope when you are grown up to be a man, my dear, you will be a comfort to your mother. She needs it, poor soul, and sakes alive, just now of all times!" I looked inquisitively into Martha's face; but she screened my eyes with her hand; and instead of further questions, I said my prayers to her.

'A few days after this I was sitting with my mother in her parlour, holding her grey worsted for her to wind, when my father entered the room and bade me put on my hat and muffler. "He is going to pay a call with me," he explained curtly. As I went out of the room, I heard my mother's question: "To your friends at the Grange, I suppose?"

' "You may suppose whatever you please," he answered. I heard my mother rise to leave the room, but he called her back and the door was shut. . . .

'The room in which the card-players sat was very low-ceiled. A piano stood near the window, a rosewood table with a fine dark crimson work-basket upon it by the fireside, and some little distance away, a green card-table with candles burning. Mr Grey was a slim, elegant man, with a high, narrow forehead and long fingers. Major Aubrey was a short, red-faced, rather taciturn man. There was also a younger man with fair hair. They seemed to be on the best of terms together; and I helped to pack the cards and to pile the silver coins, sipping a glass of sherry with Mr Grey. My father said little, paying me no attention, but playing gravely with a very slight frown.

'After some little while the door opened, and a lady appeared. This was Mr Grey's sister, Jane, I learned. She seated herself at her work-table, and drew me to her side.

' "Well, so this is Nicholas!" she said. "Or is it Nick?"

' "Nicholas," I said.

' "Of course," she said, smiling, "and I like that too, much the best. How very kind of you to come to see me! It was to keep *me* company, you know, because I am very stupid at games, but I love talking. Do you?"

'I looked into her eyes, and knew we were friends. She smiled again, with open lips, and touched my mouth with her thimble. "Now, let me see, business first, and—me afterwards. You see I have three different kinds of cake, because, I thought, I cannot in the least tell which kind he'll like best. Could I now? Come, you shall choose."

'She rose and opened the long door of a narrow cupboard, looking towards the card-players as she stooped. I remember the cakes to this day; little oval shortbreads stamped with a beehive, custards, and mince-pies; and a great glass jar of goodies which I carried in both arms round the little square table. I took a mince-pie, and sat down on a footstool near by Miss Grey, and she talked to me while she worked with slender hands at her lace embroidery. I told her how old I was; about my great-aunt and her three cats. I told her my dreams, and that I was very fond of Yorkshire pudding, "from under the meat, you know." And I told her I thought my father the handsomest man I had ever seen.

' "What, handsomer than Mr Spencer?" she said laughing, looking along her needle.

'I answered that I did not very much like clergymen.

' "And why?" she said gravely.

' "Because they do not talk like real," I said.

'She laughed very gaily. "Do men ever?" she said.

'And her voice was so quiet and so musical, her neck so graceful, I thought her a very beautiful lady, admiring especially her dark eyes when she smiled brightly and yet half sadly at me; I promised, moreover, that if she would meet me on the heath, I would show her the rabbit warren and the "Miller's Pool."

'"Well, Jane, and what do you think of my son?" said my father when we were about to leave.

'She bent over me and squeezed a lucky fourpenny-piece into my hand. "I love fourpence, pretty little fourpence, I love fourpence better than my life," she whispered into my ear. "But that's a secret," she added, glancing up over her shoulder. She kissed lightly the top of my head. I was looking at my father while she was caressing me, and I fancied a faint sneer passed over his face. But when we had come out of the village on to the heath, in the bare keen night, as we walked along the path together between the gorse-bushes, now on turf, and now on stony ground, never before had he seemed so wonderful a companion. He told me little stories; he began a hundred, and finished none; yet with the stars above us, they seemed a string of beads all of bright colours. We stood still in the vast darkness, while he whistled that strangest of all old songs—*The Song the Sirens sang*. He pilfered my wits and talked like my double. But when—how much too quickly, I thought with sinking heart—we were come to the house-gates, he suddenly fell silent, turned an instant, and stared far away over the windy heath.

'"How weary, stale, flat——" he began, and broke off between uneasy laughter and a sigh. "Listen to me, Nicholas," he said, lifting my face to the starlight, "you must grow up a man—a Man, you understand; no vapourings, no posings, no caprices; and, above all, no sham. No sham. It's your one and only chance in this unfaltering Scheme." He scanned my face long and closely. "You have your mother's eyes," he said musingly. "And that," he added under his breath, *"that's* no joke." He pushed open the squealing gate, and we went in.

'My mother was sitting in a low chair before a dying and cheerless fire.

'"Well, Nick," she said very suavely, "and how have you enjoyed your evening?"

'I stared at her without answer. "Did you play cards with the gentlemen; or did you turn over the music?"

' "I talked to Miss Grey," I said.

' "Really," said my mother, raising her eyebrows, "and who then is Miss Grey?" My father was smiling at us with sparkling eyes.

' "Mr Grey's sister," I answered in a low voice.

' "Not his wife, then?" said my mother, glancing furtively at the fire. I looked towards my father in doubt, but could lift my eyes no higher than his knees.

' "You little fool!" he said to my mother with a laugh, "what a sharpshooter! Never mind, Sir Nick; there, run off to bed, my man."

'My mother caught me roughly by the sleeve as I was passing her chair. "Aren't you going to kiss me good night, then," she said furiously, her narrow underlip quivering, "you too!" I kissed her cheek. "That's right, my dear," she said scornfully, "that's how little fishes kiss." She rose and drew back her skirts. "I refuse to stay in the room," she said haughtily, and with a sob she hurried out.

'My father continued to smile, but only a smile it seemed gravity had forgotten to smooth away. He stood very still, so still that I grew afraid he must certainly hear me thinking. Then with a kind of sigh he sat down at my mother's writing-table, and scribbled a few words with his pencil on a slip of paper.

' "There, Nicholas, just tap at your mother's door with that. Good night, old fellow"; he took my hand and smiled down into my eyes with a kind of generous dark appeal that called me straight to his side. I hastened conceitedly upstairs, and delivered my message. My mother was crying when she opened the door.

' "Well?" she said in a low, trembling voice.

'But presently afterwards, while I was still lingering in the dark corridor, I heard her run down quickly, and in a while my father and mother came upstairs together, arm in arm, and by her light talk and laughter you might suppose she had no knowledge of care or trouble at all.

'Never afterwards did I see so much gaiety and youthfulness in my mother's face as when she sat next morning with us at breakfast. The honeycomb, the small bronze chrysanthemums, her yellow gown seemed dainty as a miniature. With every word her eyes would glance covertly at my father; her smile, as it were, hesitating between her lashes. She was so light and girlish and so versatile I should scarcely have recognized the weary and sallow face of the night before. My father seemed to find as much pleasure, or relief, in her good spirits as I did; and to delight in exercising his ingenuity to quicken her humour.

'It was but a transient morning of sunshine, however, and as the brief and sombre day waned, its gloom pervaded the house. In the evening my father left us to our solitude as usual. And that night was very misty over the heath, with a small, warm rain falling.

'So it happened that I began to be left more and more to my own devices, and grew so inured at last to my own narrow company and small thoughts and cares, that I began to look on my mother's unhappiness almost with indifference, and learned to criticize almost before I had learned to pity. And so I do not think I enjoyed Christmas very much the less, although my father was away from home and all our little festivities were dispirited. I had plenty of good things to eat, and presents, and a picture-book from Martha. I had a new rocking-horse— how changeless and impassive its mottled battered face looks out at me across the years! It was brisk, clear weather, and on St Stephen's Day I went to see if there was any ice yet on the Miller's Pool.

'I was stooping down at the extreme edge of the pool, snapping the brittle splinters of the ice with my finger, when I heard a voice calling me in the still air. It was Jane Grey, walking on the heath with my father, who had called me, having seen me from a distance stooping beside the water.

' "So you see I have kept my promise," she said, taking my hand.

' "But you promised to come by yourself," I said.

' "Well, so I will then," she answered, nodding her head. "Good-bye," she added, turning to my father. "It 's three 's none, you see. Nicholas shall take me home to tea, and you can call for him in the evening, if you will; that is, if you are coming."

' "Are you asking me to come?" he said moodily. "Do you care whether I come or not?"

'She lifted her face and spoke gravely. "You are my friend," she said, "of course I care whether you are with me or not." He scrutinized her through half-closed lids. His face was haggard, gloomy with *ennui*. "How you harp on the word, you punctilious Jane. Do you suppose I am still in my teens? Twenty years ago, now—— It amuses me to hear you women talk. It 's little you ever really feel."

' "I don't think I am quite without feeling," she replied, "you are a little difficult, you know."

' "Difficult," he echoed in derision. He checked himself and shrugged his shoulders. "You see, Jane, it 's all on the surface; I boast of my indifference. It 's the one rag of philosophy age denies no one. It is so easy to be heroic—debonair, iron-grey, fluent, dramatic—you know it 's captivation, perhaps? But after all, life's comedy, when one stops smiling, is only the tepidest farce. Or the gilt wears off and the pinchbeck tragedy shows through. And so, as I say, we talk on, being past feeling. One by one our hopes come home to roost, our delusions find themselves out, and the mystery proves to be nothing but sleight-of-hand. It 's age, my dear Jane—age; it turns one to stone. With you young people life 's a dream; ask Nicholas here!" He shrugged his shoulders, adding under his breath: "But one wakes on a devilish hard pallet."

' "Of course," said Jane slowly, "you are only talking cleverly, and then it does not matter whether it 's true or not, I suppose. I can't say. I don't think you mean it, and so it comes to nothing. I can't and won't believe you feel so little—I can't." She continued to smile, yet, I fancied, with the brightness of tears in her eyes. "It 's all mockery and make-believe; we are not the miserable slaves of time you try to fancy. There must be some way to win through." She turned away, then added slowly: "You ask me to be fearless, sincere, to speak my heart; I wonder, do you?"

'My father did not look at her, appeared not to have seen the hand she had half held out to him, and as swiftly withdrawn. "The truth is, Jane," he said slowly, "I am past sincerity now. And as for *heart* it is a quite discredited organ at forty. Life, thought, selfishness, egotism, call it what you will; they have all done their worst with me; and I really haven't the sentiment to pretend that they haven't. And when bright youth and sentiment are gone; why, go too, dear lady! Existence proves nothing but brazen inanity afterwards. But there 's always that turning left to the dullest and dustiest road—oblivion." He remained silent a moment. Silence deep and strange lay all around us. The air was still, the wintry sky unutterably calm.

And again that low dispassionate voice continued: "It's only when right seems too easy a thing, too trivial, and not worth the doing; and wrong a foolish thing—too dull . . . There, take care of her, Nicholas; take care of her, 'snips and snails,' you know. *Au revoir,* 'pon my word, I almost wish it was good-bye."

'Jane Grey regarded him attentively. "So then do I," she replied in a low voice, "for I shall never understand you; perhaps I should hate to understand you."

'My father turned with an affected laugh, and left us.

'Miss Grey and I walked slowly along beside the frosty bulrushes until we came to the wood. The bracken and heather were faded. The earth was dark and rich with autumnal rains. Fir-cones lay on the moss beneath the dark green branches. It was all now utterly silent in the wintry afternoon. Far away rose tardily, and alighted, the hoarse rooks upon the ploughed earth; high in the pale sky passed a few on ragged wing.

' "What does my father mean by wishing it was good-bye?" I said.

'But my companion did not answer me in words. She clasped my hand; she seemed very slim and gracious walking by my side on the hardened ground. My mother was small now and awkward beside her in my imagination. I questioned her about the ice, about the red sky, and if there was any mistletoe in the woods. Sometimes she in turn asked me questions too, and when I answered them we would look at each other and smile, and it seemed it was with her as it was with me—of the pure gladness I found in her company. In the middle of our walk to the Thorns she bent down in the cold twilight, and putting her hands on my shoulders, "My dear, dear Nicholas," she said, "you must be a good son to your mother—brave and kind; will you?"

' "He hardly ever speaks to mother now," I answered instinctively.

'She pressed her lips to my cheek, and her cheek was cold against mine, and she clasped her arms about me. "Kiss me," she said. "We must do our best, mustn't we?" she pleaded, still holding me. I looked mournfully into the gathering darkness. "That's easy when you're grown up," I said. She laughed and kissed me again, and then we took hands and ran till we were out of breath, towards the distant lights of the Grange. . . .

'I had been some time in bed, lying awake in the warmth,

when my mother came softly through the darkness into my room. She sat down at the bedside, breathing hurriedly. "Where have you been all the evening?" she said.

' "Miss Grey asked me to stay to tea," I answered.

' "Did I give you permission to go to tea with Miss Grey?"

'I made no answer.

' "If you go to that house again, I shall beat you. You hear me, Nicholas? Alone, or with your father, if you go there again, without my permission, I shall beat you. You have not been whipped for a long time, have you?" I could not see her face, but her head was bent towards me in the dark, as she sat— almost crouched—on my bedside.

'I made no answer. But when my mother had gone, without kissing me, I cried noiselessly on into my pillow. Something had suddenly flown out of memory, never to sing again. Life had become a little colder and stranger. I had always been my own chief company; now another sentimental barrier had arisen between the world and me, past its heedlessness, past my understanding to break down.

'Hardly a week passed now without some bitter quarrel. I seemed ever to be stealing out of sound of angry voices; ever fearful of being made the butt of my father's serene taunts, of my mother's passions and desperate remorse. He disdained to defend himself against her, never reasoned with her; he merely shrugged his shoulders, denied her charges, ignored her anger; coldly endeavouring only to show his indifference, to conceal by every means in his power his own inward weariness and vexation. I saw this, of course, only vaguely, yet with all a child's certainty of insight, though I rarely knew the cause of my misery; and I continued to love them both in my selfish fashion, not a whit the less.

'At last, on St Valentine's Day, things came to a worse pass than before. It had always been my father's custom to hang my mother a valentine on the handle of her little parlour door, a string of pearls, a fan, a book of poetry, whatever it might be. She came down early this morning, and sat in the window-seat, looking out at the falling snow. She said nothing at breakfast, only feigned to eat, lifting her eyes at intervals to glance at my father with a strange intensity, as if of hatred, tapping her foot on the floor. He took no notice of her, sat quiet and moody with his own thoughts. I think he had not really forgotten the day, for I found long afterwards in his old bureau a bracelet purchased but a week before with her name written on a scrap of paper, inside the case. Yet it seemed to be the absence of this little gift that had driven my mother beyond reason.

'Towards evening, tired of the house, tired of being alone, I went out and played awhile listlessly in the snow. At nightfall I went in; and in the dark heard angry voices. My father came out of the dining-room and looked at me in silence, standing in the gloom of the wintry dusk. My mother followed him. I can see her now, leaning in the doorway, white with rage, her eyes ringed and darkened with continuous trouble, her hand trembling.

'"It shall learn to hate you," she cried in a low, dull voice. "I will teach it every moment to hate and despise you as I—— Oh, *I* hate and despise you!"

'My father looked at her calmly and profoundly before replying. He took up a cloth hat and brushed it with his hand. "Very well, then, you have chosen," he said coldly. "It has always lain with you. You have exaggerated, you have raved, and now you have said what can never be recalled or forgotten. Here's Nicholas. Pray do not imagine, however, that I am defending myself. I have nothing to defend. I think of no one but myself—no one. Endeavour to understand me, no one. Perhaps, indeed, you yourself—no more than—— But words again—the dull old round!" He made a peculiar gesture with his hand. "Well, life is . . . ach! I have done. So be it." He stood looking out of the door. "You see, it's snowing," he said, as if to himself.

'All the long night before and all day long, snow had been falling continuously. The air was wintry and cold. I could discern nothing beyond the porch but a gloomy accumulation of cloud in the twilight air, now darkened with the labyrinthine motion of the snow. My father glanced back for an instant into the house, and, as I fancy, regarded me with a kind of strange, close earnestness. But he went out and his footsteps were instantly silenced.

'My mother peered at me in terrible perplexity, her eyes wide with terror and remorse. "What? What?" she said. I stared at her stupidly. Three snowflakes swiftly and airily floated together into the dim hall from the gloom without. She clasped her hand over her mouth. Overburdened her fingers seemed to be, so slender were they, with her many rings.

' "Nicholas, Nicholas, tell me; what was I saying? What was I saying?" She stumbled hastily to the door. "Arthur, Arthur," she cried from the porch, "it 's St Valentine's Day, that was all I meant; come back, come back!" But perhaps my father was already out of hearing; I do not think he made any reply.

'My mother came in doubtfully, resting her hand on the wall. And she walked very slowly and laboriously upstairs. While I was standing at the foot of the staircase, looking out across the hall into the evening, Martha climbed primly up from the kitchen with her lighted taper, shut-to the door, and lit the hall lamp. Already the good smell of the feast cooking floated up from the kitchen, and gladdened my spirits. "Will he come back?" Martha said, looking very scared in the light of her taper. "It 's such a fall of snow, already it 's a hand's breadth on the window-sill. Oh, Master Nicholas, it 's a hard world for us women." She followed my mother upstairs, carrying light to all the gloomy upper rooms.

'I sat down in the window-seat of the dining-room, and read in my picture-book as well as I could by the flame-light. By and by, Martha returned to lay the table.

'As far back as brief memory carried me, it had been our custom to make a Valentine's feast on the Saint's day. This was my father's mother's birthday also. When she was alive I well remember her visiting us with her companion, Miss Schreiner, who talked in such good-humoured English to me. This same anniversary had last year brought about a tender reconciliation between my father and mother, after a quarrel that meant how little then. And I remember on this day to have seen the first fast-sealed buds upon the almond tree. We would have a great spangled cake in the middle of the table, with marzipan and comfits, just as at Christmastide. And when Mrs Merry lived in the village her little fair daughters used to come in a big carriage to spend the evening with us and to share my Valentine's feast.

'But all this was changed now. My wits were sharper, but I was none the less only the duller for that; my hopes and dreams had a little fallen and faded. I looked idly at my picture-book, vaguely conscious that its colours pleased me less than once upon a time; that I was rather tired of seeing them, and they just as tired of seeing me. And yet I had nothing else to do, so I must go on with a hard face, turning listlessly the pictured pages.

'About seven o'clock my mother sent for me. I found her sitting in her bedroom. Candles were burning before the looking-glass. She was already dressed in her handsome black silk gown, and wearing her pearl necklace. She began to brush my hair, curling its longer ends with her fingers, which she moistened in the pink bowl that was one of the first things I had set eyes on in this world. She put me on a clean blouse and my buckle shoes, talking to me the while, almost as if she were telling me a story. Then she looked at herself long and earnestly in the glass; throwing up her chin with a smile, as was a habit of hers in talk. I wandered about the room, fingering the little toilet-boxes and knick-knacks on the table. By mischance I upset one of these, a scent-bottle that held rose-water. The water ran out and filled the warm air with its fragrance. "You foolish, clumsy boy!" said my mother, and slapped my hand. More out of vexation and tiredness than because of the pain, I began to cry. And then, with infinite tenderness, she leaned her head on my shoulder. "Mother can't think very well just now," she said; and cried so bitterly in silence that I was only too ready to extricate myself and run away when her hold on me relaxed.

'I climbed slowly upstairs to Martha's bedroom, and kneeling on a cane chair looked out of the window. The flakes had ceased to fall now, although the snowy heath was encompassed in mist; above the snow the clouds had parted, drifting from beneath the stars, and these in their constellations were trembling very brightly, and here and there burned one of them in solitude larger and wilder in its shining than the rest. But though I did not tire of looking out of the window, my knees began to ache; and the little room was very cold and still so near the roof. So I went down to the dining-room, with all its seven candlesticks kindled, seeming to my unaccustomed eyes a very splendid blaze out of the dark. My mother was kneeling on the rug by the fireside. She looked very small, even dwarfish, I thought. She was gazing into the flames; one shoe curved beneath the hem of her gown, her chin resting on her hand.

'I surveyed the table with its jellies and sweetmeats and glasses and fruit, and began to be very hungry, so savoury was the smell of the turkey roasting downstairs. Martha knocked at the door when the clock had struck eight.

'"Dinner is ready, ma'am."

'My mother glanced fleetingly at the clock. "Just a little, only a very little while longer, tell Mrs Ryder; your master will be home in a minute." She rose and placed the claret in the hearth at some distance from the fire.

' "Is it nicer warm, mother?" I said. She looked at me with startled eyes and nodded. "Did you hear anything, Nicholas? Run to the door and listen; was that a sound of footsteps?"

'I opened the outer door and peered into the darkness; but it seemed the world ended here with the warmth and the light; beyond could extend only winter and silence, a region that, familiar though it was to me, seemed now to terrify me like an enormous sea.

' "It's stopped snowing," I said, "but there isn't anybody there; nobody at all, mother."

'The hours passed heavily from quarter on to quarter. The turkey, I grieved to hear, was to be taken out of the oven, and put away to cool in the pantry. I was bidden help myself to what I pleased of the trembling jellies, and delicious pink blancmange. Already midnight would be the next hour to be chimed. I felt sick, yet was still hungry and very tired. The candles began to burn low. "Leave me a little light here, then," my mother said at last to Martha, "and go to bed. Perhaps your master has missed his way home in the snow." But Mrs Ryder had followed Martha into the room.

' "You must pardon my interference, ma'am, but it isn't right, it isn't really right of you to sit up longer. Master will not come back, maybe, before morning. And I shouldn't be doing my bounden duty, ma'am, except I spoke my mind. Just now too, of all times."

' "Thank you very much, Mrs Ryder," my mother answered simply, "but I would prefer not to go to bed yet. It's very lonely on the heath at night. But I shall not want anything else, thank you."

' "Well, ma'am, I've had my say, and done my conscience's bidding. And I have brought you up this tumbler of mulled wine; else you'll be sinking away or something with the fatigue."

'My mother took the wine, sipped of it with a wan smile at Mrs Ryder over the brim; and Mrs Ryder retired with Martha. I don't think they had noticed me sitting close in the shadow on my stool beside the table. But all through that long night,

I fancy, these good souls took it in turn to creep down stealthily and look in on us; and in the small hours of the morning, when the fire had fallen low, they must have wrapped us both warm in shawls. They left me then, I think, to be my mother's company. Indeed, I remember we spoke in the darkness, and she took my hand.

'My mother and I shared the steaming wine together when they were gone; our shadows looming faintly huge upon the ceiling. We said very little, but I looked softly into her grey childish eyes, and we kissed one another kneeling there together before the fire. And afterwards, I jigged softly round the table, pilfering whatever sweet or savoury mouthful took my fancy. But by and by in the silent house—a silence broken only by the fluttering of the flames, and the odd far-away stir of the frost—drowsiness vanquished me; I sat down by the fireside, leaning my head on a chair. And sitting thus, vaguely eyeing firelight and wavering shadow, I began to nod, and very soon dream stalked in, mingling with reality.

'It was early morning when I awoke, dazed and cold and miserable in my uncomfortable resting-place. The rare odour of frost was on the air. The ashes of the fire lay iron-grey upon the cold hearth. An intensely clear white ray of light leaned up through a cranny of the shutters to the cornice of the ceiling. I got up with difficulty. My mother was still asleep, breathing heavily, and as I stooped, regarding her curiously, I could almost watch her transient dreams fleeting over her face; and now she smiled faintly; and now she raised her eyebrows as if in some playful and happy talk with my father; then again utterly still darkness would descend on brow and lid and lip.

'I touched her sleeve, suddenly conscious of my loneliness in the large house. Her face clouded instantly; she sighed profoundly: "What?" she said, "nothing—nothing?" She stretched out her hand towards me; the lids drew back from eyes still blind from sleep. But gradually time regained its influence over her. She moistened her lips and turned to me, and suddenly, in a gush of agony, remembrance of the night returned to her. She hid her face in her hands, rocking her body gently to and fro; then rose and smoothed back her hair at the looking-glass. I was surprised to see no trace of tears on her cheeks. Her lips moved, as if unconsciously a heart worn out with grief addressed that pale reflection of her sorrow in the glass. I took hold of the hand that hung down listlessly on her silk skirt, and fondled it, kissing punctiliously each loose ring in turn.

'But I do not think she heeded my kisses. So I returned to the table on which was still set out the mockery of our Valentine feast, strangely disenchanted in the chill dusk of daybreak. I put a handful of wine biscuits and a broken piece of cake in my pocket; for a determination had taken me to go out on to the heath. My heart beat thick and fast in imagination of the solitary snow and of myself wandering in loneliness across its untrampled surface. A project also was forming in my mind of walking over to the Grange; for somehow I knew my mother would not scold or punish me that day. Perhaps, I thought, my father would be there. And I would tell Miss Grey all about my adventure of the night spent down in the dining-room. So moving very stealthily, and betraying no eagerness, lest I should be forbidden to go, I stole at length unperceived from the room, and leaving the great hall door ajar, ran out joyously into the wintry morning.

'Already dawn was clear and high in the sky, already the first breezes were moving in the mists; and breathed chill, as if it were the lingering darkness itself on my cheeks. The air was cold, yet with a fresh faint sweetness. The snow lay crisp across its perfect surface, mounded softly over the gorse-bushes, though here and there a spray of parched blossom yet protruded from its cowl. Flaky particles of ice floated invisible in the air. I called out with pleasure to see the little ponds where the snow had been blown away from the black ice. I saw on the bushes too the webs of spiders stretched from thorn to thorn, and festooned with crystals of hoar-frost. I turned and counted as far as I could my footsteps leading back to the house, which lay roofed in gloomy pallor, dim and obscured in the darkened west.

'A waning moon that had risen late in the night shone, it seemed, very near to the earth. But every moment light swept invincibly in, pouring its crystal like a river; and darkness sullenly withdrew into the north. And when at last the sun appeared, glittering along the rosy snow, I turned in an ecstasy and with my finger pointed him out, as if the house I had left behind me might view him with my own delight. Indeed, I saw its windows transmuted, and heard afar a thrush pealing in the bare branches of a pear tree; and a robin startled me, so suddenly shrill and sweet he broke into song from a snowy tuft of gorse.

'I was now come to the beginning of a gradual incline, from the summit of which I should presently descry in the distance the avenue of lindens that led towards the village from the margin of the heath. As I went on my way, munching my biscuits, looking gaily about me, I brooded deliciously on the breakfast which Miss Grey would doubtless sit me down to; and almost forgot the occasion of my errand, and the troubled house I had left behind me. At length I climbed to the top of the smooth ridge and looked down. At a little distance from me grew a crimson hawthorn tree that often in past Aprils I had used for a green tent from the showers; but now it was closely hooded, darkening with its faint shadow the long expanse of unshadowed whiteness. Not very far from this bush I perceived a figure lying stretched along the snow and knew instinctively that this was my father lying here.

'The sight did not then surprise or dismay me. It seemed but the lucid sequel to that long heavy night-watch, to all the troubles and perplexities of the past. I felt no sorrow, but stood beside the body, regarding it only with deep wonder and a kind of earnest curiosity, yet perhaps with a remote pity too, that he could not see me in the beautiful morning. His grey hand lay arched in the snow, his darkened face, on which showed a smear of dried blood, was turned away a little as if out of the oblique sunshine. I understood that he was dead, was already loosely speculating on what changes it would make; how I should spend my time; what would happen in the house now that he was gone, his influence, his authority, his discord. I remembered too that I was alone, was master of this immense secret, that I must go home sedately, as if it were a Sunday, and in a low voice tell my mother, concealing any exultation I might feel in the office. I imagined the questions that would be asked me, and was considering the proper answers to make to them, when my morbid dreams were suddenly broken in on by Martha Rodd. She stood in my footsteps, looking down on me from the ridge from which I had but just now descended. She hastened towards me, stooping a little as if she carried a burden, her mouth ajar, her forehead wrinkled beneath its wispy light brown hair.

' "Look, Martha, look," I cried, "I found him in the snow; he 's dead." And suddenly a bond seemed to snap in my heart.

The beauty and solitude of the morning, the perfect whiteness of the snow—it was all an uncouth mockery against me—a subtle and quiet treachery. The tears gushed into my eyes and in my fear and affliction I clung to the poor girl, sobbing bitterly, protesting my grief, hiding my eyes in terror from that still, inscrutable shape. She smoothed my hair with her hand again and again, her eyes fixed; and then at last, venturing cautiously nearer, she stooped over my father. "O Master Nicholas," she said, "his poor dark hair! What will we do now? What will your poor mamma do now, and him gone?" She hid her face in her hands, and our tears gushed out anew.

'But my grief was speedily forgotten. The novelty of being left entirely alone, my own master; to go where I would; to do as I pleased; the experience of being pitied most when I least needed it, and then—when misery and solitariness came over me like a cloud—of being utterly ignored, turned my thoughts gradually away. My father's body was brought home and laid in my mother's little parlour that looked out over the garden and the snowy orchard. The house was darkened. I took a secret pleasure in peeping in on the sunless rooms, and stealing from door to door through corridors screened from the daylight. My mother was ill; and for some inexplicable reason I connected her illness with the bevy of gentlemen dressed in black who came one morning to the house and walked away together over the heath. Finally Mrs Marshall drove up one afternoon from Islington, and by the bundles she had brought with her and her grained box with the iron handles I knew that she was come, as once before in my experience, to stay.

'I was playing on the morrow in the hall with my leaden soldiers when there came into my mind vaguely the voices of Mrs Ryder and of Mrs Marshall gossiping together on their tedious way upstairs from the kitchen.

' "No, Mrs Marshall, nothing," I heard Mrs Ryder saying, "not one word, not one word. And now the poor dear lady left quite alone, and only the doctor to gainsay that fatherless mite from facing the idle inquisitive questions of all them strangers. It's neither for me nor you, Mrs Marshall, to speak out just what comes into our heads here and now. The ways of the Almighty are past understanding—but a kinder at *heart* never trod this earth."

' "Ah!" said Mrs Marshall.

' "I knew to my sorrow," continued Mrs Ryder, "there was words in the house; but there, wheresoever you be there's that. Human beings ain't angels, married or single, and in every——"

' "Wasn't there talk of some——?" insinuated Mrs Marshall discreetly.

' "Talk, Mrs Marshall," said Mrs Ryder, coming to a standstill, "I scorn the word! A pinch of truth in a hogshead of falsehood. I don't gainsay it even. I just shut my ears—there—with the dead." Mrs Marshall had opened her mouth to reply when I was discovered, crouched as small as possible at the foot of the stairs.

' "Well, here's pitchers!" said Mrs Marshall pleasantly. "And this is the poor fatherless manikin, I suppose. It's hard on the innocent, Mrs Ryder, and him grown such a sturdy child, too, as I said from the first. Well, now, and don't you remember me, little man, don't you remember Mrs Marshall? He ought to, now!"

' "He's a very good boy in general," said Mrs Ryder, "and I'm sure I hope and pray he'll grow up to be a comfort to his poor widowed mother, if so be——" They glanced earnestly at one another, and Mrs Marshall stooped with a sigh of effort and drew a big leather purse from a big loose pocket under her skirt, and selected a bright ha'penny from among its silver and copper.

' "I make no doubt he will, poor mite," she said cheerfully; I took the ha'penny in silence and the two women passed slowly upstairs.

'In the afternoon, in order to be beyond call of Martha, I went out on to the heath with a shovel, intent on building a great tomb in the snow. Yet more snow had fallen during the night; it now lay so deep as to cover my socks above my shoes. I laboured very busily, shovelling, beating, moulding, stamping. So intent was I that I did not see Miss Grey until she was close beside me. I looked up from the snow and was surprised to find the sun already set and the low mists of evening approaching. Miss Grey was veiled and dressed in furs to the throat. She drew her ungloved hand from her muff.

' "Nicholas," she said in a low voice.

'I stood for some reason confused and ashamed without answering her. She sat down on my shapeless mound of snow, and took me by the hand. Then she drew up her veil, and I saw

her face pale and darkened, and her dark eyes gravely looking
into mine.

' "My poor, poor Nicholas," she said, and continued to gaze
at me with her warm hand clasping mine. "What can I say?
What can I do? Isn't it very, very lonely out here in the
snow?"

' "I didn't feel lonely much," I answered, "I was making a—
I was playing at building."

' "And I am sitting on your beautiful snow-house, then?" she
said, smiling sadly, her hand trembling upon mine.

' "It isn't a house," I answered, turning away.

'She pressed my hand on the furs at her throat.

' "Poor cold, blue hands," she said. "Do you like playing
alone?"

' "I like you being here," I answered. "I wish you would
come always, or at least sometimes."

'She drew me close to her, smiling, and bent and kissed my
head.

' "There," she said, "I am here now."

' "Mother 's ill," I said.

'She drew back and looked out over the heath towards the
house.

' "They have put my father in the little parlour, in his coffin;
of course, you know he 's dead, and Mrs Marshall 's come; she
gave me a ha'penny this morning. Dr Graham gave me a whole
crown, though." I took it out of my breeches pocket and showed
it her.

' "That 's very, very nice," she said. "What lots of nice
things you can buy with it! And, look, I am going to give you
a little keepsake, too, between just you and me."

'It was a small silver box that she drew out of her muff, and
embossed in the silver of the lid was a crucifix. "I thought,
perhaps, I should see you to-day, you know," she continued
softly. "Now, who 's given you this?" she said, putting the
box into my hand.

' "You," I answered softly.

' "And who am I?"

' "Miss Grey," I said.

' "Your friend, Jane Grey," she repeated, as if she were fond
of her own name. "Say it now—always my friend, Jane Grey."

'I repeated it after her.

' "And now," she continued, "tell me which room is—is the little parlour. Is it that small window at the corner under the ivy?"

'I shook my head.

' "Which?" she said in a whisper, after a long pause.

'I twisted my shovel in the snow. "Would you like to see my father?" I said. "I am sure, you know, Martha would not mind; and mother's in bed." She started, and looked with quiet, dark eyes into my face. "Where?" she said, without stirring.

' "It's at the back, a little window that comes out—if you were to come this evening, I would be playing in the hall; I always play in the hall, after tea, if I can; and now, always. Nobody would see you at all, you know."

'She sighed. "Oh, what are you saying?" she said, and stood up, drawing down her veil.

' "But would you like to?" I repeated. She stooped suddenly, pressing her veiled face to mine. "I 'll come, I 'll come," she said, her face utterly changed so close to my eyes. "We can both still—still be loyal to him, can't we, Nicholas?"

'She walked away quickly, towards the pool and the little darkened wood. I looked after her and knew that she would be waiting there alone till evening. I looked at my silver box with great satisfaction, and after opening it, put it into my pocket with my crown piece and my ha'penny, and continued my building for a while.

'But now zest for it was gone; and I began to feel cold, the frost closing in keenly as darkness gathered. So I went home.

'My silence and suspicious avoidance of scrutiny and question passed unnoticed. Indeed, I ate my tea in solitude, except that now and again one or other of the women would come bustling in on some brief errand. A peculiar suppressed stir was in the house. I wondered what could be the cause of it; and felt a little timid and anxious of my project being discovered.

'None the less I was playing in the evening, as I had promised, close to the door, alert to catch the faintest sign of the coming of my visitor.

' "Run down to the kitchen, dearie," said Martha. Her cheeks were flushed. She was carrying a big can of steaming water. "You must keep very, *very* quiet this evening and go to bed like a good boy, and perhaps to-morrow morning I 'll tell

you a great, great secret." She kissed me with hasty rapture.
I was not especially inquisitive of her secret just then, and
eagerly promised to be quite quiet if I might continue to play
where I was.

'"Well, very, *very* quiet then, and you mustn't let Mrs
Marshall——" she began, but hurried hastily away in answer to
a peremptory summons from upstairs.

'Almost as soon as she was gone I heard a light rap on the
door. It seemed that Jane Grey brought in with her the cold
and freshness of the woods. I led the way on tiptoe down the
narrow corridor and into the small, silent room. The candles
burned pure and steadfastly in their brightness. The air was
still and languid with the perfume of flowers. Overhead passed
light, heedful footsteps; but they seemed not a disturbing
sound, only a rumour beyond the bounds of silence.

'"I am very sorry," I said, "but they have nailed it down.
Martha says the men came this afternoon."

'Miss Grey took a little bunch of snowdrops from her bosom,
and hid them in among the clustered wreaths of flowers; and she
knelt down on the floor, with a little silver cross which she
sometimes wore pressed tight to her lips. I felt ill at ease to see
her praying, and wished I could go back to my soldiers. But
while I watched her, seeing in marvellous brilliancy everything
in the little room, and remembering dimly the snow lying
beneath the stars in the darkness of the garden, I listened also
to the quiet footsteps passing to and fro in the room above.
Suddenly, the silence was broken by a small, continuous, angry
crying.

'Miss Grey looked up. Her eyes were very clear and wonderful in the candle-light.

'"What was that?" she said faintly, listening.

'I stared at her. The cry welled up anew, piteously, as if of
a small remote helpless indignation.

'"Why, it sounds just like—a little baby," I said.

'She crossed herself hastily and arose. "Nicholas!" she said
in a strange, quiet, bewildered voice—yet her face was most
curiously bright. She looked at me lovingly and yet so strangely
I wished I had not let her come in.

'She went out as she had entered. I did not so much as peep
into the darkness after her, but busy with a hundred thoughts
returned to my play.

'Long past my usual bed-time, as I sat sipping a mug of hot milk before the glowing cinders of the kitchen fire, Martha told me her secret. . . .

'So my impossible companion in the High Street yesterday was own and only brother to your crazy old friend, Richard,' said the Count. 'His only brother,' he added, in a muse.

From *The Riddle*.

MISS DUVEEN

I SELDOM had the company of children in my grandmother's house beside the River Wandle. The house was old and ugly. But its river was lovely and youthful though it had flowed for ever, it seemed, between its green banks of osier and alder. So it was no great misfortune perhaps that I heard more talking of its waters than of any human tongue. For my grandmother found no particular pleasure in my company. How should she? My father and mother had married (and died) against her will, and there was nothing in me of those charms which, in fiction at any rate, swiftly soften a superannuated heart.

Nor did I pine for her company either, I kept out of it as much as possible.

It so happened that she was accustomed to sit with her back to the window of the room which she usually occupied, her grey old indifferent face looking inwards. Whenever necessary, I would steal close up under it, and if I could see there her large faded amethyst velvet cap I knew I was safe from interruption. Sometimes I would take a slice or two of currant bread or (if I could get it) a jam tart or a cheese cake, and eat it under a twisted old damson tree or beside the running water. And if I conversed with anybody, it would be with myself or with my small victims of the chase.

Not that I was an exceptionally cruel boy; though if I had lived for many years in this primitive and companionless fashion, I should surely have become an idiot. As a matter of fact, I was unaware even that I was ridiculously old-fashioned —manners, clothes, notions, everything. My grandmother never troubled to tell me so, nor did she care. And the servants were a race apart. So I was left pretty much to my own devices. What wonder, then, if I at first accepted with genuine avidity the acquaintanceship of our remarkable neighbour, Miss Duveen?

It had been, indeed, quite an advent in our uneventful routine when that somewhat dubious household moved into Willowlea, a brown brick edifice, even uglier than our own, which had been long vacant, and whose sloping garden confronted ours across the Wandle. My grandmother, on her part, at once discovered that any kind of intimacy with its inmates was not much to be desired. While I, on mine, was compelled to resign myself to the loss of the Willowlea garden as a kind of No Man's Land or Tom Tiddler's ground.

I got to know Miss Duveen by sight long before we actually became friends. I used frequently to watch her wandering in her long garden. And even then I noticed how odd were her methods of gardening. She would dig up a root or carry off a potted plant from one to another overgrown bed with an almost animal-like resolution; and a few minutes afterwards I would see her restoring it to the place from which it had come. Now and again she would stand perfectly still, like a scarecrow, as if she had completely forgotten what she was at.

Miss Coppin, too, I descried sometimes. But I never more than glanced at her, for fear that even at that distance the too fixed attention of my eyes might bring hers to bear upon me. She was a smallish woman, inclined to be fat, and with a peculiar waddling gait. She invariably appeared to be angry with Miss Duveen, and would talk to her as one might talk to a post. I did not know, indeed, until one day Miss Duveen waved her handkerchief in my direction that I had been observed from Willowlea at all. Once or twice after that, I fancied, she called me; at least her lips moved; but I could not distinguish what she said. And I was naturally a little backward in making new friends. Still I grew accustomed to looking out for her and remember distinctly how first we met.

It was raining, the raindrops falling softly into the unrippled water, making their great circles, and tapping on the motionless leaves above my head where I sat in shelter on the bank. But the sun was shining whitely from behind a thin fleece of cloud, when Miss Duveen suddenly peeped in at me out of the greenery, the thin silver light upon her face, and eyed me sitting there, for all the world as if she were a blackbird and I a snail. I scrambled up hastily with the intention of retreating into my own domain, but the peculiar grimace she made at me fixed me where I was.

'Ah,' she said, with a little masculine laugh, 'so this is the young gentleman, the bold, gallant young gentleman. And what might be his name?'

I replied rather distantly that my name was Arthur.

'Arthur, to be sure!' she repeated with extraordinary geniality, and again, 'Arthur,' as if in the strictest confidence.

'I know you, Arthur, very well indeed. I have looked, I have watched; and now, please God, we need never be estranged.' And she tapped her brow and breast, making the sign of the cross with her lean, bluish forefinger.

'What is a little brawling brook,' she went on, 'to friends like you and me?' She gathered up her tiny countenance once more into an incredible grimace of friendliness; and I smiled as amicably as I could in return. There was a pause in this one-sided conversation. She seemed to be listening, and her lips moved, though I caught no sound. In my uneasiness I was just about to turn stealthily away, when she poked forward again.

'Yes, yes, I know you quite intimately, Arthur. We have met *here*.' She tapped her rounded forehead. 'You might not suppose it, too; but I have eyes like a lynx. It is no exaggeration, I assure you—I assure everybody. And now what friends we will be! At times,' she stepped out of her hiding-place and stood in curious dignity beside the water, her hands folded in front of her on her black pleated silk apron—'at times, dear child, I long for company—earthly company.' She glanced furtively about her. 'But I must restrain my longings; and you will, of course, understand that I do not complain. *He* knows best. And my dear cousin, Miss Coppin—she too knows best. She does not consider too much companionship expedient for me.' She glanced in some perplexity into the smoothly swirling water.

'I, you know,' she said suddenly, raising her little piercing eyes to mine, 'I am Miss Duveen, that's not, they say, quite the thing here.' She tapped her small forehead again beneath its two slick curves of greying hair, and made a long narrow mouth at me. 'Though, of course,' she added, 'we do not tell *her* so. No!'

And I, too, nodded my head in instinctive and absorbed imitation. Miss Duveen laughed gaily. 'He understands, he understands!' she cried, as if to many listeners. 'Oh, what a joy it is in this world, Arthur, to be understood. Now tell me,' she continued with immense nicety, 'tell me, how's your dear mamma?'

I shook my head.

'Ah,' she cried, 'I see, I see; Arthur has no mamma. We will not refer to it. No father, either?'

I shook my head again and, standing perfectly still, stared at my new acquaintance with vacuous curiosity. She gazed at me with equal concentration, as if she were endeavouring to keep the very thought of my presence in her mind.

'It is sad to have no father,' she continued rapidly, half closing her eyes; 'no head, no guide, no stay, no stronghold; but we have, Oh yes, we have another father, dear child, another father—eh . . . Where . . . Where?'

She very softly raised her finger. 'On high,' she whispered, with extraordinary intensity.

'But just now,' she added cheerfully, hugging her mittened hands together, 'we are not talking of *Him*; we are talking of ourselves, just you and me, *so* cosy; so *secret*! And it's a grandmother? I thought so, I thought so, a grandmother! Oh yes, I can peep between the curtains though they do lock the door. A grandmother—I thought so; that very droll old lady! *Such* fine clothes! Such a presence, oh yes! A grandmother.' She poked out her chin and laughed confidentially.

'And the long, bony creature, all rub and double'—she jogged briskly with her elbows—'who's that?'

'Mrs Pridgett,' I said.

'There, there,' she whispered breathlessly, gazing widely about her. 'Think of that! *He* knows; *He* understands. How firm, how manly, how undaunted! . . . *One* "t"?'

I shook my head dubiously.

'Why should he?' she cried scornfully. 'But between ourselves, Arthur, that is a thing we *must* learn, and never mind the head-ache. We cannot, of course, know everything. Even Miss Coppin does not know everything——' she leaned forward with intense earnestness—'though I don't tell her so. We must try to learn all we can; and at once. One thing, dear child, you may be astonished to hear, I learned only yesterday, and that is how exceedingly *sad* life is.'

She leaned her chin upon her narrow bosom, pursing her lips. 'And yet you know they say very little about it. . . . They don't *mention* it. Every moment, every hour, every day, every year—one, two, three, four, five, seven, ten,' she paused, frowned, 'and so on. Sadder and sadder. Why? why? It's strange, but oh, so true. You really can have no notion, child, how very

sad I am myself at times. In the evening, when they all
gather together, in their white raiment, up and up and up, I sit
on the garden seat, on Miss Coppin's garden seat, and precisely
in the middle (you'll be kind enough to remember that?) and
my *thoughts* make me sad.' She narrowed her eyes and shoulders.
'Yes and frightened, my child! Why must I be so guarded?
One angel—the greatest *fool* could see the wisdom of that. But
billions!—with their fixed eyes shining, so very boldly, on me.
I never prayed for so many, dear friend. And we pray for a
good many odd things, you and I, I'll be bound. But, there,
you see, poor Miss Duveen's on her theology again—scamper,
scamper, scamper. In the congregations of the wicked we must
be cautious! . . . Mrs Partridge and grandmamma, so nice, *so*
nice; but even that, too, a *little* sad, eh?' She leaned her head
questioningly, like a starving bird in the snow.

I smiled, not knowing what else she expected of me; and her
face became instantly grave and set.

'He's right; perfectly right. We must speak evil of *no* one.
No one. We must shut our mouths. We——' She stopped
suddenly and, taking a step, leaned over the water towards me,
with eyebrows raised high above her tiny face. 'S—sh!' she
whispered, laying a long forefinger on her lips. 'Eavesdroppers!'
she smoothed her skirts, straightened her cap, and left me; only
a moment after to poke out her head at me again from between
the leafy bushes. 'An assignation, no!' she said firmly, then
gathered her poor, cheerful, forlorn, crooked, lovable face into
a most wonderful contraction at me, that assuredly meant—
'But, *yes*!'

Indeed it was an assignation, the first of how many, and how
few. Sometimes Miss Duveen would sit beside me, apparently
so lost in thought that I was clean forgotten. And yet I half
fancied it was often nothing but feigning. Once she stared me
blankly out of countenance when I ventured to take the initiative
and to call out 'Good morning!' to her across the water. On
this occasion she completed my consternation with a sudden,
angry grimace—contempt, jealousy, outrage.

But often we met like old friends and talked. It was a novel
but not always welcome diversion for me in the long shady
garden that was my privy universe. Where our alders met,
mingling their branches across the flowing water, and the king-
fisher might be seen—there was our usual tryst. But occasion-

ally, at her invitation, I would venture across the stepping-stones into her demesne; and occasionally, but very seldom indeed, she would venture into mine. How plainly I see her, tiptoeing from stone to stone, in an extraordinary concentration of mind—her mulberry petticoats, her white stockings, her loose spring-side boots. And when at last she stood beside me, her mittened hand on her breast, she would laugh on in a kind of paroxysm until the tears stood in her eyes, and she grew faint with breathlessness.

'In all danger,' she told me once, 'I hold my breath and shut my eyes. And if I could tell you of every danger, I think, perhaps, you would understand——dear Miss Coppin . . .' I did not, and yet, perhaps, very vaguely I did see the connection in this rambling statement.

Like most children, I liked best to hear Miss Duveen talk· about her own childhood. I contrived somehow to discover that if we sat near flowers or under boughs in blossom, her talk would generally steal round to that. Then she would chatter on and on: of the white sunny rambling house, somewhere, nowhere—it saddened and confused her if I asked where—in which she had spent her first happy years; where her father used to ride on a black horse; and her mother to walk with her in the garden in a crinolined gown and a locket with the painted miniature of a 'divine' nobleman inside it. How very far away these pictures seemed!

It was as if she herself had shrunken back into this distant past, and was babbling on like a child again, already a little isolated by her tiny infirmity.

'That was before——' she would begin to explain precisely, and then a criss-cross many-wrinkled frown would net her rounded forehead, and cloud her eyes. Time might baffle her, but then, time often baffled me too. Any talk about her mother usually reminded her of an elder sister, Caroline. 'My sister, Caroline,' she would repeat as if by rote, 'you may not be aware, Arthur, was afterwards Mrs Bute. So charming, so exquisite, so accomplished. And Colonel Bute—an officer and a gentleman, I grant. And yet . . . But no! My dear sister was not happy. And so it was no doubt a blessing in disguise that by an unfortunate accident she was found drowned. In a lake, you will understand, not a mere shallow noisy brook. This is one of my private sorrows, which, of course, your grandmamma would be horrified to hear—horrified; and which, of course, Partridge has not the privilege of birth even to be informed of —*our* secret, dear child—with all her beautiful hair, and her elegant feet, and her eyes no more ajar than this; but blue, blue as the forget-me-not. When the time comes, Miss Coppin will close my own eyes, I hope and trust. Death, dear, dear child, I know they *say* is only sleeping. Yet I hope and trust *that*. To be sleeping wide awake; oh no!' She abruptly turned her small untidy head away.

'But didn't they shut *hers*?' I inquired.

Miss Duveen ignored the question. 'I am not uttering one word of blame,' she went on rapidly; 'I am perfectly aware that such things confuse me. Miss Coppin tells me not to think. She tells me that I can have no opinions worth the mention. She says: "Shut up your mouth." I must keep silence then. All that I am merely trying to express to you, Arthur, knowing you will regard it as sacred between us—all I am expressing is that my dear sister Caroline was a gifted and beautiful creature with not a shadow or vestige or tinge or taint of confusion in her mind. *Nothing*. And yet, when they dragged her out of the water and laid her there on the bank, looking——' She stooped herself double in a sudden dreadful fit of gasping, and I feared for an instant she was about to die.

'No, no, no,' she cried, rocking herself to and fro, 'you shall *not* paint such a picture in his young innocent mind. You *shall* not.'

I sat on my stone, watching her, feeling excessively uncomfortable. 'But what *did* she look like, Miss Duveen?' I pressed forward to ask at last.

'No, no, no,' she cried again. 'Cast him out, cast him out. *Retro Sathanas!* We must not even *ask* to understand. My father and my dear mother, I do not doubt, have spoken for Caroline. Even I, if I must be called on, will strive to collect my thoughts. And that is precisely where a friend, you, Arthur, would be so precious; to know that you, too, in your innocence, will be helping me to collect my thoughts on that day, to save our dear Caroline from Everlasting Anger. That, that! Oh dear; oh dear!' She turned on me a face I should scarcely have recognized, lifted herself trembling to her feet, and hurried away.

Sometimes it was not Miss Duveen that was a child again,

but I that had grown up. 'Had now you been your handsome father—and I see him, oh, so plainly, dear child—had you been your father, then I must, of course, have kept to the house . . . I must have; it is a rule of conduct, and everything depends on them. Where would Society be *else*!' she cried, with an unanswerable blaze of intelligence. 'I find, too, dear Arthur, that they increase—the rules increase. I try to remember them. My dear cousin, Miss Coppin, knows them all. But I—I think sometimes one's *memory* is a little treacherous. And then it must vex people.'

She gazed penetratingly at me for an answer that did not come. Mute as a fish though I might be, I suppose it was something of a comfort to her to talk to me.

And to suppose that is *my* one small crumb of comfort when I reflect on the kind of friendship I managed to bestow.

I actually met Miss Coppin once; but we did not speak. I had, in fact, gone to tea with Miss Duveen. The project had been discussed as 'quite, quite impossible, dear child' for weeks. 'You must never mention it again.' As a matter of fact I had never mentioned it at all. But one day—possibly when their charge had been less difficult and exacting, one day Miss Coppin and her gaunt maid-servant and companion really did go out together, leaving Miss Duveen alone in Willowlea. It was the crowning opportunity of our friendship. The moment I espied her issuing from the house, I guessed her errand. She came hastening down to the waterside, attired in clothes of a colour and fashion I had never seen her wearing before, her dark eyes shining in her head, her hands trembling with excitement.

It was a still, warm afternoon, with sweet-williams and linden and stocks scenting the air, when, with some little trepidation, I must confess, I followed her in formal dignity up the unfamiliar path towards the house. I know not which of our hearts beat the quicker, whose eyes cast the most furtive glances about us. My friend's cheeks were brightest mauve. She wore a large silver locket on a ribbon; and I followed her up the faded green stairs, beneath the dark pictures, to her small, stuffy bedroom under the roof. We humans, they say, are enveloped in a kind of aura; to which the vast majority of us are certainly entirely insensitive. Nevertheless, there was an air, an atmosphere as of the smell of pears in this small attic room—well, every bird, I suppose, haunts with its presence its customary cage.

'This,' she said, acknowledging the bed, the looking-glass, the deal washstand, 'this, dear child, you will pardon; in fact, you will not see. How could we sit, friends as we are, in the congregation of strangers?'

I hardly know why, but that favourite word of Miss Duveen's, 'congregation,' brought up before me with extreme aversion all the hostile hardness and suspicion concentrated in Miss Coppin and Ann. I stared at the queer tea-things in a vain effort not to be aware of the rest of Miss Duveen's private belongings.

Somehow or other she had managed to procure for me a bun —a saffron bun. There was a dish of a grey pudding and a plate of raspberries that I could not help suspecting (and, I am ashamed to say, with aggrieved astonishment), she must have herself gathered that morning from my grandmother's canes. We did not talk very much. Her heart gave her pain. And her face showed how hot and absorbed and dismayed she was over her foolhardy entertainment. But I sipped my milk and water, sitting on a black bandbox, and she on an old cane chair. And we were almost formal and distant to one another, with little smiles and curtsies over our cups, and polished agreement about the weather.

'And you'll strive not to be sick, dear child,' she implored me suddenly, while I was nibbling my way slowly through the bun. But it was not until rumours of the tremendous fact of Miss Coppin's early and unforeseen return had been borne in on us that Miss Duveen lost all presence of mind. She burst into tears; seized and kissed repeatedly my sticky hands; implored me to be discreet; implored me to be gone; implored me to retain her in my affections, 'as you love your poor dear mother, Arthur,' and I left her on her knees, her locket pressed to her bosom.

Miss Coppin was, I think, unusually astonished to see a small strange boy walk softly past her bedroom door, within which she sat, with purple face, her hat-strings dangling, taking off her boots. Ann, I am thankful to say, I did not encounter. But when I was safely out in the garden in the afternoon sunshine, the boldness and the romance of this sally completely deserted me. I ran like a hare down the alien path, leapt from stone to stone across the river; nor paused in my flight until I was safe in my own bedroom, and had—how odd is childhood! —washed my face and entirely changed my clothes.

My grandmother, when I appeared at her tea-table, glanced at me now and again rather profoundly and inquisitively, but the actual question hovering in her mind remained unuttered.

It was many days before we met again, my friend and I. She had, I gathered from many mysterious nods and shrugs, been more or less confined to her bedroom ever since our escapade, and looked dulled and anxious; her small face was even a little more vacant in repose than usual. Even this meeting, too, was full of alarms; for in the midst of our talk, by mere chance or caprice, my grandmother took a walk in the garden that afternoon, and discovered us under our damson tree. She bowed in her dignified, aged way. And Miss Duveen, with cheeks and forehead the colour of her petticoat, elaborately curtsied.

'Beautiful, very beautiful weather,' said my grandmother.

'It is indeed,' said my friend, fixedly.

'I trust you are keeping pretty well?'

'As far, ma'am, as God and a little weakness of the heart permit,' said Miss Duveen. 'He knows all,' she added firmly.

My grandmother stood silent a moment.

'Indeed He does,' she replied politely.

'And that's the difficulty,' ventured Miss Duveen, in her odd, furtive, friendly fashion.

My grandmother opened her eyes, smiled pleasantly, paused, glanced remotely at me, and, with another exchange of courtesies, Miss Duveen and I were left alone once more. But it was a grave and saddened friend I now sat beside.

'You see, Arthur, all bad things, we know, are best for us. Motives included. That comforts me. But my heart is sadly fluttered. Not that I fear or would shun society; but perhaps your grandmother . . . I never had the power to treat my fellow-creatures as if they were stocks and stones. And the effort not to notice it distresses me. A little hartshorn might relieve the *palpitation*, of course; but Miss Coppin keeps all keys. It is this shouting that makes civility such a task.'

'This shouting'—very faintly then I caught her meaning, but I was in no mood to sympathize. My grandmother's one

round-eyed expressionless glance at me had been singularly
disconcerting. And it was only apprehension of her questions
that kept me from beating a retreat. So we sat on, Miss Duveen
and I, in the shade, the day drawing towards evening, and
presently we walked down to the water-side, and under the
colours of sunset I flung in my crumbs to the minnows, as she
talked ceaselessly on.

'And yet,' she concluded, after how involved a monologue,
'and yet, Arthur, I feel it is for your forgiveness I should be
pleading. So much to do; such an arch of beautiful things might
have been my gift to you. It is here,' she said, touching her
forehead. 'I do not think, perhaps, that all I might say would
be for your good. I must be silent and discreet about much.
I must not provoke'—she lifted her mittened finger, and raised
her eyes—'Them,' she said gravely. 'I am tempted, terrified,
persecuted. Whispering, wrangling, shouting: the flesh is a
grievous burden, Arthur; I long for peace. Only to flee away
and be at rest! But,' she nodded, and glanced over her shoulder,
'about much—great trials, sad entanglements, about much the
Others say, I must keep silence. It would only alarm your
innocence. And that I will never, *never* do. Your father, a
noble, gallant gentleman of the world, would have understood
my difficulties. But he is dead . . . Whatever that may mean.
I have repeated it so often when Miss Coppin thought that I
was not—dead, dead, dead, dead—but I don't think that even
now I grasp the meaning of the word. Of you, dear child, I
will never say it. You have been life itself to me.'

How generously, how tenderly she smiled on me from her
perplexed, sorrowful eyes.

'You have all the world before you, all the world. How
splendid it is to be a Man. For my part I have sometimes
thought, though they do not of course intend to injure me, yet
I fancy, sometimes, they have grudged me *my* part in it a little.
Though God forbid but Heaven's best.'

She raised that peering, dark, remote gaze to my face, and
her head was trembling again. 'They are saying now to one
another—'*Where is she? Where is she? It's nearly dark, m'm,
where is she?*' Oh, Arthur, but there shall be no night *there*.
We must believe it, we must—in spite, dear friend, of a weak
horror of glare. My cousin, Miss Coppin, does not approve of
my wishes. Gas, gas, gas, all over the house, and when it is not

singing, it roars. You would suppose I might be trusted with
but just my own one bracket. But no—Ann, I think—indeed
I fear, sometimes, has no——' She started violently and shook
her tiny head. 'When I am gone,' she continued disjointedly,
'you will be prudent, cautious, dear child? Consult only your
heart about me. Older you must be . . . Yes, certainly, he
must be older,' she repeated vaguely. 'Everything goes on
and on—and round!' She seemed astonished, as if at a sudden
radiance cast on an old and protracted perplexity.

'About your soul, dear child,' she said to me once, touching
my hand, 'I have never spoken. Perhaps it was one of my first
duties to keep on speaking to you about your soul. I mention
it now in case they should rebuke me when I make my appearance there. It is a burden; and I have so many burdens, as
well as pain. And at times I cannot think very far. I *see* the
thought; but it won't alter. It comes back, just like a sheep—
"*Ba-aa-ah*," like that!' She burst out laughing, twisting her
head to look at me the while. 'Miss Coppin, of course, has no
difficulty; gentlemen have no difficulty. And this shall be the
occasion of another of our little confidences. We are discreet?'
She bent her head and scanned my face. 'Here,' she tapped her
bosom, 'I bear his image. My only dear one's. And if you
would kindly turn your head, dear child, perhaps I could pull
him out.'

It was the miniature of a young, languid, fastidious-looking
officer which she showed me—threaded on dingy tape, in its
tarnished locket.

'Miss Coppin, in great generosity, has left me this,' she said,
polishing the glass on her knee, 'though I am forbidden to wear
it. For you see, Arthur, it is a duty not to brood on the past,
and even perhaps, indelicate. Some day, it may be, you, too,
will love a gentle girl. I beseech you, keep your heart pure and
true. This one could not. Not a single word of blame escapes
me. I own to my Maker, *never* to any one else, it has not eased
my little difficulty. But it is not for us to judge. Whose
office is that, eh?' And again, that lean small forefinger, beneath an indescribable grimace, pointed gently, deliberately,
from her lap upward. 'Pray, pray,' she added, very violently,
'pray, till the blood streams down your face! Pray, but rebuke
not. They all whisper about it. Among themselves,' she added,
peering out beneath and between the interlacing branches.

'But I simulate inattention. I simulate . . .' The very
phrase seemed to have hopelessly confused her. Again, as so
often now, that glassy fear came into her eyes; her foot tapped
on the gravel.

'Arthur!' she cried suddenly, taking my hand tightly in her
lap, 'you have been my refuge in a time of trouble. You will
never know it, child. My refuge, and my peace. We shall
seldom meet now. All are opposed. They repeat it in their
looks. The autumn will divide us; and then, winter; but, I
think, no spring. It is so, Arthur, there is a stir; and then
they will hunt me out.' Her eyes gleamed again, far and small
and black in the dusky pallor of her face.

It was indeed already autumn; the air golden and still. The
leaves were beginning to fall. The late fruits were well-nigh
over. Robins and tits seemed our only birds now. Rain came
in floods. The Wandle took sound and volume, sweeping deep
above our stepping-stones. Very seldom after this I even so
much as saw our neighbour. I chanced on her one still afternoon, standing fixedly by the brawling stream, in a rusty-
looking old-fashioned cloak, her scanty hair pushed high up
on her forehead.

She stared at me for a moment or two, and then, with a
scared look over her shoulder, threw me a little letter, shaped
like a cocked hat, and weighted with a pebble stone, across the
stream. She whispered earnestly and rapidly at me over the
water. But I could not catch a single word she said, and failed
to decipher her close spidery handwriting. No doubt I was too
shy, or too ashamed, or in a vague fashion too loyal, to show it
to my grandmother. It is not now a flattering keepsake. I
called out loudly I must go in; and still see her gazing after me,
with a puzzled, mournful expression on the face peering out of
the cloak.

Even after that we sometimes waved to one another across
the water, but never if by hiding myself I could evade her in
time. The distance seemed to confuse her, and quite silenced
me. I began to see we were ridiculous friends, especially as
she came now in ever dingier and absurder clothes. She even
looked hungry, and not quite clean, as well as ill; and she talked
more to her phantoms than to me when once we met.

The first ice was in the garden. The trees stood bare beneath
a pale blue sunny sky, and I was standing at the window, looking

Mother was sitting in the wooden chair with the baby in her arms. She looked as if she was pretending. I went close and stared at her, and found that she was fast asleep. The baby was asleep too, but it scarcely seemed to be really breathing—it was like a moth fluttering on a pin; its face was quite pale and still in its sleep, but its cheeks were very red. I thought I would make a fire again without asking mother's leave, so as to be more cheerful; besides, I could feel the cold air oozing through the crannies of the timbers, and it was getting so dark I could see only the white things in the room. The rushing sound of the wind never ceased at all.

As soon as the flames began to spring up, and the sparks to crack out of the wood, my mother woke up. She looked at me with a curious face; but soon she remembered that she had been asleep, and she enjoyed the warmth of the fire.

On the next day I woke up where I had fallen asleep by the hearth, and it was a very quiet morning. I looked out of the window, and saw the sun shining yellow between the branches; and many of the boughs were now all but bare. But the fallen leaves lay thick on the ground as far as I could see, and some of them were still quite large and green. I was glad my father was gone away, because now I could do just as I pleased. I did not want the trouble of lighting the fire, so I went out into the forest, and down to visit the snares. There was a young hare caught by the leg in one, and the leaves were all round him. His eyes were bleeding, and not very bright. I killed him with a crack on the neck as I had seen father kill the hares, and carried him back by his hind legs. The leaves made an incessant rustling as I walked through them. I could see the blue sky above the trees; it was very pale, like a ribbon. I stood still a minute, carrying the hare, and listening to find if I could hear the guns. But I heard only a bird singing and a rushing sound, as if a snake were going away under the leaves. Sometimes I came to branches blown down to the ground, and even now, here and there, a leaf would fall slowly through the air, twirling, to be with all the rest. I enjoyed my broth for dinner very much, and the hare lasted for three days, with some turnips.

I asked mother how long father would be away. She said she could not tell. And I wondered how they would carry back his body if he was killed in the war.

I stayed out in the forest nearly all that day because the baby kept on crying. It was dark, and the window was lit up when I came home, and still the baby was fretting. Its eyes were gone dull, and it would not go to sleep in the night, though mother kept walking up and down, crooning and mumbling to it, and rocking it in her arms. She said it was very ill, and she held it pressed close to her. I asked her if it was going to die, but she only walked a little faster, and, as I was very sleepy, we did not talk much that night. The baby was still crying when I woke up, but not so loud. It was bleating small and shrill; like a young lamb, I told mother. I felt very refreshed after my sleep, and very hungry. I lit the fire and boiled the kettle, and put the plates on the table, and the loaf.

After breakfast I told mother I was going down to the old pool to fish, and that I would bring her some fish for dinner. But she looked at me and called me to her.

'The baby is dreadfully ill,' she said, 'and we must go without the fish. Feel its poor thin hot hands. That's the fever. Do you love it? Then take it in your arms.'

But I shook my head. It looked very ugly because its face was all puckered up, and it just wailed and wailed like a gnat in the air.

'I think I would *like* to go fishing, mother,' I said, 'and I promise you shall have the biggest I catch.'

But she kept on persisting that the baby was too ill to wait, that it was very queer, and that I must go for the doctor in the village. It wasn't so very far, she said, and I could fish to-morrow.

'But it *is* far,' I told her; 'and it doesn't look so very bad; and it might be windy and cold to-morrow. It's only crying,' I said. And I ran out before she could catch me.

But I did not catch any fish. I suppose they would not bite because I had been wicked. So I tied up my lines and came home about three in the afternoon. As I stood at the door waiting before going in, I heard a sound far away, and then, in a while, again, through the forest. And I knew it was the guns and cannons on the other side of the forest. The baby was not crying now, when I went in. But my mother did not turn her head to speak to me. She was kneeling beside its old rocking-cradle, some of her hair hanging down on her shoulders.

'I'll go for the doctor now, mother; but the guns are firing; you can hear them now if you come and listen at the door.'

But when I told her about the guns, she began to cry out loud, and hid her face in the coverlet on the cradle. I watched her a little while, and I could hear the cannons going off quite plainly now; only far away, like a drum when you put your hand on it.

I got very hot standing still, so I put my tackle on the hook and sat down by the hearth.

'Shall I go for the doctor now, mother? It 'll be dark before I get back.'

Mother turned on me very wild. 'Oh, you coward, you coward!' she said. 'Dark—it 's dark enough for me!'

She startled me very much by saying this and I felt very uncomfortable. I went nearer and looked. The baby's face was white, and its eyelids were like white wax. Its lips were the colour of its hands, almost blue.

'Is it dead, mother?' I asked. But she did not answer me, only shook her shoulders. I walked away and looked out of the door. First I felt hot and then my back shivered. And I began to cry too, because I had not gone in the morning for the doctor. I did not dry my eyes because the tears ran quite hot down my cheeks, and I could hear them dripping off my chin upon my jacket. I liked to have the door open, although it was cold and grey in the afternoon.

My mother came to the doorway and drew me close to her as if she were sorry, with her hand clutching my head. I could not cry any more now, but stood still; and even then the guns and cannons went on firing. And sometimes birds silently flew between the trees away from the sound. I wondered if father was fighting near the cannons.

The next day it was so cold again my mother made me a jacket out of an old coat of father's. It was just hemmed up, and I wore it instead of my other jacket when I went out. She had drawn the coverlet over the baby's face, so that it now lay in a kind of little house in its cradle. I thought I would please mother, so found the place and read out of the Bible about Herod; but the candle burned very sooty and smoky, so that I could not read very well, and left out the long words.

The next morning mother told me to go down to the village and tell the sexton that the baby was dead so that it could be buried in the churchyard.

I started out with my switch, about ten o'clock. It was a

warm day; so I was wearing my old jacket again, and the air smelled of the leaves, which were withered and yellow and brown. I went on, whistling; but it was more than five miles to the village. The robins were singing on the twigs, and I saw some crows flying in the sky. It was so quiet in the forest, that the cannons seemed to shake the air with their sound.

And while I was walking along, not very fast, and looking out for wild berries, I heard a noise in the distance of men running, and then the sound of a rifle quite near, and a scream like a rabbit, but much more loud and awful. I hid behind a tree, and when the forest was quiet again I ran home as quick as I could. But I did not like to tell mother that I had been frightened of the soldiers, because she had called me a coward already. So I said instead that the sexton was nowhere to be found in the village, that he must have gone to the war himself, and that no one would come for fear of the soldiers.

She looked me full in the face with her eyes. She looked so earnestly and so hard at me that I could not help moving my shoulder a little. And at that she turned away, and I felt very wretched because I knew that she had seen it was a lie. But I did not say anything.

All the while I sat there my eyes would not keep from looking at the cradle. I was very hungry. But since mother was putting on her shawl I knew that she was going out presently. Then, I thought, when she is gone, I will eat as much as ever I can. There were some bones in the cupboard well worth picking, I knew. When mother had put on her shawl and her bonnet, she lifted the baby out of the cradle.

'I must carry it to the churchyard myself,' she said, but more to herself than to me. There were no tears in her eyes; they were dark all round.

'Won't you kiss your little brother, Robbie?' It was wrapped up in her wedding shawl, which she had sometimes shown me of an evening, out of the chest. I began to cry when I kissed its forehead. It was as cold as a stone, as a piece of dough, and looked very heavy, yet thin, and its face was quite still now.

'Take care of the house, Rob,' she said. 'Don't go out; and bolt the door after me.'

I watched her hasten off along the narrow path between the trees. There was a light like crimson in the forest, and I knew that the sun would soon be setting. It was silly of her not to have gone earlier. It was very quiet now; and I was afraid it would soon be dark.

Soon she was out of sight, and only the trees seemed to come a little nearer and stand still. I left the door open, went into the room and put the candlestick on the table. I kicked the log till it began to flame. Then I went to the cupboard and took out the loaf and the bones, and a few puckered old apples. I ate from the dish, sitting by the hearth, looking out of the door. When I had finished I fell asleep for a little while.

By and by I opened my eyes, It was darker, and I saw some animal looking in at the door. I jumped up, and the animal ran away. Then I shut and barred the door and put some more wood on the fire until it was blazing high up the chimney. But I did not like to look over my shoulder towards the square window; it was so dark and silent and watchful out there. I could not hear the cannons now, either because they weren't sounding or because the flames made a loud bubbling noise as they ran up and waved. I did not dare to let them fall quiet, to only the red embers, so I kept on putting wood on the fire as fast as it burned away.

Mother did not come back, and it seemed I was sitting in front of the warm hearth in a dream that would never come to an end. All was still and motionless, and there was no ordinary sound at all that I could hear in the forest, and even the cannons were more muffled now and farther away. I could not cry, though I felt very angry at being left alone, and I was afraid. Besides, I didn't know what I would say to mother when she came back—about the food. Yet I longed for her too, and got a pain with it, and felt that I loved her, and was very sorry for my wickedness.

I fell asleep unawares. When I awoke it was broad daylight. I felt very glad and relieved to see the light, even though mother had not come back. It seemed to me that some noise had awakened me. Presently there came a groan at the doorway. Kneeling down and peeping through a crevice between the planks, I saw my father lying there on the doorstep. I took down the bar and opened the door. He was lying on his stomach; his clothes were filthy and torn, and at the back of his shoulder was a small hole pushed in in the cloth. There was dark, thick blood on the withered leaves. I tried to see his face, but couldn't very well. It was all muddy, bleared and

white, and he groaned and swore when I touched him. But he
didn't know who I was, and some of what he said didn't seem
to me to have any sense.

He asked for some water, but I could not turn him over so
that he could drink it. And it was all spilt. I told him about
the baby dying, but he didn't show that he could hear anything;
and just as I finished I heard mother coming back from the
churchyard. So I ran out and told her that it was father.

From *The Wind Blows Over.*

AT FIRST SIGHT

AT first sight any passer - by chancing to notice the grey-flannelled figure of the young man who was now making his way round the eastern horn of Galloway Crescent, would have assumed that he was blind. But this was not so. It is true the slender cane he carried in his hand was poised exploringly in front of him as he stepped quietly on, but then he never tapped with it; and though his eyes were hidden from view beneath a green silk shade attached to his head under his hat, an occasional slight sidelong movement of that head suggested that he was making at least *some* rudimentary use of them.

There was a peculiar grace in his movements, too, such as any wild but timid creature shows even when kept in a cage, and an almost absurd fastidiousness was manifest in his clothes. And though—in part, possibly, because this hideous green shade of his had always shielded his face from the furies of a London sun—his features were unusually pale, there was nothing positively effeminate in his looks. Wild things, after all, however timid, are not necessarily of the weaker sex.

Residents in Galloway Crescent were seldom visible at their windows. To many of them, none the less, Cecil must long since have become a familiar figure since the pavement between their iron balconies and their basements was part of his daily constitutional. Where old Professor Smith lived indeed, at No. 24—an old gentleman so profoundly interested in Persian literature that he had no need of 'the time'—the neat parlour-maid sometimes actually set her pantry clock by this young man. Busy at her dusting, her dark eye would glance down from the professor's first-floor drawing-room—to which she was all but the sole visitor—and would descry Cecil gently forging his way along with a motion like that of a yacht on a halcyon sea.

'Why, there's that young Mr Jennings!' she would exclaim to herself, with a thrill in her mind, and would at once run off downstairs to look at the clock to see if its hands—as they usually did—actually pointed to ten minutes past eleven.

On this particular morning, however, Cecil was at least a quarter of an hour before his time; and to judge from his progress, a stiffer breeze than usual was cat's-pawing his sea. On approaching the crescent's westerly horn, however, his footsteps began to lag. And now he seemed to be taking the liveliest possible interest in the outskirts of the scene which his shade and his affliction enabled him to command.

His slightly protruding dark-blue eyes were fixed on the pavement as if in eager search of something. They were. What indeed for days past his mind had been positively bent on was the hope of discovering—not its fellow—but the *owner* of the grey suède glove that now lay safely tucked away in the side pocket of his jacket. That hope was rapidly waning—to leave him not only restless but forlorn. This morning he was little more than pursuing its shadow, as one may pursue the vanishing memories of a happy dream.

In a monotonous life even the smallest excitement seems to have dropped clean out of the blue. And since Cecil's day-by-day had for years been as regular and punctual as Professor Smith's parlourmaid's pantry clock, to want anything badly was a novel and exciting experience. He was still in his early twenties, and in part because of his affliction, in part because of a natural shyness, he was still under the unrelaxing care of a kind of step-grandmother, Mrs le Mercier—a lady of ample means if not always of entirely transparent ends.

Cecil also had money of his own. Comfort lapped him in; every wish—within reason—could be gratified. There was only this one comparatively slight ocular disability. He might have been a cripple, or an imbecile, or a man of genius, or gravel-blind; and even then not always unhappy. But nothing so tragic as that. He was merely incapable of looking *up*. From his earliest infancy this curious and baffling derangement of his eyes had kept whatever attention he had to give fixed almost exclusively on the ground. By thrusting back his head a little he could, it is true, increase his optical range. But any effort of this kind was severe, and was apt to cause him excruciating pain. And Mrs le Mercier—'Grummumma,' as he called her—steadily set her face against these experiments. She counselled patience and moderation—to any extreme.

'I cannot bear the distress of it,' she would cry, when Cecil falteringly groped upwards with his head. And though, naturally, she had spent a good deal of money to get expert advice, she had never given up hope that time which heals all things might alleviate this, and had never been in favour of drastic measures. She hated the notion of plaguing the poor dear boy, and even of reminding him more often than was necessary to his well-being that he was different from other young men.

'After all,' she would sometimes confide in her friends, 'so long as dear Cecil is all right in *himself*, that is all that really matters. There is nothing, thank God, *abnormal* in any way, and fine frenzies, I am thankful to say, are not Cecil's forte. That is my conviction. So long as he is all right in *himself*, we must just make the best we can of his little handicap.' Still, even Grummumma occasionally had her doubts; and could be peevish when incommoded.

Standing in his shade in the middle of the luxurious, almost lush, French carpet laid all over Mrs le Mercier's drawing-room, and soundlessly rotating on his heels, Cecil could see nothing beyond a circle of a circumference of about nine or ten feet. By mounting up on to a chair he could of course extend his survey. Still, all human venture is only *human* venture. And at no time in his life had Cecil ever been tempted to become an explorer or a pioneer. He was as normal in that respect as most people. And his grandmother, in the kindness of the heart that lay somewhere within her ample bosom, had, if anything, tended to restrict his range. Whims of a contrary kind she would greet with indulgent, if not copious amusement. And as time went on—though it seemed powerless to add anything more suggestive of age than 'presence' to her general effect— that amusement grew ever more pronounced.

Inspired one April morning in his seventeenth year by a bright idea, Cecil had been discovered kneeling, hairbrush in hand, busily knocking into his bedroom wall—a foot or so above the wainscot—a tintack or two. Unframed photographs of the 'old masters' lay scattered on the floor around him.

'You know how I enjoy looking at them, as much as I *can* look at them,' he had explained to Grummumma, archly surveying him from the doorway. 'I wanted just to see if—well, you see, at *this* height——'

'And Grummumma doesn't blame her dear boy,' she had replied in that deep, rich voice of hers. 'It's the happiest of thoughts! None the less, I am perfectly certain, Cecil, you didn't want any one—one of the maids, say—who happened to be passing your door to die of laughing. You can't imagine how absurd the effect is—even to *me*. No, Cecil, we don't want that.' And Cecil had at once concurred.

It may or may not be true that *children* in general enjoy a far more comprehensive view of life than their elders are apt to surmise. It was true anyhow of Cecil: and this in spite of his poor eyes. His mother, indeed, in his quite early days, had realized this, and had always made a point of engaging tall, strapping nursemaids, to the end that the little man, while at least *she* had any say in the matter, should see as much of the world as possible.

Fortunately, too, in this respect she had not died until fully six months after he had been breeched, when to be carried about at all, even by the Queen of Brobdingnag herself, would have been a little humiliating. He had *once* enjoyed 'the larger view'; that was the point.

On the other hand, all children, however freely they may twist their big heads on their small bodies, are accustomed to being close to the ground, which may in part account for the fact that as they grow older they are apt to have a rather narrow outlook. Cecil, having as an infant spent most of his waking hours in high chairs and in the arms of these nursery grenadiers, became suddenly *shorter*, so to speak, as soon as his mother died; and Grummumma was not one to gainsay the obvious.

But then again, mere custom, while it may blunt and dull the mind, can also bless it with almost incredible funds of patience and endurance. And of an uncomplaining household—consisting of himself, Mrs le Mercier, an occasional grandniece, three servants, a gardener, his boy, and a kind of crippled old pensioner who did the boots and other odd and dirty jobs—Cecil was the most uncomplaining member. It was to outward appearance a singularly placid household. The servants kept their audibility to their own quarters; Eirene, Grummumma's grandniece, was unusually discreet for a young woman of her age; Cecil was no conversationalist; and Mrs le Mercier, though she had a temper, very rarely showed or lost it. Concealed and kept, it was, if anything, more intimidating. Even at its extreme, it dressed itself up in the mantle of a mute, peculiar, ferocious scorn.

Any kind of incompetence in any home cannot but be a burden, however philosophically that burden may be borne. The moment it threatened to become unbearable in hers, Grummumma became a dowager Mrs Christian, while remaining Mrs Worldly-Wisewoman in her methods of correcting it. She could be liberal, even magnanimous to any one really dependent on her, and she never humiliated the humble. Her husband, after a long tedious illness, had, as it were, suddenly dropped out of her life. This was years ago. She thought of him none the less kindly and even sentimentally, whenever she did think of him, because it had been a release to them both.

She had never had any children, and every scrap of maternal instinct she possessed was squandered on Cecil. He was hers 'for keeps.' 'He is "my young man,"' she had more than once fondly sighed of him over her tea-table. 'If anything happened to him . . .' a momentary frumpishness of utter dejection would settle over her copious figure; one plump ringed hand resting on the Indian tea-tray beside her while she followed up the sentence in the silence of her mind.

All this was none the less a little curious, for Mrs le Mercier couldn't endure in any human being the slightest deviation from the normal. At sight of a humpback her eyes rolled in her head. She could be charitable—but only from a distance. As a girl she had been made to read the life of St Francis. It had disgusted her. This experience—and similar compulsions —had tainted for her the very sight of a serious book. Even the marks in a strange face of poverty or sickness filled her with dismay—'froze her up.'

'I know it, my dear,' she had once confided in a friend. 'I am at the mercy of horrors.' And there came with the words such a look of helplessness into her bold and formidable face that even cruelty itself would have hesitated to set to work on such a victim.

It may have been in order to spare her own feelings, then, that though she had never desisted in her efforts to better poor Cecil's eyes, she had steadily opposed anything in the nature of an operation. Physicians and specialists from every country in Europe had been consulted, turn and turn about, and had expressed their views at large when out of hearing of their subject. For Cecil, this ordeal had almost become a habit. He knew how to avoid being hurt, became an expert in specialists' little ways, and usually feigned to be much more of a muff even than he looked. And when the specialist was gone, he would settle his silk shade over his eyes and just simply become himself again, whatever that might mean.

'We cannot be downcast,' Grummumma would sometimes declare in astonishing contradiction of her habits, 'we *cannot* be downcast, my dear boy, provided we know the worst. Face that, and all is well. Not, of course, that all these *clever* men intend to be optimistic. It's just false hopes that are the bane of most people. The poor hope to be rich, the afflicted hope to be whole, little realizing how much happier they would be if they remained contented with things as they are, and expected them so to stay. After all, Cecil, the ways of Providence are inscrutable.'

So Cecil had continued not to look up. On the other hand, there is a metaphorical use of the phrase, and Cecil had been reminded of it at rather frequent intervals. Here Grummumma and he indeed completely parted company. Particularly when Canon Bagshot came not merely to lunch but to 'help.' When Cecil was a little boy, the canon used to take him—used indeed to wedge him—between angular knees and talk to him. Being spare, dark, and tall, Canon Bagshot looked a more ascetic man even than he actually was. He had done excellent, if rather active, work in the parish and was one of the few human beings whose company Mrs le Mercier could enjoy without any symptom on his part of a polite subservience; and no local scheme of betterment was complete without him. Among these schemes, Canon Bagshot had somehow got imbedded in his mind the notion that Cecil might be cured of his physical difficulty if in *spirit*, so to speak, he could be persuaded or induced or compelled to 'look up.'

One particular catechism of this kind remained vividly in Cecil's memory, and Grummumma had been present at it, sitting with her back to the window, and drinking it all in. There was a particular large rose of many graduated reds in the beautiful carpet upon which he remembered he had then been standing. Two large bony hands had been holding his elbows, but only the extreme edges of the canon's dark, wide, dinted chin were visible as it gently wagged up and down.

'You know well, my dear boy,' the voice had assured him, 'how much we all have your happiness at heart. And if we urge you to things even a little painful in themselves, it is only for your good. And now I am told you refuse to speak sometimes when you are spoken to. Why is that?'

At the moment Cecil had no wish to refuse to speak, but his mouth was dry, he felt extremely uncomfortable, and what he most wanted to do *was* to look up into Canon Bagshot's face—though only to see if it resembled what was suggested by the tones of his voice. He meant to explain too that it was useless to ask him the same question again and again when he had already answered it. Instead of this, he at last managed to mutter: 'I don't want to.'

'But then, you see, my dear boy,' Canon Bagshot had replied firmly, 'it's just those *don't wants* that harass and impede us in life's pilgrimage. It is not what we want or don't want to do, but what we ought to do that matters. Your dear grandmamma wishes only for your *good*. "Ah," you may say, "I can't be like other boys." And that, of course, in its degree is perfectly true. God's will be done. But it doesn't mean that in many other things you cannot be *better* than other boys, setting them an example which should shame them, knowing what advantages they have, while at the same time you yourself should realize the many, many advantages denied to them which have *not* been denied to you. Do you follow me?'

The canon's voice, its mere accents, somehow reminded Cecil of an illustration in one of his story books—the picture of an Alpine guide, brass horn to lip, just vanishing round an incredibly precipitous bluff of snow and rock. It invited one on.

Cecil indeed had in actual fact been a long way in front throughout this speech. He now had to hasten back in order to nod and shake his head. This contradictory gesture was a little instinctive device of his own. If he *had* been able to raise his eyes, he might, with the same end in view, have opened them wider, then shut them.

'Precisely!' cried the canon. 'And examples are better than precepts. Are they not? You would hardly believe it, perhaps, but there is a poor old woman living in Fish Street, not a mile from here, who is compelled to lie on her back day in, day out, in one dingy little room into which I should hesitate to take a dog. She knows absolutely nothing of the gentle circumstances that surround *you*. Only one dingy old blanket to cover her; only one window, cracked and grimed, to look out of all day long. And I ask you, is she unhappy?'

'She must be very stupid if she is not,' had been Cecil's first thought. What he said was: 'I hate old women in Fish Street.'

'You will please, Cecil,' came a voice from Grummumma's bow-window. 'You will please, when you are addressing Canon Bagshot, leave off these sullen manners. Those who live with you may be accustomed to them; visitors are not. Besides, it is *very* irreverent.'

'Well, my dear boy,' continued the canon magnanimously, 'whatever you may think, you are mistaken. That poor, miserable old woman is as happy as the days are long.' The last part of the remark on this bleared winter afternoon was perhaps less appropriate than it seemed on the surface. But Cecil made no comment.

'Now to have to use physical persuasion in your case,' the canon continued, 'is the last thing any one could wish. All that I want you to remember is this: Humility, Trust, Gratitude. Say these words over to yourself night and morning. Say them now. No,' the canon rapidly added, remembering similar adjurations in the past, 'say them over when you are alone. For it is not, dear boy, as if we could plead ignorance. We *know* our duty. It is in black and white. "I must order myself lowly and reverently to all my betters." What does that mean? Surely, no scowling looks, no dumb-doggedness. Friends are constantly praying for you; sympathy is being poured out for your affliction. But though it is your lot in life to be compelled to be unable to face the world boldly, as Christian faced Apollyon, in *spirit* you can, like all of us, at least learn to look up. And I, as one of the humblest of spiritual pastors and masters, if you remain recalcitrant, must find some means of insisting upon your making the attempt. No sullenness, now, no dark clouds! *What* were our Gentle Three?—Humility, Trust, Gratitude.'

How odd a paradox. It was this Gentle Three that poor Cecil in later life had most to contend against; if, at least, there was to be any hope of *his* becoming the Happy Warrior.

But these were far-away days. Sunday by Sunday Cecil had continued to sit beside Mrs le Mercier in her pew at St Peter's and St Paul's. But the canon's sermons on these occasions were of a more general application. And since they differed as little in form as they did in matter and Cecil knew their trend by heart, much of this edifying half-hour was spent in day-dreaming. Here he had an advantage over his neighbours. For not only were the mean decorations of the Corinthian pillar and of the pitch-pine roof over his head, and the utterly dehumanized saints depicted in the stained-glass chancel windows—mustard green, blue, and crushed strawberry—out of his range, but no one could judge from his downcast eyes on what his attention *was* fixed.

But on the whole his relations with Grummumma were friendly enough, and, when visitors were present, even cordial. Then, indeed, if only in a negative sort of way, he *might* be said to look up to her, though it was difficult to tell exactly to what extent. And partly because he could not help himself and partly because of a natural indolence, he had just gone his own way—the way within, that is—without saying very much about it and without deliberately setting his will against hers.

Cecil, however, could hardly be said to be thinking of this *auld lang syne* as he gently pushed on round the crescent this particular sunny morning, one hand clasping the derelict glove in his jacket pocket. Only the faintest nebulous incubus of it hung in his mind. Meanwhile his eyes wandered restlessly and heedlessly over the ground at his feet. He had long been an expert in his own orbit. Quite apart from such manageable refuse as cigar and cigarette ends, dead matches, hairpins, footprints, pavement weeds, moss, the laying of asphalt, puddles, mud, dogs, cats, pebbles, straw, and so on, not to mention the lovely way of the wind in withered leaves or drifting snow—concerning which he was probably the only expert for miles around, he was also a connoisseur of horses' hoofs, boots and shoes, socks and laces, of the nether portion of trouser-legs, and of feminine skirts, shoes, and ankles. He was an expert, that is, without in the least being aware of it.

He had long enjoyed the habit, too, of steadily scrutinizing what happened to interest him indoors as well as out. Reading desperately tired his eyes, and so, even apart from the books his Grummumma kept out of his way, his literary range was decidedly narrow. But while he looked and read, he usually thought. He was indeed a master of his own exceedingly small fraction of the complete human range of consciousness—a range fairly considerable in itself and one which, of course, if only in the world of matter, is being steadily amplified.

But this fine morning he was anxious, uneasy, and sick at heart. His eyes wandered vacantly, his attention was elsewhere: simply because his one and only desire was to return the

rather dingy glove in his pocket to its owner. He just wanted
to say: 'You will forgive me for intruding, but I picked this up,
you see. And you may have missed it perhaps.'

It was never very easy to raise his hat when his Grummumma
whispered: 'Ssh, Cecil, there's Mrs Shrub, or Lady Linsey, or
Miss Bolsover,' mainly because he got so nervous and usually
hit with his knuckles the shade over his eyes before his fingers
reached the brim above.

But this time he was going to do it very carefully, and then
take his leave. It seemed to him a small glove compared with
Eirene's, with Mrs le Mercier's, or even with that of their parlour-
maid, Janet, which he had seen by accident hanging beside her
skirt (its hand within it), at the area gate but a few weeks ago,
after one of her 'afternoons out.'

This glove was scented, too, though not quite so delicately as
would seem to make it impossible for Grummumma to detect it
even though it lay in his pocket. Grummumma's gloves were
also scented, but rather with herself than with anything else.
He had deduced, too, that this specimen of a glove cannot have
been an expensive one. Yet the fact that it had a tiny hole in
its first finger only made him the more anxious to return it to
its owner. But—his heart had come into his mouth once more
—how on earth was he to recognize her unless she happened to
be wearing the same blue serge skirt, and the same stockings
and shoes as when she had come his way and had gone?

Never had there been such a fool as he was—he knew that well
enough. But to be a fool in public is one thing, to be a fool in
one's own private soul is another. And that was what he was
being now. He was being timid and ashamed simply because
there was the faintest possibility that Grummumma might herself be abroad that morning in her soft glacé kid shoes, or that
Canon Bagshot might come treading along in his stout parochials,
or spry, odious, mincing Miss Bolsover, with her ringing voice
and old-fashioned springsiders. All three of them would realize
at once that he was not merely enjoying his morning walk, but
hanging about, loafing. They would watch him; their gaze
would bore into his back; and by that time it might be—well,
too late. That the sun was scorchingly hot and the pavement a
continuous glare, with its sharp-cut shadows here and there and
its steady, pungent, broiling odour, was, however, a joy rather
than a martyrdom.

Cecil had by this time not only turned the corner of the crescent but was approaching the first of a row of shops. Their window-blinds hung dazzling in the sunshine, casting delightful shadows. A medley of noises zigzagged across the air. The whole vista of High Street, he knew, was steadily effervescing with traffic of matutinal gaiety and business. It was odd how one's mind roved to and fro from point to point in memory without once realizing its direction, or what had intervened. He had suddenly become a little boy again, his right hand tenaciously clutching the iron handle of a perambulator, which a plump young nursemaid, named Annie, in a stiff print gown, was pushing in front of her. At the same moment a grocer's assistant had come back to mind, a young man with a voice almost as rich in flavours as the inside of the shop in which he served. On the morning in memory he had slipped out of the shop to talk to Annie. And though Cecil could not recall any of the pleasantries they had actually exchanged, he could remember how double-voiced the young man with the frayed white apron and corrugated button-boots had seemed to be— just as if what he was saying had two meanings, one for Annie and one for himself.

And Annie had giggled on, while her cotton-gloved hand stroked gently the iron handle of the perambulator above Cecil's dumpy thumb. He hadn't liked the young man, and had even attempted to lift his young eyes just to give him a stare, to show it. The pain had dreadfully frightened him. And he was glad Annie had afterwards married a strange postman who had come to help in the district during the Valentine season.

This romantic little recollection for some reason made him still more ill at ease, and once again he reassured himself by clutching at the glove in his pocket. He hated the shops in this busier time of the day. He hated all crowds, 'gatherings,' congregations. He could tell by the legs and feet of the people thronging the street and its shop windows that from their upper parts they were also curiously examining this green-shaded stranger in their midst.

'What the devil!' he would now and then quietly mutter to himself. And then perhaps: 'Oh, mind your eye!' These hardly refined exclamations, picked up he knew not whence, were part of the life Grummumma knew nothing about. And still he held on, with that gentle antenna-like movement of his ivory-headed cane, and with rapid searching glances from under his shade at every human extremity that came into view.

This was his sixth similar excursion, and to-day he pushed on still farther—three more shops: an ironmonger's, with lawn mowers, syringes, pruning-knives, and slug-traps in the low window, all well within view; a tobacconist's—but Cecil had not been taught to smoke—and a tailor's and outfitter's.

Here for a moment he came to a pause. For a moment even his mission edged a little out of his mind. He adored clothes. Apart from his little collection of unframed prints and engravings and postage stamps, and apart of course from the plate on Sundays, they were all but his only means of being extravagant. In blind furious moments he had, it is true, more than once given every penny he had in his pocket to some dog-guarded 'blind man,' or paralytic, or forlorn-looking shrew selling matches in the street. This was not exactly charity, even though his heart seemed to gulp in his body at sight of them. It was a hostage to fortune, a clumsy attempt to call quits, perhaps.

For in general, like Grummumma, Cecil detested beggars, and edged away from anything that could be described as ghastly, horrible, or even unpleasant. He detested rags, dirt, and neglect; even the brazen spectacle of 'potatoes' in stockings or of leaking welts failed to amuse him. His shoes, his suits, his own gloves and hats and other adornments were made to measure. He enjoyed considering himself a fop; his little, innocent airs and graces were a sort of hobby. The 'man' would call at the house, and Mrs le Mercier, anxious to indulge any little harmless whim, would leave them to themselves. In all that concerns clothes and kindred matters, indeed, Cecil was at least as much of an expert as was Thomas Carlyle; and this morning he edged slowly along the display in the window, digesting for future use the exclusive shapes and tints and fabrics displayed on the other side of its plate glass.

Then suddenly at whisper of a silken *frou-frou* behind him, a flush of shame mounted into his pale cheek, and he turned about and retraced his footsteps. And Providence was watching over him. For he had trailed on not more than a dozen paces or so when, having arrived at the two private doors separating tobacconist's from ironmonger's, his anxious glance alighted on the long expected. And every drop of blood in him stood still.

The owner of this particular pair of shoes must herself have

reached the tobacconist's while he had been engaged at the outfitter's.   And, though the indiscriminate noises of the street had
suddenly mounted up into a prolonged roar, and then had ceased,
and though every fibre of Cecil's body seemed to be at an
affrighting stretch, he knew as well as if an angel had whispered
it into his ear, that she—the longed-for stranger—was now
actually surveying the peculiar creature he appeared to be.

In a strange, dizzy eternity, every forecast of this meeting,
turned over and over in his mind night after night of late before
he had fallen asleep, fled on the four shining winds of heaven.
It was as if he had come to the very end of a long straight road
—and then, nothing.

He had forgotten Grummumma, Canon Bagshot, Miss Bolsover, Mrs Grundy, all the conventions and his manners; he had
forgotten himself, his shade, the glove, the universe.   There was
nothing anywhere but just this mute unknown figure, of whose
slim person in its black-braided blue serge skirt less than one-
third was visible to him.   How odd that even in a world renowned for its oddities just a scarcely perceptible flaw in the
sewing of a toe-cap would alone have been enough to distinguish
those shoes from every other 'foot-wear' in man's five continents!

Perceptible—no, that was not the real mystery.   The shoes,
the skirt, were all he could see; and yet it seemed the presence of
this unknown girl, the very being of her, flooded his senses, his
mind, and—one might almost add—his soul.   There was not
even the perfume of the glove to help him.   Possibly that slim
malacca cane of his had now become in sober truth one of a pair
of human antennae.   What he had meant to say, what he had
heard himself saying again and again—not a single syllable of it
recurred to his mind.   His chin had lifted itself by a fraction of
an inch.   He could scarcely breathe, and his heart, as though
it were a hare on a dewy hillside when distant hounds are
hallooing, seemed to be sitting perfectly still in its ribbed cage.

'Forgive me,' he heard a voice utterly unfamiliar and yet his
own, pleading, 'please forgive me.   I have been looking for you
for days and days and days.   This is your glove.'   He was
holding it out, as if, poor young man, it was the very secret
of his life.

At this the feet beneath his gaze seemed to have planted themselves a little more firmly in their shoes.   There was an enormous
pause, while instinctively the young woman hesitated to thrust

out her gloved right hand or her bare left, till this moment concealed in her skirt. As a matter of fact, it was the bare left
hand that came into Cecil's view. And at first glimpse of it—
though Cecil was unconscious of the cause for at least half an
hour afterwards—a frigid and nauseating misgiving and disappointment had swept over him.

'And here,' said the voice, 'here's the very hand it belongs to.
Thank you *ever* so much.'

Perhaps because their fellow-servants, his eyes, were unable
to be of as much service as they might have been, Cecil's ears
were acuter than most. Before that voice's sound had come to
an end, he had half-consciously examined and dissected its every
minutest cadence and nuance, just as a connoisseur may sit down
to the critical enjoyment, say, of a fugue by Bach, or a melody
of Handel's. It rang within him—it very quietly rang within
him—and he never doubted in the least that he could read not
only much of its owner, but even of its owner's past in its inflexions. How strange; for never in the world was there such
a benighted ignoramus, such a poor, abandoned creature on a
remote atoll, as he.

'Yes,' said the voice, 'that's *it* right enough. I should know
it, if by nothing else, by the hole in the first finger. I hate
mending, and I haven't much time. But how you came to
know it was mine, and why you should have taken so much
trouble about it simply beats me. It simply beats me, I confess.'

Every vestige of self-confidence had by this time evaporated
in Cecil's mind. Yet—and how he managed it he could not
conceive—the next remark he heard himself making appalled
him by its boldness: 'I want, if you don't mind,' he said, 'to keep
it. Or will you please let me give it you another time?'

He could not see the longish nose and the dark eyes beneath
the delicate curved dark eyebrows of the face now confronting
him beneath its cheap straw hat. Its whole attention was
steadily, the least bit suspiciously, and yet with immeasurable
candour, fixed on his mouth. 'It isn't of much *value*,' said the
voice, but without the faintest trace of mockery in it.

'No, but you see,' blurted Cecil anxiously, 'I have kept it so
many days now, and should miss it. . . . I haven't very much
to do, you see. And, of course, not many friends.'

This was well on the right side of exaggeration, since in sober
fact and in any real meaning of the word, he hadn't any friends

at all. For though his rather remote cousin Eirene seemed to be almost more often in the house than not, and was occasionally accompanied by familiars of her own of both sexes, Cecil could never be perfectly at his ease with her, let alone with them. Nor could he ever be quite sure why she was so persistently sympathetic. He hated that even more than he deplored her silly French shoes and the colours and patterns she chose for her clothes. As for her friends, they never took any notice of him, no more at least than if he were a rather unusual chair, a dumb animal, or a pet canary that spent its existence pecking at a blunt-headed yellow spray of groundsel and enjoying an unlimited supply of lump sugar.

'Well,' responded the clear, crisp voice, 'even if you haven't, you don't seem to mind very much.'

'I mind *enormously*,' cried the young man, so loudly that he positively alarmed a little old gentleman with a purplish face and pale blue eyes who happened to be passing at the moment, and who whipped round on him like a startled bird.

'Then why don't you make some?' inquired the voice.

'I meant not friends—the glove,' blurted Cecil desperately. 'I mean, I want to *keep* it. May I give it you next time? To-morrow?'

'I am not so sure as I can get out,' replied the stranger.

'Well, if you please could and *would*,' he said, 'I shall be waiting here at this time. I shall be waiting here until——'

'Until?' echoed the other.

'Why, until,' he trailed on, 'there is no hope at all of your ever coming again.'

Once more there came a pause. The eyes regarding him had fallen, and were now overwhelmed, though evidently not for the first time, by a cloud of doubt and perplexity.

'Well, I really don't know that I ought to be seeing you again, I really don't——' the stranger's voice was repeating, as if she were speaking to herself. 'We don't know one another, and it isn't as if *you* . . . Not that I should—necessarily—mind that.'

For the breath of an instant Cecil's hand had fluttered towards his pocket as if to produce a card. It dropped again. 'My name is only Jennings,' he said. 'And I have a perfectly silly Christian name though it exactly describes me, I suppose—what I look like, I mean. So perhaps you wouldn't mind about that. And though, if you don't mind, I won't ask you yours—not here

and now, I mean; surely we do know one another now—a little?
And you will *come*?'

He awaited her answer, lips ajar, shoulders stooping, as if in
expectation of manna from heaven.

'And meanwhile, I suppose, I am to keep *this* hand somehow
covered up!' There may have been the faintest ring of defiance
in her tone, and yet, it seemed, not defiance of *him*. 'Very well,
then. I'll come. And then you promise to give me my glove?
Not because it's of much value—even to me; but because I was
already thinking of buying another pair of gloves and—and
losing *them* and so—well, that's settled, then.'

At this poor Cecil was more confused and dismayed than he
could have imagined possible. He had suddenly become aware
of but one small fraction of himself, the dove-grey, suède-clad
hand that held his cane. 'I don't see how you can *ever* forgive
me,' he blurted with crimson cheeks beneath the green. 'I had
no idea——'

'Why, how should you? And there's nothing to forgive as
I know of. And now I *must* be off.'

She was gone. Cecil was alone again. As much alone as if
he stood high up on a desert island, safe after shipwreck. But
gradually the bustle and babel, the sights and sounds and smells
of the street returned to his perception. He came to himself,
and suddenly realizing the enormity of these proceedings, was
utterly at a loss how to look, to move, to free himself, to find his
bearings. But the hateful shops at last were left behind him;
and, gently forging his course along familiar pavements and yet
all but into a world that until that moment he had never even
dreamed to exist, he was soon safely home.

Until that now remote day when Cecil had picked up the
stranger's glove, his secrets had been chiefly of an inward kind.
His outer life, his funny little groping ways and traits and fads
and interests and everything he possessed, including his tailor's
and hatter's bills—all these Grummumma had shared to the
full. Not that she ever openly intruded. Not that she exacted
confidence. There are other methods of opening a lock than
by forcing it. But apart from that, it is difficult to associate
ladies of unusually ample proportions with the activities of the
spy. Cecil knew perfectly well, and had been again and again
assured that anything Grummumma might do would always be

kindly meant. She invariably had his happiness at heart and watched over it, too. It was her nature, not only in regard to Cecil but to the world at large. Indeed, those fine black eyes of hers appeared to have so extensive a range that any attempt at concealment or subterfuge would be a mere waste of ingenuity.

What passed within was another matter. By steadily following the path of least resistance, though he was candour and openness itself by impulse, Cecil had tended as he grew up to become more and more secretive concerning anything that happened in his mind. That mind had thus become the queerest of little refuges all his own. To watch him *there* was almost like watching the innocent inmate of a private lunatic asylum or a novice in a nunnery. None the less this 'closeness' was due, not to the inability to say anything, but to the want of anybody to say all that he wanted *to*. The garden itself was choked to overflowing; at times he felt he *must* jump over its wall and bolt.

So it must have been merely because Grummumma was not interested in his mental states that she now failed to notice anything unusual. She remarked, it is true, at luncheon that morning, glancing at him over a forkful of green peas, that he seemed a little out of sorts.

'If I may venture, Cecil, upon a piece of advice,' she said when the peas had been safely steered to their destination, 'and it is none the worse because, as you know, I have long since acted upon it myself, I should eat a little less *meat*.'

He made no reply; and it was perhaps unfortunate that, as usual, she was unable to see his eyes—eyes now bent on the tiny slice of lamb on his plate and with an expression so innocent of any particular interest in it that she might for once in her life have been tempted to speculate on what he was thinking about. As a matter of fact, Cecil's whole being was tossing at this moment on a positive sea of the unusual. He *was* incredibly, immeasurably 'out of sorts.' A complete convoy of ideas, fancies, interests, circumstances that had hitherto accompanied him in his voyage from one eternity into another, had simultaneously foundered before his very eyes. Had foundered in an ocean immense, unimaginable, its crested billows of a dazzling whiteness, its arching skies of an unplumbable blue.

It was odd indeed, though he hadn't realized the oddity, that in his *imagination* no effort had been needed to survey whatever dizzy heights and depths might there suddenly reveal themselves. 'Meat!' He had never felt less hungry in his life. How rare an experience to be welcoming Grummumma's advice! He pushed aside untasted his remnant of lamb, and even the three new, innocent, little potatoes that accompanied it on his plate. He regaled himself with the green peas; and it seemed as though every single hour of his life—or at least of all its solitude —had been merely waiting for this morning.

Grummumma—crooking that charming little finger of hers on her plump white hand—having tossed off the last drops of her customary glass of sherry; the crumbs of her Bath Oliver having been already neatly brushed up into a heap on the damask tablecloth—rose at last to her feet.

'This afternoon,' she explained, with a last hasty brush of her table-napkin over her lips, 'I have to see Colonel Sprigge with reference to the Home.' Her Home, that was, for Girls; not the one whose roof so capaciously sheltered herself and the young man still seated at the table. 'And what are *you* proposing to do?' She archly wagged her head at him.

Cecil's head with its peaked shade, as it slowly veered round in her direction, had a peculiar resemblance to a searchlight, though a searchlight has no cowl.

'I thought, you know,' he said, 'of looking over my arrow-heads. Or I might, perhaps, take another little stroll.'

'Well, my dear boy, no matter,' returned Grummumma in that ample fashion which somehow always seemed to suggest a tinge of magnanimous impatience, 'do exactly what you please. But don't for mercy's sake fatigue your eyes with those dreadfully uninteresting, and I am sure, perfectly murderous, scraps of flint. We can imagine to what dreadful bloodthirsty uses *they* must once have been put. And if you *do* take a walk, keep out of the sun. Tea, then, in your own room, at half-past four. If my talk with Colonel Sprigge permits it, I shall be home about six.'

She was gone, silks, voice, presence, and all. And Cecil was left alone with his raspberry tart and cream, and his thoughts. He sat on until he heard the large varnished door emphatically shut. For a few minutes even after that he remained absolutely still in his chair. And then the skirts of the parlour-maid sounded at the door. He rose and, seizing his grey felt hat and his malacca cane, followed Mrs le Mercier out into the afternoon sunshine.

He had armed himself with the key to the gate of the neighbouring 'Gardens,' the freedom of which Grummumma shared with her discreet neighbours. Following a winding, bushscreened, gravel path, he came to a seat beside a patch of ornamental water; and there he sat down.

An immense dejection, hardly due to any heedlessness of diet, had taken possession of him. All that he had intended to say to his stranger—all, rather, that deep down in his mind, even though unexpressed in words, he had hoped to make clear to her—welled up into remembrance. All that he had actually said and done, those clumsy, stuttered speeches, the absurd, motionless way in which he had stood, that conceit about his own silly name, the hideous discourtesy of refusing to share hers after practically asking her to tell him it, all that miserable meaninglessness — the whole scene came flooding back to remembrance.

He did not mind the young woman's thinking him anything she pleased except only the feeble nincompoop he had shown himself to be. The clear, cool voice re-echoed in his mind— her openness, the frank, matter-of-fact tone in which she had claimed the missing glove. He knew exactly how she had stood there, poised and still, searching him with her eyes. Why, he hadn't even offered her his hand when he had said good-bye. Had he even raised his hat? His thoughts whirled impotently in a vortex. He longed to go fumbling off once more into the High Street with the faintest shadow of a hope that she might by a miracle be there. And to think that, when she had appeared, he had been gloating into a hatter's! And now a whole day to go; and that voice echoing on—unnaturally quiet, surely, for her age! Supposing she fell ill, or—why, anything might happen to prevent their meeting again. And he hadn't even the smallest notion where she lived!

Perhaps she was just being kind to him. He was used to that. Why should she really have had the faintest intention of meeting him again, of being made horribly conspicuous by standing there in that vile crowd of sightseers talking into a kind of green silk funnel. Perhaps she had just wanted to get rid of him.

No, no. Nothing mattered. He must just wait. Just wait for the chance to put everything right; to *tell* her that nothing mattered, except only that she must not let him be any kind of a trouble or burden; that he would never bother her again. And might he perhaps . . .?

The strained eyes remained tightly shut for a few moments. When they opened again, a solitary swan that had somehow contrived to keep its pride and beauty even in the muddy shallows of this 'ornamental water,' had floated in close under the bank, as if in need of company, or possibly of crumbs. Cecil stared at the creature from under his shade. Its virgin snow burned in the sunshine at least as purely as those on the far mountain-tops he would never see. The arched plumes of its wings were softly mantled. Its round eye glittered. Its dark-webbed feet were softly paddling beneath the greenish oil-like water.

It was an awful thing to sit there looking at it, and be so unhappy. Cecil was torn to pieces with longing. He didn't want to live any more. If the first real miracle that had happened in his life could leave him as miserable and dejected as this, what of the rest, of the years that remained? If only he had had a little worldly wisdom, he might at least have known what *not* to say. He could at least have shown the rudiments of courtesy. Why, she must have scarcely any money at all, not enough even to buy a new pair of gloves with, and he had forced the confession of it out of her like the most unutterable of cads!

But there comes an end at last even to self-abasement. A wan and rather sickly smile had spread over Cecil's face as he continued to watch this sequestered bird on the water. He took the scapegoat glove out of his pocket and examined the little, round, worn hole in the first finger of it. A sigh that was uncommonly like a sob shook him. 'May God bless you for ever and ever!' he muttered in an anguish of sentiment, and pushed it back into his pocket again. And as if the swan had been positively tarrying in the narrow creek beneath him for this precise benediction, it now unruffled its rose-flushed wings and, steering into the blaze of the sun, oared itself out of his sight.

Cecil turned home. There was one thing to be thankful for. He had been given a latchkey—to save the servants. He turned that key very quietly in the lock. It was twenty minutes to five, though how his charming watch had managed to deceive itself into making hours of what had seemed a few minutes completely baffled him.

His tea was awaiting him in the large white sitting-room that adjoined his bedroom. He poured it out—tepid, rich, red-brown, and there under the cover of the dish was the particular kind of scone with a trace of butter on it that he had detested the taste of ever since he could remember. And there too was yesterday's slice of plum cake. And out *there* the chirruping of sparrows. Everything was exactly the same as it had always been; and he himself—gross, clumsy, dull-witted—was merely somebody in a dream that had already come to an end. It was monstrous, this 'life'!

He put down his cup, rose to his feet, tiptoed out of the room, and having reached his dressing-table, took up the brushes he found there. But this was pretence of course; he had not come to brush his hair. He had come to see as much as possible of the self that she had seen from top to toe. For a minute or two he stood listening, then raised his face by a painful inch or so to peer in at what was confronting him in the wide mahogany looking-glass. And almost before the slightest sensation of the agony that would ensue, if he persisted, had made itself felt, almost before he had time to realize the fatuity of the attempt, he had turned abruptly away and was presently nibbling his buttered scone, and, despite Grummumma's warnings of the perils of indigestion, had poured himself out an even richer and redder cup of tea.

The sparrows continued to chirp, the western sunlight to pour into the room. But the waft of steam with its gentle gyrations on the surface had thinned away and the contents of the handsome Dresden cup were stone cold before Cecil came out of his second long reverie that day. It was not a happy reverie; for one tiny memory that had been steadily skulking at the back of his mind had at last gnawed its way out. And the process had left him with a deadly hollow ache beneath his heart. Grummumma might be a jealous goddess, but until this instant Cecil had never been conscious of such pangs. Yet, as he gazed on in memory at the shoes, the skirt, the sleeve, and the bare hand that had for an instant touched his own, he was conscious of but one corroding doubt—that ring!—a ring of discoloured turquoises which he had seen encircling the third finger of that left hand!

Yet when he raised his head at last, something very like serenity had come back into his mind. He would explain everything to-morrow. He would be perfectly calm and collected. He would give back the glove and prove at any rate that he was 'gentleman' enough, however queer a specimen, to withdraw out of this stranger's life with a little more courtesy and less confusion than had accompanied his intrusion into it.

To judge from Grummumma's *sotto voce* remarks to the parlourmaid during their solitary dinner that evening, the consultation with Colonel Sprigge on the affairs of the Home had tried her patience. Apart from this, the courses followed one another in silence. And the occasional diamond-like effects of Grummumma's eyes in her rather wax-like face, owing to this preoccupation, were otherwise engaged than in scrutinizing the young man who sat opposite her.

When, next morning, Cecil glided rapidly past under Mr Flaxman Smith's drawing-room window, the pretty parlourmaid, glancing down at him, discovered two things, and both of them to her consternation, for to-day was her afternoon out: first, that it looked as if a storm was coming on, and next, that her kitchen clock had once more and quite unaccountably lost at least half an hour.

But it was Cecil who paid for them by finding himself at his trysting-place exactly that much before his time. He hated being a spectacle, yet this morning it didn't seem in the least to matter. Waiting gave him the opportunity, too, to get cool again and to recover externally, at any rate, his usual fastidious serenity and aloofness. If only his thoughts would follow suit! If only he could breathe more easily! If only he could for an instant suppose that she would come!

So helpless and motionless the figure of the young man showed at last, standing there like a sentry close up against the private doors of the tobacconist's and the ironmonger's shops, that a tender-hearted young woman, taking him for an unfortunate aristocrat who had come down in the world, actually pressed a threepenny-piece into the loose, dangling hand, and then sped rapidly on. Little actions may have large effects. Cecil's icy-hot chagrin had instantly given way to an almost childish amusement. Threepenny-bits are for luck. And Cecil actually lifted the coin to his lips and deliberately spat on it before pushing it into his waistcoat pocket. It was money gotten under false pretences. He might at any moment be run in.

A shudder of sheer dare-devilry coursed down his spine. Let come what would—if only it were she! This peculiar smile was still hovering over the lower part of his face when, indeed, the young woman, as punctual as May Day, and as unexpected as a miracle, was suddenly once more in his company; and Cecil found himself in gentle motion at her side.

The grotesquely intense face of the day before could not so much as have hinted at the joy that now radiated from it—from his very finger-tips. And but one glance at it affected the mind this young stranger supposed she had 'made up.' None the less, 'Look here, before I go,' she was saying breathlessly, 'I have been thinking over what happened yesterday. And what first I can't understand is why you shouldn't have given me my glove then and there.'

Cecil's fingers holding his cane managed somehow also to clasp tight the threepenny-bit in his waistcoat pocket, while his other hand kept guard on the glove. His good angel was smiling at him from over his narrow shoulder.

'Why, you see,' he said, with an instinctive little bow that might have graced a Spanish grandee, 'it seemed so horribly public, and I knew you hated being looked at. Besides, you said I might keep it. Of course,' he added as if almost driven into a corner, 'I ought to have gone straight off to the police.'

'The police, *that* thing! The things you say! Still, I *do* say you must have picked it up very, very quickly. I came back the next moment to look for it, and there was nothing and nobody there—besides all this, I mean. It seems so very odd to me you didn't *notice* who had been so stupid. I am always losing things; though I really don't see why I should be reminded of it by—by strangers.' There was a pause, and then in a flash, and sharp as a dart, came the question: 'Had you ever seen me before?'

Cecil faltered. 'If you are going to be angry,' he said, 'I don't think I shall be able to do or say anything at all. All I want is just to try and explain myself and to give you the glove back. At least I don't, I mean, *want* to do that, but must. It was hateful of me to keep it. You see, I hardly know anybody, though that is not why—I wanted to know *you*. I had never, never seen you before, on my oath—and now . . . I suppose you 'd hardly believe it possible, but—since then, I have thought of *nobody*, of *nothing* else.'

The dark, attentive eyes had slipped over his delightfully tasteful apparel, head to heel. How little it told her. And yet that 'I don't know why,' and the quiet, restful sigh that had followed his last words had suddenly stilled the cautious, suspicious mind within.

'You don't know anybody! Then in that case how can you possibly *want* to know anybody you know absolutely nothing about? Why, it's broad——' and again she could have bitten her tongue off at such clumsiness—'You haven't even,' she rapidly corrected herself, 'asked me who I am. Quite the contrary. What is more, I can't stop talking to you in this hateful mob of people. Probably you don't know how they stare—and don't care. But I *have* got appearances to keep up.'

'That's just it, that's just it,' cried the young man as if in the depths of despair. 'I care enormously. I loathe them. Isn't there *any*where we could go to be quiet for a moment? I only just want to say, however absurd it may sound, that I *do* know you—I didn't know I could ever know anybody so well, and that it was utterly mean of me not to give you back your glove at once. And to keep you like this being stared at! Oh, if you only knew how I detest these horrible legs scissoring round us, you would at least realize I didn't mean to do *that*.'

A curious, crooked expression—expectation, incredulity, longing, dismay—hung over the face he couldn't see.

'Look here,' she said, 'I didn't mean to be a pig about it. I don't suppose——' she flung back her head a little—'I don't suppose you have ever so much as guessed that you are not the only young fellow loafing about on the "Parade." It is hateful to talk here, and I'd like to explain a little, too. What's more, by God's help, it happens to be early-closing day. I'm in a linen-draper's shop, you know—serve out the gloves I can't afford to buy. There is the river. Shall we go there? But I mustn't be very long.'

At least a dozen considerations came cluttering into Cecil's mind. To become the busiest of conspirators needs very little practice in conspiring. There was Grummumma, there was luncheon. There were the private gardens. There were the grounds of the rectory at the corner where you turn in by the bridge to the tow-path. To put anything off might be absolute disaster. Above everything in this world he wanted not to be remembered as one of the young fellows on the Parade. That vista appalled him—though he hardly knew why. Skunks, musk-rats, and boa-constrictors couldn't have a nastier flavour. Could he possibly get to the river without being seen? Could he possibly take *any*thing of a look round? And supposing . . . And then, in an instant, nothing seemed to matter. He was at peace and at ease.

'I can walk quite fairly fast,' he replied cheerfully, 'if you would just let me keep what I can see of you in the corner of my eye while we are crossing the road. May it be the river?'

It must be confessed there was no extravagant oddity in the outward appearance of the two of them, as, busily talking, they steered their way across from Messrs Ewart & Sons, the ironmongers, to the corner a little beyond the post office, and then on down Unicorn Street round by the sawmills. Furtively skirting the Bagshot orchard, they presently found themselves breathing the cool but stagnant sweetness of the air by the river. Its meadows on the farther side were fringed with drifts of fool's parsley; and on this side were tented with round, leafy, verdant lime trees; while nearer the water, glassing themselves in its flowing dark, hung the whispering green-grey of pollard willows.

Why this young stranger hurried quickly past a seat with a sloping back to it no more than a pace or two from the water and under an Eden-like bower which the authorities had somehow refrained from polling, and why she chose instead a low, hard one of oak full in the thinning glare of the sun, Cecil did not even attempt to guess. His only hope was to postpone for an hour or so the thunderstorm which was obviously completing its preparations; to say all that he wanted to say; and to hear as much as possible of what he longed to hear before it was too desperately near the stroke of one.

Here, then, these two seated themselves. And she herself, her bare hands, on either side of her, clasped on the edge of the hot wood, her narrow face now averted, now swiftly glancing at him, at once began talking so fast that he could scarcely find breath enough to follow her up.

'I don't really want to know who you are,' she said once more. 'I don't see that it matters, at least not to me. Not a bit. I *believe* you about the glove. I don't believe you have told me anything that is not the truth. So if you *do* make anything up—just taradiddles, you know—you may as well realize that

I shall probably believe you. Then it will be *my* responsibility. And yet—well, I don't think somehow you will do that either; though I shouldn't blame you if you did. *I* never knew any that didn't, anyhow. If you'd like to keep the glove, why, keep it. There's not very much in this world that seems to *me* much worth troubling about. They don't even *want* to mean what they say. But if any one had told me two or three days ago that I should be sitting here with you this morning, when I had promised to—to go out with a cousin of mine, well—' the dark eyes continued to brood over the now strangely shadowed meadows on the farther bank of the river, 'well, what I say is, that's *my* business. I'm free to do what I like, I suppose, whatever they may say. Still, you *are* rather— rather out of the usual, you know.'

And yet, though she had all but implored Cecil not to tell her who he was, 'or anything like that,' he was presently pouring out very little else. As usual, his mind began to hunt about in what she had been saying like a terrier suddenly let loose in a rabbit warren. Where next, and where next? Perhaps it was the echo in his mind of the word 'cousin' that at last made an end to these confessions. His lips closed a little tighter.

'This is a horribly personal question,' he faltered, 'and you need not answer it, of course, if you feel you don't want to; but would you perhaps mind telling me—' he pointed a forefinger to within an inch of the turquoises that showed bluer, it seemed, because of the bleached grey of the wood that surrounded the finger which they encircled, 'would you mind telling me if you are engaged to be married?'

His companion positively gasped. A crimson flush mounted up into her cheeks. She buried her hands in her lap. 'And so you *think*,' she cried, stooping forward over them, her head twisted awry almost under the very rim of his unsightly eye-shade, 'you *think* I should be sitting here with you if the man I was engaged to was waiting to—to go out with me? My God! It just shows what horrible mistakes one can make. I don't say a girl shouldn't do as she pleases,' she went on even more rapidly, and stooping closer over her lap, her eyes fixed straight in front of her on the worn green grass at their feet. 'I *am* free to do just what I like. But if you think—after what you have said—that I would do a thing like that—when I positively kept my promise to the very minute to be fool enough, after all I've gone through, to come and wait *there* for you in the street—well, all I can say is, I understand exactly the *kind* of old lady the one you say you live with *is*.'

Apart from anything else this impassioned speech might imply, it shot a bleaker shaft of light on Grummumma than Cecil even in his most discontented moments had so much as conceived possible. Grummumma!—somehow to get rid of her, to put her exactly in her right place, seemed to be his only way of escape, or at any rate the only possible way of keeping this explosive, enigmatic stranger sitting here beside him in this paradise amid the encircling gloom for just a few minutes longer.

'I assure you, I swear to you,' he said, 'that she is not so bad as that. She has been immensely kind to me. How would *you* like to have to take charge, or whatever you like to call it, of a person who, who—well, like *me*! I realize, of course, you must hate the thought of being *seen* with me. You needn't suppose I don't know what they have done for me in making me like this. But I swear, I *swear* I always supposed a ring on the third finger of anybody's left hand *meant* an engagement.' He groped round as if his mind were absorbed in an inextricable mathematical problem. 'And after all it *is* on your left hand!'

A dead silence fell between them. The hands in the worn blue-serge lap tightly clasped themselves together; that was all. The young woman never stirred.

'Wasn't that funny of me?' an almost unrecognizable voice a minute or so afterwards questioned him. 'Goodness! if I *was* engaged to my cousin—though this particular he happens to be a she—why, pray, *shouldn't* I be sitting here putting things right with you and keep him waiting a bit? I have precious little time to myself. I've had my fill of what they really want. And he wouldn't keep me long engaged if he made a fuss about that, *I* can tell you. I just—if you must know the truth—I wear this ring *now* because I prefer to be alone. I'm sick of the way they—well, *that*'s why. And now, please don't think I am asking this for any—for any horrible motives; but if you *did* see this thing on my finger yesterday, why didn't you give me back my glove?'

In the comparatively few years of his secluded existence, Cecil had become thoroughly accustomed to being catechized. But not exactly like this. And now, unlike most such little experiences in the past, his one aim and desire at this moment was to

share with his inquisitor every single little bit of truth that was
in him. He succeeded in this so admirably at length that the
two of them had soon abandoned all misgivings and reserve and
were chasing together every least little thought and experience
that happened to poke up its happy head into the wilderness of
their minds.

It was a wilderness that had begun to blossom like the rose.
They had discovered the solitude only two can share. By now,
indeed, not a single human soul was to be seen near at hand.
And for obvious reasons.

But though Cecil was capable of leaping blindly to conclusions
on what for most people would be the most inadequate grounds,
though but one glance at the sullen surface of the water, one
moment's attention to the torpid hush that was now hanging
its ever-thickening veils around them, would instantly have
warned him of what was coming, he was far too intent on other
things to heed. And his companion didn't care. Never, never
could either of them have guessed what an immense reservoir
of living water had lain treasured up and concealed in memory.
One twist of the fingers that now lay unfolded in the stranger's
lap beneath his very eyes—why, even that empty glove—had
suddenly turned on the tap. It seemed the flood would never
cease.

As for herself, a courageous, if not dare-devil heedlessness of
the future was her unrealized philosophy. She knew well
enough what they were in for. It was there before her eyes,
in her blood, in her brain, in every nerve. She was its centre,
its very eye. And the sudden dartings of her dark glances
to and fro drank in the complete menace of the scene with
avidity.

As she herself had repeatedly hinted, 'young fellows' of the
utmost assurance and aplomb were to be found in full display
morning and night, parading the pavements of the High Street.
And yet this young man who now shared the river seat with her,
with whom she was actually talking indeed as if they had shared
the same nursery, had somehow managed to stay clean outside
that dashing category. He was different in appearance, in talk,
in manners, in the complete, odd effect he had on her mind, as
a coral island is from darkest Africa.

She knew 'a thing or two' as well as any thing or two *can* be
known. And the knowledge had sufficed for most little crises in

what had been a fairly lively but what could hardly have been described as a lavish existence. She had even confessed to Cecil only a moment or so ago that though the cousin already mentioned had had nothing to do with it, except as a confidante, she had herself already been, as she supposed, more than once in love. Just to say it all quite easily like that seemed somehow to prove how irremediably *out* of love she was now. The confession seemed to be its own absolution. And yet, with another sudden flaming of colour in her cheek, she had easily managed to refrain from expressing her sentiments concerning the young man who had been responsible for the last experiment.

She could at least play fair even on behalf of a creature who hadn't the least notion of what the phrase meant. And she had twisted what had first sprung to her lips into: 'I didn't see as how I *could* go on caring for him. There isn't much in me, but I do believe in trying to be—if you understand what I mean —all of oneself there is. It was no fault of his, not at least that he'd know of, but—' once more the deep, dark, and tragic eyes stole over the louring meadows that lay beyond the water, 'well, there, you may think me a beast, if you like, but I came at last to hate him. Oh, how I hated him! It's gone now; it's over; and yet it has dyed me through and through. At least so I thought until—I didn't see *what* could come of it, I mean, but just a sort of suffocation if . . .'

Cecil had waited patiently for the end of the sentence.

'Well, if we had got married,' she added, as if the word meant hanged-drawn-and-quartered. 'Not that I suppose we ever should have been. It sounds awful, I know, as my friend said at the time; but I don't care even if it does. I am *glad* it . . .' Again she broke off, as if in sudden dread of her own impetuosity. 'There! that's all, that's all! I can't go back. No one could ask me to.' And the fixed wide eyes which the rejected young man had never really seen, and Cecil couldn't, were the very straightest of witnesses to the honesty of her tongue.

When at least half a dozen thoughts are entangled together in one's mind, it is difficult to express any. And Cecil had been utterly unable to make any comment on this statement before the young woman had swiftly dropped the clue. She could not imagine why her cheeks hadn't the sense to keep their natural pallor this morning; it wasn't a habit of theirs to go on in this silly fashion. Yet why on earth should it matter *what* they did,

when that funny green shade prevented anybody worth looking
at them from seeing them?

'Here I am,' her voice ran on breathlessly, in broken cadences
up and down its scale—a clear, challenging voice; 'here I am,
talking and talking, yet you are telling me nothing at all about
yourself. And soon there won't be another chance.'

'Another chance!' cried Cecil in guttural tones. 'You mean
you won't see me again? You can't mean that! Why, here
I am, seeing you now—if,' he added dismally, 'if seeing is the
right word to use. And yet I still keep on saying to myself:
"It's not the ten-thousandth part." Please do try and understand: I want to see *you*—*you*. Oh, your very self! You
couldn't have meant that.'

'*Me* ?' returned a faint and rather shaken voice. 'Me! there's
nothing in *me*. Besides,' and the tones flattened a little in spite
of the fact that a faint smile had crept into her eyes, 'that would
be seeing me double.'

'I said it. I mean it,' said Cecil stubbornly. 'I don't believe
it would be possible for me ever to know you enough. Everything you say leads me on as if, oh! into another world, and even
this one—I can't explain. I never knew there was such a place
to be in as where we are now, and yet,' it was as if a sudden light
had flooded his mind, 'what you have said as yet has been
nothing but—sign-posts.'

The dark eyes pondered. 'I think,' she said, 'if I thought you
were not meaning every syllable you say I should never hold up
my head again.'

The thin, delicate face was now averted; the narrow left hand,
as if purely of its own volition, had turned itself palm upward on
her knee. Even a young man twenty times less accustomed to
looking down than Cecil might have noticed it. But if he did,
he made no movement. He merely sat a little stiller.

'Mean? You!' he said, as if in utter perplexity. 'Why, even
to be seen with a creature like me must be a—an imposition.'
His head stared round on its shoulders. 'I assure you,' he said
with a sudden gleam of humour, 'it's an imposition even to me.'

Hardly had the little rill of answering laughter sounded out in
the sullen air when a headlong rush of wind swept over the
motionless meadows that lay opposite to them, turning their rich
seeding brown to a livid green, and sweeping the waters of the
river into a rippled shield of beaten metal. Dry leaves were

flying in it. The tree above them was swept as if by one vast, multitudinous sigh. There came a pause; and then out of the blue-black, cloud-vaulted heavens above their heads, a thin river of light suddenly flickered, like the fangs of a serpent. And as if at a signal, the solid globe beneath this day-benighted couple shook beneath a rattling crash of thunder.

Of the two, the young man must have been the least prepared for this assault. He showed not the faintest trace of being startled, however. He just quietly laid his hand on the up-turned palm and in his haste almost whispered: 'Quick, how high is the tree above us? I don't know this place. You are frightened. Where shall I take you? Quick!'

The fingers beneath his remained perfectly passive. The laughter that came in reply seemed almost as meaningless as a child's, and as full of gaiety.

'It's the littlest tree I've ever seen,' she answered, 'and the loveliest. Green and round and bushy, like a toy tree. And they go on like a row of umbrellas right along the bank. So unless they are really aiming at us up there, nothing will matter. Frightened! Please, please understand, I love it all. It's only the rain I am thinking of. What happens to me never, never matters. But what will your—what will the lady you spoke to me about think if you get back wet through?'

'Will you *please* not talk like that. Please not to. It's you I am thinking of, and——'

'And here it comes,' cried the young woman triumphantly. Her 'it' was neither lightning nor thunder, but a dense, league-long veil, part hail, part rain, that had now come sweeping over the all but blotted-out expanse of country before her eyes. Its *avant-couriers* smote ferociously and with a sharp *tap, tap, tap* on Cecil's silk shade. The wind swept over them as if it were perceptibly condensed against their bodies. An enormous confusion filled the air.

And then, well, indeed you never knew what this odd young man would be doing next. At this moment he was unbuttoning his coat. 'You must take this,' he was saying; 'you have got only the flimsiest things on. Why, I can see your arm through the silk.'

'Please, please,' she cried, catching both his wrists in her entreaty, 'don't do anything so utterly stupid. Oh, please—just think! Whatever would they say! And you'll get your

death of cold.   Look now, see, we'll get round to the other side.
There.   Do you realize it's a lime tree over us; and it's coming
into flower.   There's nothing to do—nothing, I *swear*—but just
to stay here quietly underneath it until the rain's over.'

Quite apart from the haste with which she had panted these
sentences, the clamour of the storm now almost drowned her
voice.   But actions speak louder than words.   Cecil struggled
no more.   And the two of them cowered as close as they could
against the dark, smooth bole of the young linden tree now
tenting her bright green branches over their heads.

When Nature is in one of her passing fits of hysteria, poor
little humans must just sit still and smile.   Nevertheless, any
chance observer of one of these young faces, and of all that was
visible of the other, would hardly have described them as smiling.
There is a happiness of the spirit that seems to draw an almost
grotesque mask over human features, that distorts and makes
strange and absurd and yet seems to irradiate them, as if they
were merely of glass made for a light to show through.

The next few days of Cecil's life were spent in bed and were
at the same time (so far as his mind was concerned), the most
active, the most wretched yet rapturous, and the longest he had
ever known.   The lime tree had proved to be an imperfect
umbrella.   Cecil had hastened home at last through the rain-
washed streets—blindingly silver-bright in the sunshine—in an
amazed happiness, on tenterhooks of anxiety, and soaked to
the skin.

Grummumma had listened steadily on to his rambling explana-
tions, at the same time rapidly comparing his attempts at
chronology with the dining-room clock.   Though he had an
advantage denied to most men, in that his tell-tale eyes were
concealed, Cecil hadn't the making of a skilful prevaricator.
This unusual eloquence in so reticent a young man was suspicious.   Grummumma, like an immense well-fed cat at a mouse's
hole, watched his lips and his hands as he sat there, attempting
to swallow his belated luncheon without exhibiting too obvious
an effort.   But whatever speculations she may have pursued
within remained unexpressed.   She was all credulity and indulgence.   Even when next morning she stood over him, clinical
thermometer between finger and thumb, and announced that
his temperature was 101°, she refrained from any 'I told you so.'

After all, the mouse was safely in its hole again, and there would be ample time to find out where it had been straying.

The storm was followed—a rather unusual caprice in an English summer—by a spell of happy, halcyon weather. The patient, however, lying there on his back in his beautiful brass bed, the blinds at the window all but shrouding his room, his shade over his eyes, enjoyed it only at second hand. When Mrs le Mercier was not either giving him his physic or sitting over him while he consumed milk pudding, his cousin Eirene was. She, however, was the more restless nurse of the two, and again and again would interrupt the *Cranford* she was reading to him in order to mince over to the window and peep out at the day.

'You can't think how lovely it is,' she would cry gaily over her shoulder. 'It's a *thousand* pities, you poor thing. And I simply can't imagine why you didn't take shelter in a shop. You always go that way, don't you, Cecil?'

And once more Cecil would be compelled to remember the precise terms of the rather fantastic little story he had invented to explain his sousing, a story received by Eirene with a variety of reactions. After what was perhaps the fifth attempt to glean a little further information, she returned to his bedside and, so to speak, took the bull by the horns.

'What auntie, you know, has perfectly made up her mind about *now* is that you really want somebody to take more care of you. And I am going to be one of the "somebodies." You are getting mopish, Cecil. You just shut yourself up away from everybody, though you *know* how sympathetic we all can't help being. And what's more, I believe you make things out worse than they are, just to spoil yourself a little. The doctor was saying only the other day that, even if it is a little painful, you ought to try ever so little to—you know what I mean—to *make* yourself better.'

'My eyes, you mean?' interjected Cecil from his pillow.

'And aren't our eyes,' cried Eirene brightly, 'almost, as it were, ourselves? Why, *you* see things that I have never even noticed at all. It's quite, quite wonderful. Still, you mustn't mind my speaking out a little, even though you never seem to be really listening to half I say. You couldn't tell me a single word about that last chapter I have been reading, now, could you? And I can't bear reading aloud, especially in a room like a vault.'

Cecil remained perfectly still in his bed. 'You have been kindness itself, Eirene,' he replied in a flattish voice; 'and it's

hateful to keep you here. Do please take a little rest. And—
and might I have half an hour's more *Cranford after* dinner?'

'Well, if I must, I must, you naughty boy. But promise me,
if I do, that you 'll get a little sleep. We all do so much want to
help you all we can. It 's *so* difficult—just groping in the dark.'

There was almost a hint of tears in her voice, and she stooped
prettily, though not very far down, as if to blow him a kiss right
in underneath the green shade, for as a matter of fact she had
always felt a peculiar disinclination to confront those hidden
eyes. How was she to tell, then, if her incipient kiss had reached
its destination? She eyed the long, green-cowled hummock
mistrustfully. 'And you 've *promised* to turn over a new leaf?'
she concluded.

The door gently closed, and the rack on which Cecil lay
resumed its more leisurely activities. Of all the rats that were
gnawing at his mind, one was never for a moment satisfied—
what must his stranger be thinking of him now? With unpre-
cedented presence of mind, his last words had been that he
would be found edging along around the shop-end of the crescent
at a quarter-past eleven every morning, *ad infinitum.* Just about
then, it appeared, would be her only chance of a few free minutes
except in the evenings, and on Thursdays; and even they were
precarious. Why, Cecil had not attempted to find out.

Sheer instinct had told him that circumstances had never been
very kind to her. He realized she must be 'poor,' and the very
sound of the word sent him rushing away from it in his mind as
fast as ever he could. From infancy he had been lapped in
comparative luxury, and the merest suspicion that beneath
Luxury's silken skirts were concealed two bony knees filled him
with incredible dismay. None the less he knew with the immense
assurance of mere faith that somehow or other she was not going
to be poor for very long; that he was going to just sweep those
circumstances up into a pile and burn them.

There never was a more helpless creature than himself; he
knew that, too. And yet, once or twice in his life, he had determined to have his own way, and this was going to be another
time. But how see her? How keep his trust? How write to
her? How let her have but one word to show that it was only
a silly old temperature and a Grummumma and a doctor and
a quick-witted, nimble-tongued cousin that were for the moment
keeping him away?

He had so many times re-explored in imagination that hour by the river that he now knew every inch of it by heart. And what is more, huddling there beside her under the linden tree, he had actually managed to speak of his infirmity. It was the one thing in the world his tongue hated and detested having anything to do with. Still, it had somehow stumbled out; and the ordeal had not only proved an immeasurable relief but had also won an immeasurable reward.

'Think worse of you for *that*! Oh, what an utter meanness you must feel in me! Why, all along I have almost hoped you were *blind*; for then, you see, I might have been of help, though I don't quite see how—*if* ever, I mean, we *are* going to meet again. "Worse," indeed! I'd ask the thunder just to swallow me up if I even so much as thought you thought it.'

Her face had been turned away from him as she spoke; and the grass at his feet, studded with small, snow-white daisies and here and there a yellow dandelion, had showed a wild, violent green beneath yet another riot of lightning.

But why did that particular 'blind' still make his heart stand still with delight, while Eirene's nattier little pronunciation of the word just now, rankled in his side like a poisoned arrow? Could anything be odder? And what, indeed, was the matter with Eirene?

Two days ago she was just a first cousin much removed, waiting for him like a lightship, so to speak, irremovably in the offing, both a warning and an eventual refuge against all life's storms. He had always known that if nobody more satisfactory turned up for her Eirene would probably decide to marry him. Grummumma had often spoken about it, quite plainly, however playfully; and since Cecil had always hated thinking of the future, he habitually left that future to wait until the present caught up with it.

And now the present had actually done so. And he knew as well as if it had been written down on paper, first that Eirene had suddenly made up her mind—just as if *his* chill had been *her* conflagration, and next, that he had also made up his own. He didn't know exactly how he could manage to persuade his stranger to accept for the time being about two-thirds of his modest income. But it was his, and he was going to do so, and by sheer logic Eirene was therefore *not* going to marry him.

And then, Cecil had suddenly stopped thinking and had actually found himself attempting to put Eirene's advice into practice. Hands clenched, heart pounding, pulses drumming, he was endeavouring, if only by the remotest fraction of an inch, to raise these abject eyes of his in their sockets. A horrible sweat broke out on his forehead. He was shivering from head to foot. He persisted, none the less, until it seemed the very brain beneath his skull was splitting into fragments, and incandescent stars and arrows of light were raining out of the darkness. And then, poor spoiled invalid, he flung himself over on to his pillow, and turning his back upon paradise, wept with rage and chagrin.

When calm returned, there returned with it, hungry as ever, the same old rat. How was he ever to assure the stranger that he was not—well, just another 'young fellow'? And once more the words that had haunted him repeated themselves over and over again in his mind: 'I came at last to hate him—to hate him.' He lay there—stiff and still. Grummumma's step was sounding on the stair; the First Wardress was approaching. Despair swept over him. The nameless, longed-for one must in sober fact be hating *him* with all her heart and soul this very moment.

But Grummumma (followed by the parlour-maid carrying on a silver salver a dish of sole and a glass of hock), was bringing him, apart from these dainties, news which proved at least that, however extreme that hatred might now be, it was not going to prevent the young people from meeting again. First, she assured him he was much better. That being so she paid very little attention to the grey, damp underpart of the face that lay on the pillow, though even the hair on that pillow was dank with sweat. Being better, he might sit up this afternoon and come down to-morrow. And the afternoon after that he was to receive a visitor. 'And I wonder, my dear boy, if you can guess who that will be?'

There had been only the faintest trill on the 'that,' yet at sound of it his heart stood still. 'Is it Canon Bagshot?' he muttered stonily.

'Him, too,' breathed Grummumma, 'but who else?'

'Eirene's not going away, is she?'

'Not quite yet,' smiled Grummumma. 'But then, Cecil, she is coming back for good.'

'I give it up,' said Cecil. 'And anyhow I should much prefer to be left alone.'

'My dear boy,' replied Grummumma, with that hint of unction in her voice she could never keep out of her kindest remarks, 'you would always prefer to be left alone. And what do you mean by that, may I ask? Left alone with whom? There are limits surely to one's poor little self. I agree you are tied. But, as Eirene was saying, how long is it since you have made any effort to undo the knot?'

Cecil made no reply.

'You have unnumbered blessings,' went on the philanthropist. 'Solicitous friends, a little income of your own. And though I agree the handicap has been extreme; yes, Cecil, you even have brains. And people with brains, my dear boy, don't dash their heads against brick walls; don't fly into silly entanglements out of which even the most clear-sighted minds find it difficult to extricate themselves. You *make* little difficulties. And as Dr Lodge agrees, and indeed as specialist after specialist has assured me, a physical habit is bound to reflect itself in the mind, and also, no doubt, in the heart. And if in our various spheres of society we have not a certain amount of proper respect for things as they are; if, that is, we don't draw the line somewhere, the consequent difficulties merely end in disaster. And *do*, my dear boy, show *some* little appreciation of that delicious-looking sole before it is stone cold on the dish. No; I didn't mean to be led away into a discussion on the physical side'—she flickered in a charmingly helpless fashion her little, fat, ringed hand in the air—'I know nothing of all that. All that I merely wanted to tell you was that I have invited a young lady—a friend of yours —to *tea.*'

'A young lady—a friend of *mine?*' Cecil mumbled, as if incredulous of such a marvel.

'Exactly that,' cried Grummumma brightly. 'She is an assistant in that large new draper's, poor thing; and, considering the practice she has, I must say she writes a charmingly illegible hand.'

Cecil plunged clean into the deep end of the bath prepared for him. 'I am delighted,' he said.

'About the handwriting?' inquired Grummumma.

'That she is coming to tea,' said Cecil.

'In my young days, gallantry would have suggested *suggesting* that Miss Simcox should come to tea. Wasn't it in the nature of things that we should wish to know her—after you had met, well, as you did meet. You must have realized long ago that I am never likely to be a stickler for *mere* conventions. Why, then, may I ask, have you been hiding the young lady under your bushel?' The voice was almost prattling in its geniality.

Cecil took a gulp of hock before replying. 'Why, Grummumma, since you have asked her to tea, I don't see where the bushel comes in?'

The black, handsome eyes had fixed their whole attention on his lips. 'But why not at *your* suggestion, Cecil? It was *that* I was asking.'

'But surely, Grummumma, one's invitations are pleasanter when they are given on one's own initiative. Yours must be, I am sure.' The water was proving more buoyant than he had expected.

'My dear!' she acquiesced. 'Then why didn't *you* indulge in one? I find no difficulty in believing that Miss Simcox would have come to tea on Friday with even greater alacrity and pleasure if my poor little note had been in your handwriting.'

'You didn't call on her, then?' mumbled Cecil.

'I proposed to myself the pleasure of her calling on *me*,' replied Grummumma. 'And to whom, my dear boy, do you owe what I am sure must be this charming acquaintance?'

Cecil never lied. And a kind of nausea at the thought of any further fencing or prevarication suddenly swept over him. If the fat was already in the fire, why shouldn't he set it blazing? He sat up on his bed prim and stiff, his snowy pillows for background; 'I *believe*,' he stolidly replied, 'I just woke up.'

'Charming, my dear Cecil, most romantic! But my actual question,' Grummumma persisted equably, 'was to *whom* do we owe it?'

Cecil jerked up even a little higher and the shade tilted itself almost to the angle of the peak of a guard's signalling lamp. But, if anything, and in spite of it, the light beneath was red rather than green.

'To whom *does* one owe any kind of awakening? Why sometimes, I suppose'—and the voice had fallen flat and cold—'to sheer, downright Providence.'

'I must ask Canon Bagshot to give us an address one Sunday

on false gods, Cecil. You might learn a little more of the other One—by sheer force of contrast.'

There was a pause.

'Will Eirene be here?' Cecil inquired at last, his head now lowered again over his clammy sole.

Mrs le Mercier's kid-clad right foot was at this moment beating softly on Cecil's deep-piled bedroom carpet. It was her method of purring. She was looking at the china on the luncheon-tray and smiling gently, as if consciousness were just over the border of a charming reverie. Then she laid her other little card on the table, patly and finally, since sooner or later it would almost certainly have to be disclosed. 'Why yes, Eirene will be with us—would make a point of being with us. Hasn't she the positive privilege? Even if it were not a pleasure, dear boy, to share your friends, it would be little short of a duty. And Miss Bolsover is coming too. It will be quite a pleasant little party for Miss—Miss Simcox.'

She paused once more, but this time paused in vain. 'Go on then, my dear boy, as fast as ever you can, getting *better*!' she harangued him. 'The removal of almost every little misfortune in this life, except those that come from above, is merely a question of time.'

Cecil sat up (physically speaking), and as she had prognosticated, that afternoon, and he went downstairs the next. But so assiduous were those who watched over his convalescence that, except after he had blown out his candle for the night, he was not for a moment left to mope alone. One can mope to some little purpose, however, in the gayest of company. During the forty-eight hours that succeeded the sole, apart from those which he passed in restless sleep, he enjoyed not a single moment of peace of mind. Nor was the faintest chance given him of bringing his inward conflict into the open. Short of speaking out, which every nerve in him forbade, he might drag one red herring after another across the trail in the hopes of leading Grummumma on. But she seemed to have lost all interest in the chase. How had she found him out? Did he talk in his sleep? How had she discovered Miss Simcox's name —and where she lived? What, *what* had she said to her? But Grummumma positively refused to budge. She believed that silence was best. Miss Simcox was never even mentioned again.

At a quarter to five, however, on the day before the tea-party, and when Eirene was in charge, Cecil made his first and only frontal attack. His feverish cold had left its marks behind it. There was something unusually invalidish in the look of the young man when, without the faintest preparation, he suddenly blurted out his challenge. 'I want—' he said, 'Miss Simcox's address!'

'Cecil!' cried his remote cousin in unconcealed amazement, 'you don't even know so much as her address!'

'No,' said Cecil, 'not so much as her address. And I want to write to her *now*.'

'But, *my dear*, the creature will be here to-morrow afternoon. Surely you need not be so intemperate as all that?'

The young man sat as still as a draper's model in his arm-chair. 'I don't know what you mean by "intemperate,"' he said, 'and I don't much care. The point is, I want to write to her. And I want you to give me the chance of doing so when Grummumma is not here. What's more, Eirene, if you breathe a word of what I am saying to a living soul—then, I assure you, you will regret it.'

Eirene had never before heard trumpets in her cousin's voice and had never before noticed that he sometimes sat so motionless as to resemble not exactly granite, but at least Portland stone. Her hands clasped themselves in her lap. 'I think it's perfectly monstrous of you,' she cried lamentably, 'to talk to me like that. Why, you are threatening me, Cecil! And who am I, may I ask, to be a skulking go-between? A nice kind of a creature this friend of yours must be to reduce you to that. I simply flatly refuse. Besides, I don't *know* her address.'

'How did Grummumma find her out?' said Cecil. 'Did *you* help?'

'My Heavens!' shrilled Eirene. 'And now you accuse me of being a spy! As if any one like you isn't conspicuous a mile off. Even a shop-girl might have known that. I expect she did.'

'And do you suppose I *mind* having been seen?' cried Cecil furiously. 'But I'm not going to argue about that. You are merely misleading me. Please keep to the point. You swear you haven't her address?'

'I will swear nothing,' said Eirene. 'It isn't right. I *say* I haven't her address. And I simply don't care *where* she is— or ever will be.'

'Then I believe you,' said Cecil out of a horrible vacancy and

yet as if he were conferring a royal favour. 'But please understand, if you repeat a single word of what I said just now to any
one—well—we shall both of us be sorry for it.'

Eirene rose to her feet. 'To think,' she sobbed, 'that I should
live to listen to this. Why, you must have known her for ages.
She has corrupted every vestige of nice feeling you ever had.
And you sit there without caring a fig what I suffer. I detest
the very sight of you.' She broke into a renewed flood of tears,
and hastened out of the room.

Strangely enough, though her last remark was intended to be
the truth, the frail creature had suddenly discovered that she was
as near as she ever would be to being in love. In her frantic
haste to be alone with her rage and resentment, she managed to
push past Grummumma, who attempted to intercept her in the
hall. She managed even to refrain from enlightening that lady
regarding the cause of the little scene she had been too late to
interrupt. Grummumma, however, was by nature and habit a
sagacious woman, and knew when to hold back. To have succeeded in pumping a little emotion into Eirene was almost as
much of an achievement as to have succeeded in pumping whatever she had managed to pump into the mind of Miss Simcox.
She awaited her little tea-party with folded hands.

And almost before Cecil had any opportunity to realize that
the tournament had begun, it was over. The odds had been
appalling. The only ally of the young stranger had scarcely
uttered a word. With eyes fixed now on the floriations of the
drawing-room carpet, and now on Canon Bagshot's ecclesiastical
boots, Cecil had sat mutely listening to the talk. Indeed, no
better prize could be offered in recognition of Grummumma's
tactics than the fact that never at any moment was there any
real opening for him. No kind of social gathering from a school
treat to a *tête-à-tête* with a philanthropic duchess could exhaust
Canon Bagshot's finesse. And Mrs le Mercier had all her life
apparently been an authority on the grievances of shop-assistants.
Eirene, with her puffy hair, elegant hands, and pale, fine features,
merely held a watching brief, though she saw to it that their
guest was never without the creamiest and the chocolatest of the
cakes for tea—just to give her something to do with her fingers
while she tried to hold her own with her tongue.

As for 'dear Miss Bolsover,' she rolled her blue eyes and
occasionally tapped with her blunt-toed shoe (but rather like

dog thumping its tail-stump than a cat purring), and remained tactful to the last degree. If the parlour-maid had been given three guesses as to which of the party in the drawing-room had been responsible for the presence of the young lady in black in its midst, Miss Bolsover would almost certainly have been given the glory of being the last runner-up.

And the dark young lady herself—poor Cecil writhed in the consciousness that the fatal hindrance to any possibility of her enjoying this little parlour game was his own share in it. There was a cold, clear ring in her voice, as different from the others as a silver bugle is from a bassoon. She was being flayed alive, of course, as dexterously as a professional Chinese could have managed it. But then life, even the few years she had enjoyed of it, had more or less accustomed her to the process. And it is miraculous how swiftly Nature can produce new skins. Besides, how much easier it is to endure any kind of torture, even that of tongues, in a good cause! And good cause it must be, since it was poor Cecil's, sitting there as dumb as a fish, and that out of water, in his dark-green shade. That he could hardly boast of being much in the way of a 'young fellow' was proved by the elegant company she was keeping. That he therefore needed her championship the more was somehow proved by the fact that Canon Bagshot was at this moment urbanely stooping over her with a second cup of tea.

'I garther, then, Miss Simcox, the Roman Carthotic Church is a little less intrusive than it is usually assumed to be.'

'Though not, it seems,' interrupted Grummumma, 'to the extent of allowing you to join a Guild in connection with a Sister Establishment. Otherwise, I understand, you are free to believe pretty much what you prefer.'

Miss Simcox was at this moment doing her utmost to appear at her ease with a cup of tea in one gloved hand and the cream-clogged éclair that Eirene had hospitably palmed off on her with the other. 'Oh, no, not *believe*,' she cried almost brightly. 'I thought you were referring to what it would be good for me to *do*.'

'And surely,' mused Grummumma persuasively, 'actions speak louder than words.'

'But that's a proverb, isn't it?' suggested her visitor doubtfully. 'I remember once hearing someone say that very thing to Father Browne; I forget what about.' At her glance, Canon

Bagshot hastily resumed the smile that had begun to fade away across his face.

'And what was Father Browne's reply?' he inquired indulgently.

'He said, in that case, one should take very good care not to deafen oneself.'

'And what do you imagine, Miss Simcox, he meant by that?' inquired Mrs le Mercier, with a roll of her fine eyes.

'Answers are useless,' interposed Miss Bolsover, 'that merely confuse things, and especially where principles are at stake.'

'What do *you* think, Cecil?' continued Grummumma, swooping round on her grandson with the *éclat* of a squadron of cavalry. 'You are being remarkably silent this afternoon, even for you. Though no doubt you have discussed the question?'

The green shade shifted uneasily. 'I suppose what Father Browne meant,' Cecil faltered, 'is that what one does is not necessarily a proof of what one is. At least one may hope not—always. I suppose motive counts, and that we can never really know one another. What's inside, I mean. The rest may be chiefly advertisement. But it's not much good asking me. I don't indulge in actions.'

'Dear, dear, dear!' cried Grummumma crisply, 'deeper and deeper! I wonder what Canon Bagshot is thinking of such heresies.'

She did not pause, however, to inquire, but at once turned the stream of conversation in the direction of the Shop Acts, and was presently assuring her visitor how much, *much* brighter she must be thankful to realize her lot in life now was, compared with that of the young ladies who worked in drapers' establishments twenty or thirty years ago, when there was no early closing, when no 'assistant' was *ever* out on the streets until after ten o'clock, and on Saturdays—imagine it!—not before midnight. 'The evils of such a system! And the living-in conditions!' She lifted her plump hands in horror from her lap. 'They were, I understand, simply too dreadful for description. Anaemia, pernicious and otherwise, was rampant, I believe. And far worse things than anaemia! The committee of which my dear father was chairman was shocked beyond words. But now everything is changed. You are free, Miss Simcox, for a little pleasant gossip, are you not, almost at any hour of the day?'

The dark eyes of her visitor, from under her small black hat, watched every expression of the old handsome face. Except for a slight increase of pallor, her own showed no trace of the fires that were smouldering within. Her wits, too, a little more nimble perhaps than Grummumma supposed them to be, were rapidly accustoming themselves to a method of attack with which they were not wholly unfamiliar. It would be as refreshing as a plunge into a cold bath to let these good people realize her real opinions of them—to give as good as she was getting, and so quietly too that 'moddam' would remember it to her dying day.

Her glance wandered for an instant resolutely from face to face, passed on softly from flaxen Eirene's, then rested on Cecil. He was sitting with folded hands and downcast head as if, poor thing, this was a Home for the Feeble-minded and she herself was an applicant who could not afford the fees. If he had been a blind mute, he could hardly have looked more immobile. The angry flames within languished, went out. She felt suddenly limp and helpless and was just about to prove to Grummumma how swimming a victory was hers, when the groping figure in front of her pushed out his chin and remarked that if what Mrs le Mercier had said were true, then men must be worse devils than he had thought possible. 'If I had my way,' he burst out passionately, 'I'd burn the whole "Parade" down.'

'Exactly, my dear boy,' retorted Grummumma, 'and be off next morning (if you escaped the police) to find another hatter and hairdresser and haberdasher. Oh, Cecil, Cecil! Miss Simcox is perfectly well aware, my dear boy, of her employer's difficulties. We have in this world to face things as they are. And civilization is impossible without give and take on all sides.'

'Yes,' cried Cecil ferociously, 'and who does the taking, I should like to know?'

'But surely, dear lad,' urged Canon Bagshot amiably, 'we must not mix up things as they ought to be with things as they are. We must push gently on from one to the other. Progress is step by step, not by violent eruptions.

Not in vain [*he cleared his throat*], not in vain the distance beacons.
　　Forward, forward let us range:
Let the great world spin for ever down the ringing grooves of
　　change.

That surely is not only poetry, but all that makes for sobriety and discretion. And are we not missing the whole point of what has been said? It is that the conditions of shop life have been very much *improved*. We are—I agree in only a small respect—*congratulating* ourselves. Is not that so, Miss Simcox?'

Miss Simcox had put down her cup once and for all at last. She glanced a little hesitantly about her. The green shade had lowered itself once more. Not a feature was visible; the delicate hands were clenched tight on the chair. 'Shop life?' she said, 'Oh, yes!' And she looked at Canon Bagshot. 'But then I don't see how people *can* know what other people's lives are really like. And what does it matter? I am perfectly happy as I am.'

'And *that*,' said Grummumma, rising with an almost majestic urbanity, 'is the most sensible remark I have heard for many a day. If every class and degree could say that, our difficulties would be at an end. My stepdaughter—my grandson's mother— Mrs Mortimer FitzKelly—once had a young nursemaid who . . .' With the amplest of smiles and the most elastic of gestures she had inserted herself between the two young people, and was already proffering her hand. Eirene had slipped over to the piano, in hasty search apparently of a suddenly remembered promise to perform. Miss Bolsover had already engaged the canon in talk. The contest was over.

And at this precise moment Cecil dragged himself to his feet, as if to re-enter the lists. But in vain. He blundered forward only to find that Grummumma had exquisitely eluded him, and that their guest was already well on her way out—out of touch, out of hearing, even of hail.

His head twisted aimlessly on his shoulders, like a rusty smoke cowl in a breeze. A cloud swept over his dejected eyes. He turned irresolutely as if for help.

'You poor dear boy,' cried Mrs le Mercier, as she hastily re-entered the room, 'I am afraid Dr Lodge has been far too precipitant. You look positively worn out.'

But Cecil was already pushing his way out of the room. And as with hand upon the banisters he groped his way on from stair to stair, he caught only the last word or two of what Grummumma was saying: 'Just a soupçon of *savoir-faire*, poor little thing; and she might be almost presentable.'

* D 940

It was Eirene who tapped at his door a few minutes later. She turned the handle, but in vain.

'Cecil, dear,' a whisper came, 'it's only me. Are you ill? Is anything the matter?' But since no answer of any kind sounded out of the vacancy beyond, there was nothing for it but to hope for the best.

Miss Simcox's champion can hardly be said to have appeared in shining armour. For an unconscionable time he sat by his dressing-table, his hands clasped between his knees. He was attempting to think, to argue, to explain, to plan, and all this at the same moment. The result was little more serviceable than the rotations of a squirrel in a cage. Nor did the chattering of his teeth afford him any particular help in the crisis.

During the next few days, though never before in his memory had balms so gentle and precious been poured upon his head, Cecil realized that he was a prisoner closely guarded, with a family physician for chief warden. Of his two devotees, he much preferred Grummumma. She at least made no attempt to suggest that she was an ally he had treacherously stabbed in the back.

It was the faint, far-away pathos in Eirene's tones, the gentle insinuations in her manner—'See how forbearing I am!' —that corroded every hour he spent in her company; while always between them lurked the remembrance, never referred to, that he had asked her help, had flung himself on her mercy, and that she had at least not given him away. She had so little given him away, indeed, that every touch of hand and wooing cadence of the grieved voice assured him that she was in fact keeping him entirely for herself. Moreover, what she and Grummumma might have managed unaided was made the more easy by the thermometer and the weather.

There was no doubt Cecil was ill, though the most distressing of his symptoms—the mind that revolved on and on in anguish at his own helplessness—remained concealed. It was a helplessness, none the less, awaiting only the very shadow of an opportunity to break free.

About eleven o'clock on the Tuesday morning after Mrs le Mercier's unusual visitor had come and gone, the clouds over Cecil's birthplace broke gently and then cleared completely away. It fell to Eirene to take him, well wrapped up and looking more like a hopeless invalid than ever, on his next constitutional. And Cecil chose for it a route exactly opposite to that which would have led them towards the shops.

'I often wonder,' she began speculating, in her lately acquired plaintive tones, 'what you really and truly think of people, Cecil. You always seem to me to have much more definite "views" about them than most men of your age. And they don't seem to be very high ones—the views, I mean. Why's that?'

'You mean,' said Cecil, speaking out of the turned-up collar of his overcoat, 'that as I can only see their lower halves, I cannot be any judge of their upper. You don't seem to realize that a person's character is scrawled all over him—over his boots even, rough-hew them as he will.' The reply would have been almost sprightly if it had not sounded so bitter.

'You don't mean surely that cheap shoes and cotton stockings necessarily mean common minds? That would be *too* unfair.'

'I mean,' said Cecil stubbornly, 'that what's bred in the soul comes out in the ankle. It's not merely what a person puts *on* his feet, but how he uses them. Besides, aren't there laces and buttons and buckles and so on? Don't we walk? Compare the kindly cow with the gazelle. And my God, Eirene, you don't suppose I can't even see up as far as the breast-bone where the hollow is where the heart should be?'

'I really don't know what's come over you,' said Eirene. 'It doesn't even seem to be yourself talking. You seem to have got so dreadfully clever and *never* to mean what you say. When you are not purposely misunderstanding one, you are—well once you wouldn't have said, 'my God,' Cecil. And you used not to be *coarse*.'

'No,' said Cecil.

'And I didn't realize until this moment,' she pursued, 'that you were an expert in ankles and that kind of thing. You remember how we once agreed that we could always guess in whose company Kitty had been by her manner. She just catches whoever's about,' she added sportively, 'a sort of social mumps or German measles. But I never noticed that in *you* before. Besides,' and there was now a genuine hint of anxiety in her voice, 'you don't look a bit better. You talk to me as if you hated me body and soul; as if you almost detested me—physically, I mean. And the whole time I am with you—and

Auntie agrees—you appear to be thinking of something else. What is the good of it all? Do you suppose I have never had my own little disillusionments and am not perfectly thankful to have found out that they *were* disillusionments? Nothing I can do or say seems of the least good. Why, if you had even asked my *help*——' The voice really faltered now, and fell silent.

But Cecil, unlike most young men, could not realize how disturbing an experience it can be to be walking in the street with a companion positively shedding tears. He just walked on. He continued meanwhile for a moment or two to explore what Eirene had said.

'I think,' he replied at last, faintly but firmly, 'I have had enough of this ridiculous imitation street. And I hate the mock. We'll turn back.'

There was little of the war-horse apparent in him as he wheeled. His mind had none the less suddenly cleared. It was finally made up. And he stepped out before his companion as if they had once and for all arranged the future between them. At the gate—the bland, white face of Grummumma's house, flinging its reflected sunshine in their faces under the low, delicate, pale blue arch of the sky—Eirene paused. 'You mean,' she said with a choking voice, 'that you would prefer me to be—*not* to be a friend. Well, so be it, Cecil. I can't help myself. I must just bear it. But you shall find that I *am* in spite of you.'

This pathetic challenge, however, only served to consolidate Cecil's resolution. At three o'clock in the afternoon Grummumma was accustomed to shut herself up in her bedroom for half an hour—to relax. She relaxed inch by inch, and then the complete area. It was Eirene's turn to be sentinel again. She now sat playing very plaintive Mendelssohn in the drawing-room with the door wide open, and most of her attention, if not her actual eye, fixed on the staircase that descended into view beyond it. Cecil had left her there after lunch, and, as she had expected, now sat in his own room, drinking in the winning strains.

At half-past four he sent word by the parlour-maid that he would not be down to tea; and Grummumma having returned from relaxing, the two confederates nibbled their thin bread and butter in secret, and exchanged policies. None the less, as if a bird in the air had carried the note, Cecil with door ajar realized the trend of their hushed talk, though he was honestly beyond the possibility of catching any single word of it. 'What was to happen now?' he was thinking, the eyes in his aching head fixed upon his tea-cup. At half-past five Grummuma went out. Eirene was evidently doing double duty.

At a quarter to seven Mr Mallow, Canon Bagshot's latest curate, looked in, with a new novel from Mudie's under his arm. This, he assured Eirene so eagerly that he might himself have been its author, was well worth reading. 'There's so much clap-trap, so much positive slush published nowadays,' he asserted, 'that any piece of fiction with a trace of conviction in it —and I don't mean necessarily moral conviction—just conviction, is something to be thankful for. One must face the facts.'

It was at this moment that Cecil came groping silently down the staircase, as if he were a thief in his own house, breaking not in, but out. Mr Mallow was possessed of a resonant voice, a gift that is singularly fortifying when a slim, fair, and possibly slightly feline young woman is sharing its charms. The young man on the other side of the drawing-room wall now had his ungloved fingers on the latch.

'Face the facts?' Eirene was trembling. 'How very interesting, Mr Mallow. I should love to read it. There are some novels, you know, that really are rather awful. Still, I *believe*'—she opened her blue eyes wide just to show how much she meant it—'I believe I almost prefer some of my facts done up in pretty paper. Is that *very* weak of me? *Men* like things so dreadfully bare!'

Cecil was so much engrossed in his private affairs that he did not pause to wonder why Eirene never talked with this particular timbre in her voice in her intercourse with himself. Mr Mallow's robuster tones broke out once more. 'You see, dear young lady, nowadays novelists may be said to be divided into three camps. On the one hand we have these deplorable realists who think that by calling a spade a spade they are bound to use, and are justified in using, the most deplorable language. On the other we have what I should call the serio-sentimentalists, who try to show life devoid of shadows and who therefore cannot see it whole. And last we have the Shocking School merely out to pull any leg that shows. As for the Feminists —but I am not suggesting, of course. . . .'

But Cecil had by now released the catch of the lock and the heavy door had been softly shut behind him. He was free. And his one desperate desire now was to make that freedom secure. It being Professor Flaxman Smith's parlour-maid's afternoon out, she was given no opportunity to open her bright blue eyes wide with astonishment at the sight of 'that young Mr Jennings' positively running, even though at best it was but a shambling run. But he was covering the ground.

All the peculiar paraphernalia of his life—cracks in the pavement, little windy orgies of dust and straw and dried dung, that same dust stilled and sodden after the night's rain, hairpins of every shape, metal, size, and degree of elegance, dead leaves, running ants, scraps of paper, sparrows, drowsing cats, questioning dogs, area railings, basement bars, cooks, kitchen tables, meat on them, fires in summer—all these phenomena now floated past his downcast eyes unheeded. It was Thursday. It was early closing day. With nothing but a name in his mind, and no address, with only the most meagre of hopes in the old trysting-place, he hastened on, determined that unless somehow or other Grummumma managed to circumvent him, he was going to assure himself of one single thing before he returned home. What exactly that thing was, he did not attempt to put into words. He wanted to say something, but first he must find the human being whom he wanted to say it *to*.

If the rather starchy-looking, blue-spectacled, elderly Cecil Jennings of thirty years later had ventured out on a similar quest, he would have had an extra hour of daylight, of Summer Time, to help him. This particular evening Cecil's allowance of light was by that much the more brief. But the skies were fair, the air was fresh and gentle. And after a narrow escape from being run over by a brewer's dray, he safely circumnavigated the rectory garden wall, and when he had pushed on along the river path to within a few hundred yards or so of the row of bright green lime trees, immediate risk of recognition was safely over.

The quality of the town were not accustomed to enjoy the river path at so late an hour. Maybe too because the day was Thursday and its usual frequenters were farther afield, or maybe because fortune was for that one evening in league with him, very few wayfarers indeed were about. The flowers of the dying grass from the first hayswathes in the meadow beyond the stream burdened the air with their strange sweetness. Swallows with tiny clash of beak and *skirr* of wing were hawking up and down the placid water; gnats in their dervish dancing drifted softly in every caprice of the breeze.

With little breath left either in body or spirit, Cecil came to a standstill. His mind was like a deflated balloon. The whole brave venture had suddenly become the stupidest goose chase. What preposterous self-confidence had brought him here? What justification, for that matter, had he for being a mere makeweight in the world at all? The burning heart had suddenly become like lead within him. An ailing half-wit dazzled by a shop-girl—the miserable folly of it all! The very beauty of the scene was a mockery and a sneer.

And now that the little sacred wooden bench would soon come within hail, every vestige of confidence forsook him. He felt as helpless and forlorn as a butterfly perishing in the vain attempt to extricate itself from its chrysalis skin. In the innocent hope of disguise, he had crammed on to his head an old soft hat discarded at least five years before. Nor were his clothes of his latest punctilious cut. It was no use. The whole attempt was fatuous. Nothing he could ever do would carry him farther than half-way. He might as well return to the High Street and apply at the Town Hall for a list of drapers and landladies and knock them up one by one. After the deliberate insult of that tea-party, even if he were successful, would she so much as consent to speak to him again? He buttoned his coat, shifted his eye-shade a little from the fretting line it had in his haste bitten into his forehead, and plodded on.

The lime tree was already disclosing the buds of its green-gold dangling racemes that would in a day or two be filling the air with a liquid sweetness as delicious as that of the withering grass. Here and there circlets of ripples showed where rising fish had rent the silken surface of the water. The river flowed on under the evening skies without haste between its banks. Summer comes, and goes. How was it possible that, only a few days before, this lovely, gentle, melancholy retreat had shown him a glimpse of Paradise, a paradise ablaze with lightning and shaken with thunder. The very bench, its timber still dark with a shower that had fallen, was eloquent with deprecation.

It was anguish to linger here, useless to venture farther, futile to go back. He must just give the problem up, that was all.

And all this concern, this fatuity, interjected a sardonic voice (and one not entirely unlike Grummumma's), from somewhere within his mind—all this for the sake of a green-sick shop-assistant! A young woman ineligible even for the parochial guild. A horrid Jesuitical Cartholic! A Cartholic, too, who for curiously conscientious reasons had only just escaped becoming the wife of one of the young puritans of the 'Parade.' He listened with absolute calm to this harangue, as he stood leaning against the trunk of the tree. 'But it doesn't matter, my dear,' he muttered as if in hope his whisper might penetrate to the ear of the secret Dryad slumbering beneath its smooth, dark rind. 'Nothing in the world would matter if only you would come!'

Humanity for the most part is so confident in the skill of its senses that it seldom realizes how severe are their limitations. Not to be able to divine where the long-sought-for lost thing lies concealed in one's own small earthly house; not to be able to see through even a sheet of paper; not to be aware that one's nearest and dearest at but a hundred paces' distance is in deadly danger; not to hear the faintest echo of the burning or icy thoughts in a close companion's mind—such is man's queer fate in his inexhaustibly rich environment. And yet poor Cecil never regretted the agony of the next few minutes of irresolution and despair, even though, as he was to discover when they were over, it was only a universal insensitiveness that was keeping him unaware.

Unaware, that is, that not twenty yards distant, and seated on the damp grass on the shelving bank of the river, her hands clasping her knees, was the young woman he longed for, her head turned towards him at an acute angle, her dark, quick eyes drinking him in. It seemed that she had made up her mind to give him time, and to give him his own time. Without otherwise stirring, she turned her head away again, and once more steadily surveyed the flowing water.

The narrow cheek-bones under the low brow and the straight black eyebrows were as pale as ivory in the reflected light of an almost colourless sunset. It was in part the usual pallor of shop life and in part the result of poor food and indifferent sleep. But then ivory itself does not take to itself this particular bloom until the animal that grew it has gone into the dark. Peace itself to be sitting here now after the awful conflict, inward and outward, of the last few days. Other battles had left ugly indelible scars, and yet she had come through—what was left of her. The long agonized inward conflict of the last few days was over. All was lost. And yet the world had never looked so lovely, so hard to abandon, nor had she herself ever been so utterly at rest. She had never much cared what became of her, not at least until that absurd morning when her missing glove had been all but restored. And now, after a black, exhausting night, when dreams in the shallow sleep that had at last closed in upon her mind at the first cheeping of the sparrows had only increased her torments by a conviction of hopeless inefficiency, she knew exactly *what* was to become of her. But she had never for an instant foreseen that in the meantime she would meet again the one human being who had been the final cause of her decision.

Already in the waning light her face appeared a little duskier, its grave scrutiny fixed on that profoundly lustrous and fluid looking-glass. She speculated how deep it actually was; smiled inwardly at the thought of how shallow it need be. She gazed across the sliding water and watched a moment with a curious spiritual greed in her eyes the haze-swathed fields with their fringe of solemn and gigantic elms. Her nostrils quivered as if with a suppressed sigh or shudder as she breathed in the honey of the first few linden flowers. It was a mysterious thing to be alive, or rather, not so much to be alive as to be one's only means of sharing all this. When she was gone it would be all gone too—except, of course, what might come after. And she hadn't much time to think very closely about that.

Still, she was quite accustomed to finding pinned on with a midget pin in the corner of every scrap even of machine-made lace or the flimsiest of handkerchiefs that she proffered across the counter its precise price to the uttermost farthing. So she was unlikely to fail to realize that not only whatever happens in this world, but whatever one is responsible for in it, and buys or sells of oneself, has had affixed to it its own price also. And that, too, to the uttermost farthing. And yet it was a luxury to feel her hands clasped round her bony shins and to be huddling like this with her limbs and body close together in this quiet, rain-soaked grass that would certainly teach her all in good time not to be so imprudent. An overwhelming remorse for the fate of her own body suddenly swept over her. It would be a pity to waste it.

And then, very cautiously, stealthily almost, as if even the soundless grinding of one sinew of the neck against another might be audible in this intense hush of evening, she turned her head once more and surveyed the stiff, awkward-looking shape now humped up so inanimately on its wooden bench under the tree. It would be silly, as well as unkind, perhaps, to keep him there any longer. She gave a little sort of nod at the water, much the same sort of little nod that she was accustomed to give when she had jotted down the total of a customer's bill on the piece of cardboard at the end of her shop-book. Then she rose, stole up the bank, and went over to where Cecil was sitting.

'Good evening,' she said close to him. 'Here's a bad penny, you see.'

His whole body turned round in her direction. He thrust out his hands as if to ward off an unexpected enemy. But she made no move to reassure him.

'I didn't know you were there,' he said. 'Is there anybody else near?'

She laughed softly. 'So you have discovered at last, then, that I am not the kind of person to be seen with.'

He rose to his feet and stood perfectly still, his hands trembling a little in spite of himself.

'I could say things like that too,' he replied, 'but I should hate myself for doing so.'

'Which might be,' she retorted, 'the beginning of a perfectly horrid quarrel. But I didn't mean anything at all. I just said it. One must say something. I learned that the other day.'

'This is all so horribly open,' said the young man, sweeping his cane round with an incredibly magnificent gesture as if in proof of it. He might be Satan himself, surveying from his mountain-top the outstretched Kingdoms of the World. 'Could we go on a little farther, do you think?'

'Farther!' she answered. 'To Land's End, if you like—if we could. But I've got to be out of the streets by ten, or say eleven, or I shall be on them for good on Monday.'

'I never knew any one,' said Cecil, 'who had such a dreadful way of telling the truth. You must be very young for that.'

An inexhaustible serenity seemed to have descended upon

him. It seemed that he hadn't an enemy in the world, that before them lay an infinity of space fenced in only by an infinity of time. 'If you only knew what I feel at being with you again,' he muttered. 'I have been waiting for you for ages. But had —had given you up. I have been kept in again, you see—idiot that I am.'

'Well,' she said in a curiously flattened voice, which yet seemed to conceal an intensity of music, 'never mind that! Here I am. I don't mind, I don't mind even if you have been at death's door, as long as you too are with *me* again. You see, I am always more or less contented when I haven't any decisions to make. I am sick of them, but there are none left now.'

She smiled to herself as fondly as a beauty at the image in her glass. 'I didn't suppose I should see you again, and yet even impossibilities come true sometimes.' She turned her head away and went on with an effort: 'You see, I couldn't pretend I'm sorry to see you. I ought to. But nothing now, nobody in the world—or out of it either—could make me say that.' Once more she twisted about. 'Is *that* a common and horrible way of telling the truth? Like losing a whole boxful of gloves, I suppose.'

'You never say anything,' he replied gently, conscious, it seemed, while they loitered slowly on, of every saw-edged, exquisite blade of grass stooping green under the evening sky and here and there laden with a drop, a crystal universe, of rain-water—'you never say anything without saying something different immediately after. I don't see, I mean, why you should always give a sting to everything. Mayn't we be—just friends, for now? You see,' he hastened on, 'I want to speak to you very badly indeed. I have got to make plans. And I am wondering if you would help me.'

'Where did you leave Mrs le Mercier,' she inquired, 'and— and that other young lady? I enjoyed that tea party. But I had, of course, *heard* of Canon Bagshot before—often. He's a little like a vulture, isn't he?'

'I have left them at home,' he answered amiably, 'or rather, Grummumma will be at home by now.'

'Will they be sending a rescue party, do you think—from the street girl?'

'Oh,' he said helplessly, 'you will just break me in pieces if you go on talking like that. You don't know what I have been through these last few days—knowing what you must have thought of me. I deserve it all.'

For the moment Miss Simcox made no reply. Her inward glance had vaguely returned with a wry little grimace to scan the vista of her own last few days; but she was not going to say anything about that. Instead, and as usual for no clear reason, a flush of colour slowly spread over her pale face. She could feel the heat of it as she blurted out: 'Then you 've missed me? *Missed* me—missed *me*?' With a wrench she regained her self-control. 'Well, then, all I can say is, that I 've missed you too. I mean, if you are kind enough to talk to me, I *like* talking to you. In the whole of my life I have never talked to any one like you. I mean that *I* have never really talked before to *any* one, and that I have never talked to any one like *you*. Do you see *now* what I mean?'

'I hear what you say,' said Cecil in despair. It was odd that anything so substantial as the ground upon which they were walking should seem to be at least as precarious yet as buoyant as the water of which it was the restraining buttress. 'I can't think what you can find in me?' he added lamely.

'And me?'

'I don't find anything, I *am* you. You are *here*.' As if even the sweet, pure air of a summer evening might be a little suffocating in certain conditions, his companion had lightly touched her throat with outspread fingers. 'Do you,' he went on hastily, 'do you understand what I mean?'

He came to a standstill, gesticulating with his hand as if over a mathematical problem. 'The moment you come, my mind is like another place. I have never seen anything of this before —this green, this loveliness, that water. I don't even know what they are; they have gone back to their own secrets, as, do you remember—when you were a child . . .?'

Her only answer to that was a vigorous, tragic little nod he couldn't see. 'Don't let us say any more about that,' she went on with a shudder. 'There are worse things than *not* seeing. . . . I wonder if, do you think, just for this once I might take your arm? I assure you there is not a soul in sight now. There was a blackbird calling on the other side of the river a moment ago, and just now I saw a bat in the air. Up there is the first star. Do you understand what *I* am saying? All it means is that I have gone to heaven—before I die!'

She had slipped her ungloved fingers through his arm, and the pair of them paced on towards—though they did not know it—towards the sea, and not towards the source of the river. They looked just like what they were—two commonplace sweethearts aimlessly wandering on together. And a sentimental passer-by might have thought how pleasant it was that a young man so severely handicapped should yet have been able to find a future helpmate.

But then this kind of foolish self-sacrifice is expected of the gentler sex, though as a matter of fact there was an odd suggestion of the masculine in the way in which this silk-shaded young man's companion walked along beside him. There was a hint almost of the athletic in her every movement this evening, which is only to say, after all, that even in the indifferently nourished bodies which civilization is so freely responsible for, some spring of the wild animal may still remain.

The two young people went on in an eternity that was a moment until they had reached a point where a few silver birches and hazels thinly screened them from the world they had for that moment left behind them. There the young woman came suddenly to a standstill.

'I must go back in a minute,' she said. 'And if you don't mind, I would prefer to go back alone. Meanwhile we are here, and even a little time is a long time when there's not much left.' She laughed softly.

Irked by the obstacle of the rooty bank at this bend, the water gurgled as if in echo of a never-ending lullaby. At least to some ears it might sound so, though for Cecil it resembled the monologue of a hopeless voice babbling of everlasting darkness. 'You have only just come,' he said, 'and now you talk about saying good-bye.'

'I didn't wish to. I must.'

'Well, then,' he said, 'all I am going to say to you is this; and would you please listen as patiently as you can? Without interrupting me, I mean. It's—it's nothing much.' He waved his fingers in the air, took a deep breath, and plunged on. 'What I mean is this: I haven't very much money now, but I have some. A little income, you know, only four or five hundred a year—but certain. It's horribly little to go on with, but even Grummumma can't keep me out of a good deal more than *that* in a few years' time. Can't. Apart from that, and I don't mind saying it a bit, she can't live for ever. I don't want her even to live as long as that. Honestly I don't. I wouldn't so much mind if she had driven me—just harassed me, you know. It would have done me good. But she's held so tight to the bit, that my mouth's all covered with blood. I know now what's gone on all along. It's her way, her self, her domination. *That's* what Scarlet Women are made of. I see it now even though they—well, that's what I *mean*. And I simply can't stand it any longer. Possibly I should have stood it—at least for some little time—if *you* hadn't come. If *you* hadn't come, I believe I should have gone mouldering on like a suet pudding in a damp pantry. Oh, yes, I know what I am talking about all right! I saw a slice of that once—mildewed—on my own plate, when my nurse didn't think my eyes could see under the bandage.'

Cecil breathed again. He paused. Then: 'What I am saying is this,' he went on tranquilly, 'would you mind telling me how we can get married? I mean what do they do? I don't mean the Canon Bagshot way. I know that's impossible. But isn't there some place where you can get married just for the time being, without, I mean, going to a church? And especially, if you are a Roman Catholic. Couldn't we go to a church later on, don't you think, when we have got safely away? I want to get married to you *at once* if we can—if I may. And yet I don't think I have even told you I love you. I don't think there was any reason to say that. You must have thought me even a more unutterable idiot than you must think me if you think that. I don't want to be impatient. I mean, I don't want to vex you into saying, no—that is, if you *won't* marry me. You see, I am so dreadfully ignorant of all these things. But you said just now that if you weren't back in your home by eleven it would be the streets on Monday. What did you mean by that, please?'

It was ludicrous what a muddle the young man was in; and yet how easy his listener was finding it to sort him all out and to see exactly not only where the commas and semicolons ought to have come in this remarkable piece of oratory, but also the full stop, the 'period,' as she had been taught to call it when she was (for a year or two) at school. That was before the drapery business set in. That was before her father went off with the other woman. That was before even the none-too-particular but good-humoured woman next door began to take care of her for a time and to learn her in certain ways how it is possible when the worst comes to the worst, to take care of oneself. But all this was quite a long, long, long time before she had met this young man with the green shade over his eyes.

There was the look almost of a half-witted creature on her face as she now stood staring at the water. And yet, like a singularly intelligent canary or like a singularly instinctive black-cap or mocking-bird, she was trying over—as rapidly as a Paganini might a phrase in Mozart—she was trying over half a dozen tunes in which to reply. She chose the hardest.

'When I was engaged—and never mind who,' she said, 'we found out about getting married without a parson. He knew all about all that. You go to what is called a Registry Office. We thought—we might have to. Do you see? It would, of course, have been everlasting damnation to me, if we had; or at any rate a good many centuries of Purgatory. And to you —why! Oh, don't I *know* it!—it would be the dismalest and most horrible thing you ever conceived of doing in the whole of your life. No, no, I can't marry you. I don't wish to. Oh, no. Don't let us waste this little time in talking of foolish things like that. I couldn't marry you. I couldn't. I don't wish to. Not go down like that, after all you have been, and said. I don't even mind confessing now—as you see!—that I thought all this out even after the first time we met on the Parade. It was vile of me, I know, but it's my character. I always see ahead. From the very first instant. When you are in my—well, some girls wait for marriage, just for the chance. They even. . . . But never mind; that's all over now. Until you came I never had a friend—not a *friend*. Did you really think I would ever risk—when you knew everything—losing. . . . Oh, you don't seem to realize'—she suddenly turned on him—'how hopelessly, blindly unpractical and unworldly you are. You say you are a fool: well, you *are*. A fool in all that *I'm not*. I have been soaked in the other thing ever since I was born. If you asked me to go to the devil with you, I'd go—gladly. But you wouldn't. And knowing that, I'd rather go alone. And yet, before God, I love you. I say, I love you. It breaks my heart to say it. I didn't know it was possible. I didn't know what it meant. And yet, though you won't, though you can't understand about the rest of me. . . . But don't listen to that. What's the use if I never could and never, never would say, yes. Just listen only to what I am saying now. I love you. It's spelt l-o-v-e.' She gazed at the half-hidden face with an agonized smile. 'And simply because of that, it must be—we must leave each other here. It's almost night now. Don't let us talk any more. But you *must* be able to see I couldn't go back with you now. My legs wouldn't bear me. And honestly I don't think I could manage to *say* good-bye. So would you'—a fantastic, almost jocular note had edged into her curious voice—a voice like that of a delicate instrument whose sound-box has somehow or other become cracked, muting the clearer timbre of the thing, 'so would you please kiss me, and I'll be gone.'

Cecil groped for the hand that hung limp and inert beside the old serge skirt. He lifted it, and looked at its fingers. He counted them. They were long and narrow-boned fingers, and belonging, as they did, not to her right hand, they were a little less marked with work.

'I don't want to tell you,' he muttered as if to himself at last, and still examining them in the clarifying focus afforded by his shade, 'I don't want to tell you how shockingly miserable you are making me. You think I am a coward. You don't believe I could ever do anything, ever break free. You say you love me—you *say* you do—but you don't believe in me, not at all. I might just as well be a child for all that you are saying. But then I know it can't mean anything. I mean, I know you couldn't help saying it, and I can't tell you what I think of you for *having* said it. But you see, what I feel is that if you are going to keep to what you say—even if after all you weren't utterly meaning it—then I *must* see your face. I couldn't kiss you until I had, and it may be more than I can bear, more than I can manage, I mean. There isn't any moon, either,' he added helplessly. 'Would you mind taking tight hold of both my hands?'

She flung her arms away from him, took a quick step backwards, stooping low, like a dangerous animal about to spring. 'Do you mean you are going to try *that* horrible thing—now?' she cried at him. 'Be quiet, do. You don't know what you are saying. Be quiet, do. Here I am. All you can see. What *more* has anybody wanted. Oh, you won't be content till you've skinned me to the very bone. Look at *me*! Oh, you will hurt yourself. You said you might die. And'—her voice ran down the scale until she was scarcely more than whispering—'and how, pray, do you know what I look *like*? *I* do. You should see the looking-glass my landlady gives me. *That*'s where I powder my nose!' A corrosive sardonicism had come into her voice. A look of fierce vindictiveness distorted her narrow face and her blazing, disquieted eyes. 'Oh, for God's sake,' she said, 'do try and be a little kind to me. There won't be very much time for it, if you only knew.'

But Cecil had followed her up, and she could retreat no farther unless she was to plunge at once into the swirling water a foot or two beneath the bank. He was lifting his chin with convulsive efforts and had thrust both hands on her shrinking shoulders as he did so. And at last, with a strangled sob, he found himself gazing eye to eye with this phantom of his dreams.

Strangely enough, he *had* been without the least expectation of what that face looked like. It hadn't seemed to matter. And now that he was scrutinizing it, only half conscious of the appalling pangs which were darting from skull to spine, it was not as if he had merely recognized her, but as if this were the first face that as a mortal creature he had ever seen at all—a landscape, a garden, a marvel, before time, lovely, earthly, yet unbelievable, all-pitying, burnt up with pain, never to be forgotten, never to be exhausted, never to be understood.

And before he could make the slightest movement, she had taken him in her arms and had hidden his anguished and distorted and transfigured face on her breast. 'Oh!' she cried. 'How could you do it! How dared you! Oh, dear, my dear! Oh, my dear, my dear, my dear! Have a moment's peace. Don't you see it will be mine too?'

Cecil had lost ages ago all but the faintest remembrances of his childhood; or rather, he had never let himself think about it. And now he had reached a momentary, yet eternal, oblivion, though it was an oblivion fenced in by misery and pain.

'Listen,' he said, drawing back at last, still clutching at her hands, 'I know now what you meant just then; I know what you meant. You meant you had made up your mind to kill yourself to-night—to drown yourself *there*. Well, then, listen to me. You don't move an inch until you have sworn to me by the Holy Ghost you won't do it. Do you understand? I can't keep you,

I know that. I only ask you to go away and to think it over, and to come back again here in the morning. I shall be here. But before you go, even if it's for ever—and surely you couldn't, you wouldn't treat me like that!—you will promise me not to do *that*. Not to be so hopelessly wicked, you understand. You simply couldn't do it, leaving me the burden.'

The fingers in his grip seemed to consist of little else than thin bones. 'There!' she cried into Space, 'isn't that the Man all over. You don't know what you are condemning me to, you cruel boy. You don't *know*. If I told you,' she went on rapidly, 'that to stay here—to stay on this earth as I am—will be only to go from one thing on to another, pillar to post until . . . Do you suppose yours is the only tender-hearted Grandmamma in the world? Or, if you knew how I long, and now of all times, to get away. And I believe even God would forgive me, if He has any longing left. Ah, well, you *don't* know. And what's the good of talking!'

'But you promise?' Cecil repeated. 'For, after all, you are not thinking of me. You haven't remembered what my life has been like—silly fop that I am.'

'My dear,' she sobbed brokenly, 'your hands are all wet. I can't really see your face, but you are shuddering all over. I will take you home after all. We can walk well apart. . . . But no—no!'

'But you promise?' he repeated.

Her eyes strayed from the hideous pent-house shade to the dark, secret water.

'No,' she said, 'I cannot promise. . . . But there!—God helping me—I won't.'

Nothing seemed to matter now. She knew all that she was. Every thought in her had seemed to have foundered in an unfathomable pit of darkness. 'But you don't know what you are asking,' she added again, with a sound that might almost have been taken for laughter. 'You are asking me to go on loving you, and that I don't see how I shall be able to bear.'

She drew her hands gently away and stood for a moment quietly looking at her solitary companion, as if uncertain whether or not she had ever seen him before. But in a while the illusion cleared away and she realized where she was; the darkened wood, the secret gurgling water, the empty starry sky.

'Listen,' she said at last, stooping forward, her shoulders

seeming to fold themselves a little together like the curve of a bird's wings. 'Are you safe now?'

He nodded.

'Not in pain?' He shook his head in his agony.

'And you won't quite forget me?' He made no answer.

'Well, then,' she went on earnestly, like a child repeating its catechism, 'never forget that I came to the *end* of my life when you came to its beginning. I didn't know what it meant to love anybody. And I'd rather have gone. For, you see, when you looked up at me, something came *here*—I can't explain, I . . .'

Nor did she ever come back to explain. The sun was riding high in the heavens next morning, and the scene around Cecil alive with its scintillating summer beauty—skylarks in the empty blue, butterflies wavering from flower to flower, the bosoming waters radiant with light—when, too much worn out with pain and hopelessness to pay any attention to such elusive and illusory promises, he realized at last that she was gone never to return, and he groped his way back to Grummumma and his life.

From *On the Edge.*

THE THREE FRIENDS

THE street was narrow; yet, looking up, the two old friends, bent on their accustomed visit, could discern—beyond a yellow light that had suddenly shone out into the hushed gloom from an attic window—the vast, accumulated thunder-clouds that towered into the darkening zenith.

'That's just it,' continued Mr Eaves, more emphatically, yet more confidentially, 'it isn't my health, Sully. I'm not so much afraid of my health. It's—it's my . . .' He took off his hat and drew his hand over his tall, narrow head, but pushed on no further towards the completion of his sentence.

Mr Sully eyed him stonily. 'Don't worry, then,' he said. 'Why worry? There's worry enough in the world, old sport, without dreaming about it.'

'I know,' said Mr Eaves; 'but then, you see, Sully——' They had paused at the familiar swing-door, and now confronted one another in the opaque, sultry silence. And as Mr Sully stood for an instant in close contact with his old crony in the accentuated darkness of the mock-marble porch, it was just as if a scared rabbit had scurried out of Mr Eaves's long white face.

'Look here,' Mr Sully exclaimed with sudden frivolity, 'we'll ask Miss Lacey'; and was followed by his feebly protesting companion into the bar.

The long black stuffed bench and oblong mahogany table, darkened here and there by little circular pools of beer, stood close against the wall, and Mr Sully began to divulge his friend's confidences even before Miss Lacey could bring them their glasses. A commissionaire sat in the further bar, nodding over an old newspaper; and Mr Eaves kept his eyes fixed on his oblong lurching head, while he listened, fascinated and repelled, to his friend's facetiousness.

'Now, supposing, Miss Lacey, my dear,' began Mr Sully shrewdly, half-closing his eyes as if to gloss over his finesse, 'supposing a young man, a nice, curly-headed young man—just about our old friend's age here'—Miss Lacey, with a kind of arch and sympathetic good-nature, leaned a large, dark head to glance at Mr Eaves—'supposing a nice young gentleman—just as it might be our old friend himself here—came, like an innocent, to entrust to your blessed bosom a secret—a sacred secret: what would you do?'

'Lor' bless me, Mr Sully, sir, is that all you was coming to. A secret? Why, keep it, to be sure; and not the first time neether.' Miss Lacey advanced to the bar, black, precise and cheerful, with the two small, thick glasses in her hand.

'Good,' said Mr Sully, with an almost professional abandon. 'Good. *So* far. But step number two; supposing, my dear, you couldn't for the life and love of you *help* him in his little difficulty—dependent on his secret, let's say—what then?'

'Why, I'd keep it all the more,' cried Miss Lacey brightly.

'A woman's answer, Eaves; and none the worse for that,' said Mr Sully. 'But on the other hand, supposing you were a practical'—he paused with the little water-jug hovering an inch or two above his friend's glass—'supposing you were a practical, unromantic old blackguard like me—why, you'd go and tell it to the first lovely blooming creature that came along.' He eyed her steadily yet jocosely. 'And that's why I'm going to tell it to you, my dear!'

'How you do tease, to be sure!' said Miss Lacey. 'He's a real tease, isn't he, Mr Eaves?'

Mr Sully's eyes suddenly sobered with overwhelming completeness. He pointed coldly with his stick. 'He's been dreaming of hell,' he said.

Mr Eaves, on his part, withdrew large, weak, colourless eyes from the uneasy head of the commissionaire, and turned them on Miss Lacey. She glanced at him swiftly, then stooped, and took up a piece of sewing she had laid down on her wooden chair, in the little out-of-the-way bar.

'I don't approve of such subjects,' she said, 'treated frivolous.'

'Gracious goodness, Eaves,' said Mr Sully, 'she says "frivolous." Hell—"frivolous"!'

'Why,' said Miss Lacey lucidly, 'I'm not so green as I look.'

'Well, you couldn't look younger, if being young's to be green,' said Mr Sully; 'and as sure, my dear, as that was a flash of lightning, it—it's the real thing.'

When the faint but cumulative rumble of thunder that followed had subsided, Miss Lacey seemed to have withdrawn her attention. Mr Sully edged slowly round on his feet and faced his friend. 'You old skeleton at the feast! You've alarmed the poor child,' he said.

Miss Lacey spoke without raising her eyes, bent closely on her needle. 'Not me,' she said; 'but I don't hold with such ideas.'

'Tell her yourself,' said Mr Sully to his friend; 'tell her yourself: they never *will* believe *me*.'

Mr Eaves shook his head.

'Why not?' said Mr Sully.

'God bless me,' said Mr Eaves, with sudden heat, 'I'm old enough to be her father.'

Miss Lacey looked up over her sewing. 'You'd scarcely believe *me*,' she said mysteriously; 'but there was a young gentleman down Charles Street, where I used to be, that had dreams—well, there, shocking! Nobody but me had the patience to listen to him. But you can't give all your attention to one customer, can you? He,' she cast a curious glance into the shadows brooding over the commissionaire—'he got up out of his bed one night, just as you or me might—he was living in private apartments, too—struck a match, so they said, and cut his throat. Awful. From ear to ear!' Her thimbled finger made a demure half-circuit of the large pearls of her necklace.

Mr Sully gazed roundly. 'Did he, though? But there, you see,' and he leant in great confidence over the counter, 'Mr Eaves here doesn't shave?'

Mr Eaves smiled vaguely, half-lifting his stick, as if in coquettish acknowledgment of his friend's jest.

'No, no, old friend,' he said, 'not that, not that, I hope.'

'Gracious goodness,' said Mr Sully cordially, 'he mustn't take it to heart like that. A dream's a dream.'

'Why, of course, it is,' said Miss Lacey. 'You ought to take more care of yourself, sir; didn't he, Mr Sully?'

Mr Eaves gazed dispassionately, and yet with some little dignity, in the isolation of attention he had evoked. He turned slowly towards the bar, and stooped a little—confidentially. 'Not once, not twice,' he said ruminatingly, 'but every blessed night. Every blessed night.'

Miss Lacey eyed him with searching friendliness.

'Tell her,' said Mr Sully, walking slowly and circumspectly to the door, and peeping out through the cranny into the darkened street.

Mr Eaves put his empty glass deliberately upon the counter, drew his hand slowly across his lips and shook his head. 'It's nothing to tell, when you come to that. And . . .' He nodded a questioning head towards the solitary occupant of the other bar.

'Oh, fast: bless you,' said Miss Lacey. 'As reg'lar as clock-work—you'd hardly believe it.'

'He'll break his neck, some day,' remarked Mr Sully tersely, 'with that jerking.'

'You see, my dear,' continued Mr Eaves trustfully, 'I don't mind my old friend, Mr Sully, making a good deal of fun at my expense. He always has: eh, Sully? But he doesn't *see*. You don't *see*, Sully. There the thing is; and truth all over it. Facts are facts—in *my* belief.'

'But fire and brimstone, and suchlike; oh no!' said Miss Lacey with a dainty little shudder. 'I can't credit, reelly; oh no! And poor innocent infants, too! You may think of me what you like, but nothing'll make me believe *that*.'

Mr Sully looked over his shoulder at Mr Eaves. 'Oh, that,' said his old friend, 'was only Mr Sully's fun. He says it's hell. I didn't. My dream was only—*after*; the state after death, as they call it.'

'I see,' said Miss Lacey, lucidly, summoning all her intelligence into her face.

Mr Eaves leaned forward, and all but whispered the curious tidings into her ear. 'It's—it's just the same,' he said.

'The same?' echoed Miss Lacey. 'What?'

'The same,' repeated the old man, drawing back, and looking out of his long, grey, meaningless face at the little plump, bright satiny woman.

'Hell?' breathed Miss Lacey.

'The state after death,' called Mr Sully, still peering into the gloom—and stepped back rather hurriedly in the intense pale lilac illumination of a sudden flickering blaze of lightning.

Thunder now clanged directly overhead, and still Mr Eaves gazed softly yet earnestly into nothingness, as if in deep thought.

'Whatever you like to call it,' he began again steadily pushing his way, 'that's how I take it. I sit with my wife, just the same; cap and "front" and all, just the same; gas burning, decanter on the table, books in the case, marble clock on the mantel-piece, just the same. Or perhaps I'm walking in the street, just the same; carts and shops and dogs, all just the same. Or perhaps I'm here, same as I might be now; with Sully there, and you there, and him there,' he nodded towards the commissionaire. 'All just the same. For ever, and ever, and ever.' He raised his empty glass to his lips, and glanced almost apologetically towards his old friend. 'For ever, and ever,' he said, and put it down again.

'He means,' said Mr Sully, 'no change: like one of those blessed things on the movies; over and over again, click, click, click, click, click; you know. I tell him it's his sentence, my dear.'

'But if it's the same,' Miss Lacey interposed, with a little docile frown of confusion, 'what's different?'

'Mark me, Eaves, my boy,' cried Mr Sully softly at the door; 'it's the ladies for brains, after all. That's what they call a poser. "What's different," eh?'

Mr Eaves pondered in a profound internal silence in the bar. And beyond the windows, the rain streamed steadily in a longdrawn gush of coolness and peace. 'What's different?' repeated Mr Sully, rocking infinitesimally on his heels.

'Why,' said Mr Eaves, 'it seems as if there I can't change; can't. If you were to ask me how I know—why, I couldn't say. It's a dream. But that's what's the difference. There's nothing to come. *Now:* why! I might change in a score of ways; just take them as they come. I might fall ill; or Mrs Eaves might; I might come into some money; marry again. God bless me, I might *die!* But there, that's all over; endless; no escape; nothing. I can't even die. I'm just meself, Miss Lacey; Sully, old friend. Just meself, for ever, and ever. Nothing but me looking on at it all, if you take me—just what I've made of it. It's my'—his large pale eyes roved aimlessly —'it's just what Mr Sully says, I suppose; it's my sentence. Eh, Sully? wasn't that it? My sentence?' He smiled courageously.

'Sentence! Oh, no! Sentence? You!' cried Miss Lacey incredulously. 'How could you, Mr Sully? Sentence! Whatever for, sir?'

Mr Eaves again glanced vaguely at the sleeper, and then at his friend's round substantial shoulders, rigidly turned on him. He fixed his eyes on the clock.

'You've never done no harm, Mr Eaves!' cried Miss Lacey, almost as if in entreaty.

'You see,' said the old gentleman, glancing over his shoulder, 'it isn't what you do: so I seem to take it.' Mr Sully half turned from the door, as if to listen. 'It 's what you are,' said Mr Eaves, as if to himself.

'Why, according to that,' said Miss Lacey, in generous indignation, 'who 's safe?'

A day of close and tepid weather followed the storm. But it was on the evening of the next day after that—an evening of limpid sunshine and peace, the sparrows chirping shrilly in the narrow lights and shadows of the lane, that Mr. Sully came in to see Miss Lacey.

She was alone: and singing a little quiet tune to herself as she went about her business. He shook his head when she held up two glasses; and raised just one forefinger.

'He 's dead,' he said.

'Oh, no!' cried Miss Lacey.

'This morning . . . in his sleep.' He gazed at her with an unusual—with a curiously fish-like concentration.

'Poor, poor gentleman,' said Miss Lacey. 'He *was* a gentleman, too; and no mistake. Never a hard word for nobody; man, woman, or child. Always the same. But it 's shocking. Well, well. But how dreadfully sudden, Mr Sully, sir!'

'Well, I don't know,' said Mr Sully almost irritably. 'And if so, where 's the change?' His round shoulders seemed with slight effort almost to shrug themselves.

'Goodness gracious,' Miss Lacey cried, 'you don't mean—you don't mean to think—you don't say it 's true? What he was telling us, Mr Sully?'

'I 'm not so sure,' her visitor replied vaguely, almost stubbornly. 'Where else, after all, knowing all that, why, where else *could* he go?'

'Mr Eaves, Mr Sully? Him? Oh, no!'

Mr Sully, in the intense clear quiet of the bar, continued to stare at her in a manner something like that of an over-glutted vulture. He nodded.

Miss Lacey's kind brown eyes suddenly darkened as if with a gust of storm. 'But, then, what about us?' she cried piteously, and yet with the tenderest generosity.

'Well,' said Mr Sully, opening the door, and looking out into the sunny evening air, 'if you ask me, that 's merely a question of time.'

From *The Riddle.*

E 940

MISSING

IT was the last day of a torrid week in London—the flaming crest of what the newspapers call a *heat wave*. The exhausted inmates of the dazzling, airless streets—plate-glass, white stone, burnished asphalt, incessant roar, din, fume, and odours—have the appearance at such times of insects trapped in an oven of a myriad labyrinthine windings and chambers: a glowing brazen maze to torture Christians in. To have a *mind* even remotely resembling it must be Satan's sole privilege!

I had been shopping; or rather, I had been loafing about from one department on to another in one of the huge 'stores' in search of bathing-drawers, a preventative against insect bites, and a holiday 'shocker,' and had retired at last incapable of buying anything—even in a world where pretty well everything except peace of mind can be bought, and sold. The experience had been oppressive and trying to the temper.

Too hot, too irritable even to lunch, I had drifted into a side street, and then into a second-hand bookshop that happened still to be open this idle Saturday afternoon; and having for ninepence acquired a copy of a book on psycho-analysis which I didn't want and should never read, I took refuge in a tea-shop.

In spite of the hot-water fountain on the counter it was a degree or two cooler in here, though even the marble-top tables were tepid to the touch. Quiet and drowsy, too. A block of ice surmounted the dinner-wagon by the counter. The white clock-face said a quarter to three. Few chairs were now occupied; the midday mellay was over. A heavy slumbrousness muffled the place—the flies were as idle as the waitresses, and the waitresses were as idle as the flies.

I gave my order, and sat back exhausted in a listless vacancy of mind and body. And my dazed eyes, having like the flies little of particular interest to settle on, settled on the only fellow-reveller that happened to be sitting within easy reach. At first glimpse there could hardly be a human being you would suppose less likely to attract attention. He was so scrupulously respectable, so entirely innocent of 'atmosphere.' Even a Chelsea psychic would have been compelled to acknowledge that this particular human being had either disposed of his aura or had left it at home. And yet my first glimpses of him had drawn me out of the vacuum into which I had sunk as easily as a cork is drawn out of an empty bottle.

He was sitting at a table to the left, and a little in front of me. The glare from the open door and the gentler light from the cream-blinded shop window picked out his every hair and button. It flooded in on him from the sparkling glittering street, focused him, 'placed' him, arranged him—as if for a portrait in the finest of oils for next year's 'Academy.' Lime-light on the actor-manager traversing the blasted heath is mere child's play by comparison.

Obviously he was not 'the complete Londoner'—though that can hardly be said to be a misfortune. On the other hand, there was nothing rural, and only a touch or so of the provincial in his appearance. He wore a neat—an excessively neat—pepper-and-salt tweed suit, the waistcoat cut high and exhibiting the points of a butterfly collar and a triangle of black silk cravat slipped through a gold mourning-ring. His ears maybe were a little out of the mode. They had been attached rather high, and flat on either side of his conical head with its dark, glossy, silver-speckled hair.

The nose was straight, the nostrils full. They suggested courage of a kind; possibly, even, on occasion, bravado. He looked the kind of man, I mean, it is well to keep out of a corner. But the eyes that were now peering vacantly down that longish nose over a trim but unendearing moustache at the crumbs on his empty plate were too close together. So, at least, it seemed to me. But then I am an admirer of the wide expressive brow —such as our politicians and financiers display. Those eyes at any rate gave this spruce and respectable person just a hint, a glint of the fox. I have never heard though that the fox is a dangerous animal even in a corner; only that he has his wits about him and preys on geese—whereas my stranger in the tea-shop had been refreshing himself with Osborne biscuits.

It was hot. The air had grown more stagnant. And heat—unless in Oriental regions—is not conducive to exquisite manners; far otherwise. I continued to watch this person, indo-lently speculating whether his little particularities of appearance

did not match, or matched too precisely. Those ears and
that cravat, for example; or those spruce-moustached nostrils
and the glitter of the close-neighbouring eyes. And why had
he brought to mind a tightly-packed box with no address on it?
He began to be a burden, yet I could not keep my eyes away
from him—nor from his hands. They were powerful and hairy,
with large knuckles; and now that they were not in use he had
placed them on his knees under the dark polished slab of his
marble table. Beneath those knees rested his feet (the toes
turned in a little) in highly-polished boots, with thickish soles
and white socks.

There is, I agree, something peculiarly vulgar in thus picking
a fellow-creature to pieces. But then Keats so dissected Miss
Brawne even when he was in love with her, and it was certainly
not love at first sight between myself and this stranger.

Whether he knew it or not, he was attaching himself to me;
he was making his influence felt. It was odd, then, that he
could remain so long unconscious of so detached a scrutiny.
Maybe that particular nerve in him had become atrophied.
He looked as if a few other rather important nerves might be
atrophied. When he did glance up at me—the waitress having
appeared with my tea at the same moment—there was a far-away
startled look in his bleak blue-black eyes—as if he had been
called back.

Nothing more; and even at that it was much such a look as
had been for some little time fixed on the dry biscuit crumbs in
his empty plate. He seemed indeed to be a man accustomed to
being startled or surprised into vigilance without reason. But
having seen me looking at him, he did not hesitate. He carefully took up his hat, his horn-handled and gold-mounted
umbrella, and a large rusty scaling leather bag that lay on a
chair beside him, rose, and stepping gently over with an almost
catlike precision, seated himself in the chair opposite to mine.
I continued to pour out my tea.

'You will excuse me troubling you,' he began in a voice that
suggested he could sing tenor though he spoke bass, 'but would
you kindly tell me the number of the omnibus that goes
from here to King's Cross? I am a stranger to this part of
London.'

I called after the waitress: 'What is the number of the bus,'
I said, 'that goes from here to King's Cross?'

'The number of the bus, you si, that goes from here to King's Cross?'

'Yes,' I said, 'to King's Cross.'

'I 'm sure *I* don't know,' she said. 'I 'll ask the counter.' And she tripped off in her silk stockings and patent leather shoes.

'The counter will know,' I assured him. He looked at me, moving his lips over his teeth as if either or both for some reason had cause to be uneasy.

'I am something of a stranger to London altogether,' he said, 'and I don't usually come these ways: it 's a novelty to me. The omnibuses are very convenient.'

'Don't you? Is it?' I replied. 'Why not?' They were rather point-blank questions (and a gentleman, said Dr Johnson, does not ask questions) but somehow they had slipped out as if at his pressing invitation.

He looked at me, his eyes seeming to draw together into an intenser focus. He was not exactly squinting, but I have noticed a similar effect in the eyes of a dog when its master is about to cry 'Fetch it!'

'You see,' he said, 'I live in the country, and only come to London when I seem to need company—badly, I mean. There 's a great contrast between the country and this. All these houses. So many strange faces. It takes one out of oneself.'

I glanced round at the sparsely occupied tables. A cloud apparently had overlaid the sun, for a faint coppery glow was now reflected from the drowsy street. I could even hear the white-faced clock ticking. To congratulate him on his last remark would hardly have been courteous after so harmless an advance. I merely looked at him. What kind of self, I was vaguely speculating, would return into his hospitality when he regained his usual haunts.

'I have a nice little place down there,' he went on, 'but there 's not much company. Lonely: especially now. Even a few hours makes all the difference. You would be surprised how friendly a place London can be; the people, I mean: helpful.'

What can only be described as a faint whinny had sounded in his voice as he uttered that 'helpful.' Was he merely to prove yet another of those unfortunate travellers who have lost the return halves of their railway tickets? Had he marked me down for his prey?

'It is not so much what they say,' he continued, laying his

hand on the marble table; 'but just, well, their company, you know.' I glanced at the heavy ring on its third finger and then at his watch chain—woven apparently of silk or hair—with little gold rings at intervals along it to secure the plait. His own gaze continued to rest on me with so penetrating, so corkscrew-like an intensity, that I found myself glancing over my shoulder in search of the waitress. She, however, was now engaged in animated argument with the young lady at the pay-desk.

'Do you live *far* from London?' I ventured.

'About seventy miles,' he replied with an obvious gulp of relief at this impetus to further conversation. 'A nice old house, too, considering the rent, roomy enough but not too large. Its only drawback in some respects is there's nothing near it —not within call, I mean; and we—I—suffer from the want of a plentiful supply of water. Especially now.'

Why so tactless a remark on this broiling afternoon should have evoked so vivid a picture of a gaunt yellow-brick building perched amid sloping fields parched lint-white with a tropical drought, its garden little more than a display of vegetable anatomies, I cannot say. It was a house of a hideous aspect; but I confess it stirred my interest. Whereupon my stranger, apparently, thought he could safely glance aside; and I could examine him more at leisure. It was not, I have to confess, a taking face. There was a curious hollowness in its appearance. He looked like the shell of a man, or rather, like a hermit-crab—that neat pepper-and-salt tweed suit and so on being a kind of second-hand accumulation on his back.

'And of course,' he began again, 'now that I am alone I become'—he turned sharply back on me—'I become more conscious of it.'

'Of the loneliness?' I suggested.

Vacancy appeared on his face, as if he had for the instant stopped thinking. 'Yes,' he replied, once more transfixing me with those clear close eyes of his, 'the loneliness. It seems to increase more and more as the other slips away into the past. But I suppose we most of us have much the same experience; just of that, I mean. And even in London . . .'

I busied myself with my tea-things, having no particular wish at the moment to continue the conversation. But he hadn't any intention of losing his fish as easily as all that.

'There's a case now here in the newspaper this morning,'

he went on, his glance wandering off to a copy of the *Daily Mail* that lay on the chair next the one he had just vacated. 'A man not very much older than I am—found dead. Dead. The only occupant of quite a good-sized house, I should judge, at Stoke Newington—though I don't know the place personally. Living there for years on end without even a charwoman to do for him—to—to work for him. Still even there there was some kind of company, I suppose. He could look out of the window; he could hear people moving about next door. Where I am, there isn't another house in sight, not even a barn, and so far as I can see, what they call Nature doesn't become any the more friendly however long you stay in a place—the birds and that kind of thing. It may get better in time; but it 's only a few months ago since I was left quite like this—when my sister died.'

Obviously I was hooked beyond hope of winning free again until this corkscrew persistent creature had had his way with me. The only course seemed to be to get the experience over as quickly as possible. It is not easy, however, to feign an active sympathy; and mention of his dead sister had produced in my mind only a faint reflex image of a dowdy lady no longer young in dingy black. Still, it was an image that proved to be not very far from the actuality.

'Any close companionship like that,' I murmured, 'when it is broken is a tragic thing.'

He appeared to have seen no significance in my remark. 'And you see, once there were three of us. Once. It never got into the papers—at least not into the London papers, except just by mention, I mean.' He moistened his lips. 'Did you ever happen to come across a report about a lady, a Miss Dutton, who was "missing"?'

It was a pretty stupid question, for after all, few human beings are so gifted as to be able to recall the names even of the protagonists in genuine *causes célèbres*. To bear in mind every sort of Miss Dutton whose disappearance would be referred to only in news-snippets borrowed by the Metropolitan press from the provincial, would be rather too much of a tax even for those interested in such matters. I sipped my tea and surveyed him as sagaciously as possible; 'Not that I can actually recall,' I said. 'Miss—Dutton? It isn't a very uncommon name. You knew her?'

'Knew her!' he repeated, placing his hands on his knees and

sitting stiffly back in his chair, his eyes unflinchingly fixed on mine. 'She lived with us a matter of two years or more. It was us she left. It was my house she was missing from. It caused quite a stir in the neighbourhood. It was the talk of the countryside. There was an inquiry; and all that.'

'How long ago?'

'Pretty near a year ago. Yes; a year yesterday.'

'Do you mean the inquiry, or when Miss Dutton disappeared?'

'The inquiry,' he replied in a muffled fashion, as if a little annoyed at my want of perspicacity. 'The other was—oh, a month or more before that.'

The interview was becoming rather a laborious way of extracting a story, but somehow its rudiments had begun to interest me. I had nothing to do. Judging from the look of the street, the quicksilver in the thermometer was still edging exquisitely upwards. I detested the thought of emerging into that oven. So apparently did my companion, unless the mere sound of his voice seemed to him better entertainment than, say, the nearest picture palace—where at least one would be out of sight and it would be dark.

'I should have thought,' I began again in a voice as matter-of-fact as I could manage, 'that living as you do, a stir in the neighbourhood would not much matter, though I agree that the mystery itself must have mattered a good deal more. It must have been a great shock to you both.'

'Ay,' he said, with a gleam in his eye, 'but that's just what you Londoners don't seem to understand. You have your newspapers and all that. But in most ways you don't get talked about much. It's not so in the country. I guarantee you might be living right in the middle of the Yorkshire Fells and yet, if it came to there being anything to keep their tongues wagging, you'd know that your neighbours were talking of you, and what about, for miles around. It gets across—like those black men's drums one hears about in West Africa. As if the mere shock of the thing wasn't enough! What I feel about it is that nowadays people don't seem to show any sympathy, any ordinary feeling with—with those in such circumstances; at least, not country people. Wouldn't you say yourself,' he added, with feline rapidity, 'that if *you* were reported as missing it would be rough luck if nobody cared?'

'I don't quite see what you mean,' I replied. 'I thought

you said that the disappearance of your friend made a stir in the neighbourhood.'

'Yes; but they were not thinking so much of her as of the cause of it.'

We exchanged a long glance, but without much addition to my own small fund of information. 'But surely,' I ventured, 'that must depend upon where she was supposed to have disappeared *to*?'

'That,' he replied, 'they never knew. We couldn't find out one iota about it. You 've no idea'—he drew his hand down over his face as if to clear away a shadow from his eyes—'you 've no idea. Since she has gone I feel almost sometimes as if she can never have been real. *There,* but not real; if you understand me. I see her; and then the real thing goes again. It never occurred to me, that.'

'The psychologists would tell us something about that.'

'The what?' he asked sharply.

'People interested in the working of the mind, you know. After all, we can't definitely say whether that teapot there is real—what it is in itself, I mean. And merely to judge from its looks,' I added, 'one might hope it was a pure illusion.'

He looked hard at the teapot. 'Miss Dutton was a very well-preserved woman for her age,' he said. 'And when I say "not real," it 's only in a manner of speaking, I mean. I 've got her portrait in the newspaper in my pocket-book. That ought to prove her real enough. I never knew any one who was more "all there," as they say. She was a good friend to me—I have every reason to remember her. She came along of her own free will—just a chance meeting, in Scarborough, as a matter of fact. And she liked the comforts of a home after all those hotels and boarding-houses.'

In the course of these ruminating and mournful remarks—and there was unmistakable 'feeling' in his tones—he was rather privily turning over the contents of an old leather pocket-book with an inelastic black band. He drew out a frayed newspaper cutting, and put it down on the table beside the teapot.

'Looking at that, you wouldn't be in much doubt what Miss Dutton was in herself, now, would you? You 'd recognize her,' he raised his eyes, 'if she were—if you met her, I mean, in these awful streets? I would myself.'

It was impossible to decide whether this last remark was

ironical, triumphant, embittered, or matter-of-fact; so I looked at Miss Dutton. She was evidently a blonde and a well-preserved woman, as my friend had intimated; stoutish, with a plump face, a plump nose, infantile blue eyes, frizzy hair, and she wore (what a few years ago were old-fashioned and are now new-fashioned) long ear-rings.

It was curious what a stabilizing effect the ear-rings produced. They resembled the pole Blondin used to carry as he tripped across his rope over the Niagara Falls. Miss Dutton was looking out of her blurred image with a sort of insouciance, gaiety, 'charm,' the charm that photographers aim at but rather seldom convey. Destiny, apparently, casts no retrospective shadow. I defy anybody to have found the faintest hint in that aware, vain, commonplace, good-natured face which would suggest Miss Dutton was ever going to be 'missed'—missed, I mean, in the sense of becoming indiscoverable. In the other sense her friends would no doubt miss her a good deal. But then boarding-houses and hotels are the resorts rather of acquaintances than of friends.

The owner of the newspaper snippet was scrutinizing the gay, blurred photograph with as much interest as I was; though to him it was upside-down. There was a queer fond look on his face, a little feline, perhaps, in its sentimentality.

I pushed back the cutting across the marble table and he carefully reinterred it in his pocket-book. 'I was wondering,' he rambled on as he did so, 'what you might have thought of it—without prejudice, so to speak, if you had come across it —casually—like; in the newspaper, I mean?'

The question was not quite so simple as it sounded. It appeared as if my new acquaintance were in wait for a comment which he himself was eager to supply. And I had nothing much to say.

'It's difficult, you know, to judge from prints in newspapers,' I ventured at last. 'They are usually execrable even as caricatures. But she looks, if I may say so, an uncommonly genial woman: feminine—and a practical one, too. Not one, I mean, who would be likely to be missing, except on purpose—of her own choice, that is.' Our eyes met an instant. 'The whole business must have been a dreadful shock and anxiety to you. And, of course, to Miss . . . to your sister, I mean.'

'My name,' he retorted abruptly, shutting his eyes while a

bewildering series of expressions netted themselves on his face, 'my name is Bleet.'

'Miss Bleet,' I added, glancing at the pocket into which the book had by now disappeared, and speculating, too, why so preposterous an *alias* should have occurred to apparently so ready a tongue.

'You were saying "genial,"' he added rapidly. 'And that is what they all agreed. Even her only male relative—an uncle, as he called himself, though I can swear she never mentioned him in that or in any other capacity. She hadn't always been what you might call a happy woman, mind you. But they were bound to agree that those two years under my care—in our house—were the happiest in Miss Dutton's life. We made it a real home to her. She had her own rooms and her few bits of furniture—photographs and boxes and so on, quite private. It 's a pretty large house considering the rent —country, you know; and there was a sort of a new wing added to it fifty years or more ago. Old-fashioned, of course—open fireplace, no bath, enormous kitchen-range—swallows coal by the bushel—and so on—very inconvenient, but cheap. And though my sister was not in a position to supervise the house-keeping, there couldn't be a more harmless and affectionate creature. To those, that is, who were kind to her. She 'd run away from those who weren't—just run away and hide. I must explain that my poor sister was not quite—was a little weak in her intellects—from her childhood. It was always a great responsibility. But as time went on,' he drew his hand wearily over his face, 'Miss Dutton herself very kindly relieved me of a good deal of that. You said she looked a practical woman; so she was.'

The narrative was becoming steadily more personal, and disconcerting. And yet—such is humanity—it was as steadily intensifying in interest. A low grumble of thunder at that moment sounded over the street, and a horse clattered down with its van beyond the open door. My country friend did not appear to have noticed it.

'You never know quite where you are with the ladies,' he suddenly ejaculated, and glanced piercingly up—for at that moment our waitress had drawn near.

'It 's a 'Ighteen,' she said, pencil on lip, and looking vacantly from one to the other of us.

''Ighteen,' echoed her customer sharply; 'what's that? Oh, the omnibus. You didn't say what you meant. Thank you.' She hovered on, check-book in hand.' And please bring me another cup of coffee.' He looked at me as if with the intention of duplicating his order. I shook my head. 'One cup, then, miss; no hurry.'

The waitress withdrew.

'It looks as if rain was coming,' he went on, and as if he were thirsting for it as much as I was. 'As I was saying, you can never be quite sure where you are with women; and, mind you, Miss Dutton was a woman of the world. She had seen a good deal of life—been abroad—Gay Paree, Monte Carlo, and all that. Germany before the War, too. She could read French as free and easy as you could that mennoo there. Paper-bound books with pictures on them, and that kind of thing.' He was looking at me, I realized, as if there were no other way of intimating the particular kind of literature he had in mind.

'I used to wonder sometimes what she could find in us: such a lonely place; no company. Though, of course, she was free to ask any friends if she wanted to, and talked of them too when in the mood. Good class, to judge from what she said. What I mean is, she was quite her own mistress. And I must say there could not be more good humour and so on than what she showed my poor sister. At least, until later. She'd talk to her as if conversing; and my sister would sit there by the window looking back at her and smiling and nodding just as if she were taking it all in. And who knows, perhaps she was. What I mean is, it's possible to have things in your head which you can't quite put into so many words. It's one of the things I look for when I come up to London: the faces that could tell a story though what's behind them can't.'

I nodded.

'I can assure you that before a few weeks were over she had got to be as much at home with us as if we had known her all our lives. Chatty and domesticated, and all that. And using the whole house just as if it belonged to her. All the other arrangements were easy, too. I can say now, and I said it then, that we never once up to then demeaned ourselves to a single word of disagreement about money matters or anything else. A woman like that, who has been all over the Continent, isn't likely to go far wrong in that. I agree the terms were on the generous side; but then, you take me, so were the arrangements.

'She asked herself to raise them when she had been with us upwards of twelve months. But I said "No." I said: "A bargain's a bargain, Edna"—we were "Edna" and "William" to one another, by then, and my sister too. She was very kind to my poor sister; got a specialist up all the way from Bath—though for all his prying questions he did nothing, as I knew he wouldn't. You can't take those things so late. Mind you, as I say, the business arrangements were all on one side. Miss Dutton liked things select and comfortable. She liked things to go smoothly, as we all do, I reckon. She had been accustomed to smart boarding-houses and hotels—that kind of thing. And I did my level best to keep things nice.'

My stranger's face dropped into a rather gloomy expression, as if poor humanity had sometimes to resign itself to things a little less agreeable than the merely smooth and nice. He laid down his spoon, which he had been using with some vigour, and sipped his coffee.

'What I was going to explain,' he went on, rubbing at his moustache, 'is that everything was going perfectly easy—just like clockwork, when the servant question came up. My house, you see, is on what you may call the large side. It's old in parts, too. Up to then we had had a very satisfactory woman —roughish but willing. She was the wife, or what you might just as well call the widow, of a sailor. I mean he was one of the kind that has a ditto in every port, you know. She was glad of the place, glad to be where her husband couldn't find her, even though the stipulation was that her wages should be permanent. That system of raising by driblets always leads to discontent. And I must say she was a fair tyrant for work.

'Besides her, there was a help from the village—precious little good *she* was. Slummocky—and *stupid*! Still, we had got on pretty well up to then, up to Miss Dutton's time, and for some months after. But cooking for three mouths is a different thing to two. Besides, Miss Dutton liked her meals dainty-like: a bit of fish, or soup occasionally, toast-rack, tantalus, serviettes on the table—that kind of thing. But all that came on gradual-like—the thin edge of the wedge; until at last, well, "exacting" wasn't in it.

'And I must say'— he turned his wandering eye once more on

mine—'I must say, she had a way of addressing menials which sometimes set even my teeth on edge. She was a lady, mind you—though what *that* is when the breath is out of your body it's not so easy to say. And she had the lady's way with them —those continental hotels, I suppose. All very well in a large establishment where one works up against another and you can call them names behind their backs. But our house wasn't an establishment. It wouldn't do there: not in the long run, even if you had an angel for a general and a cook to match.

'Mind you, as I say, Miss Dutton was always niceness itself to my poor sister: never a hard word or a contemptuous look —not to her face nor behind her back, not up to then. I wouldn't have tolerated it either. And you know what talking to a party that can only just sit, hands in lap, and smile back at you means, or maybe a word now and then that doesn't seem to have anything to do with what you've been saying. It's a great affliction. But servants were another matter. Miss Dutton couldn't demean herself to them. She lived in another world. It was, "Do this"; and "Why isn't it done?"—all in a breath. I smoothed things over, though they got steadily worse and worse, for weeks and weeks, ay, months. It wore me to a shadow.

'And one day the woman—Bridget was her name—Irish, you know—she flared up in earnest and gave her, as they say, as good as she got. I wasn't there at the time. But I heard afterwards all that passed, and three times over—on the one side at least. I had been into the town in the runabout. And when I came home, Mrs Tantrums had packed up her box, got a gig from the farm, and was gone for good. It did me a world of harm, that did.

'Pretty well upset, I was too, as you can imagine. I said to Miss Dutton, "Edna," I said, "all I am saying is, was it necessary to go to such extremes? Not," I said, "mind you, Edna, that she was all sugar and honey even to me. I knew the wrong side of her mouth years before *you* appeared on the scene. What you've got to do with such people is—to manage —be firm, keep 'em low, but manage. It isn't common sense to cut off your tongue to spite your teeth. She's a woman, and Irish at that," I said, "and you know what to expect of them."

'I was vexed, that's a fact, and perhaps I spoke rather more sharply than need have been. But we were good friends by that time: and if honest give-and-take isn't possible between friends, where are you? I ask you. There was by that time too, nothing left over-private between us, either. I advised her about her investments and so on, though I took precious good care not to be personally involved. Not a finger stirring unless she volunteered it first. That all came out too. But it was nothing to do with me, now, was it, as man to man, if the good lady took a fancy into her head to see that my poor sister was not left to what's called the tender mercies of this world after my death?

'And yet, believe me, they fixed on that, like leeches. My hell, they did! At the Inquiry, I mean. And I don't see how much further their decency could have gone if they had called it an Inquest; and——'

Yet another low (almost gruff) volley of thunder interrupted his discourse. He left the sentence in the air; his mouth ajar. I have never met any one that made such active use of his chin in conversation, by the way, as Mr Bleet did. It must have been exceedingly fatiguing. I fancy he mistook just then the expression on my face for one of inquiry. He leant forward, pushing down towards me that long hairy finger on the marble table-top.

'When I say "tender mercies,"' he explained, 'I don't mean that my sister would have been left penniless, even if Miss Dutton or nobody like her had come into the house. There was money of my own too, though, owing to what I need not explain'—he half swallowed the words—'not much.' He broke off. 'It seems as if we are in for a bit of a thunderstorm. But I'd sooner it was here than down my way. When you're alone in the house you seem to notice the noise more.'

'I fancy it won't be much,' I assured him. 'It will clear the air.'

His eyes opened as if in astonishment that any mere act of nature could bring such consolation.

'You were saying,' I exclaimed, 'that you lost your maid?' He glanced up sharply. 'Though, of course,' I added hastily, 'you mustn't let me intrude on your private affairs.'

'Not at all; oh, not at all,' he interrupted with relief. 'I thought you said, "lost my head." Not at all. It makes all the difference to me—I can assure you, to be able to go over it like this. Friendly-like. To get a listener who has not been fed up on all that gossip and slander. It takes some living down, too. Nothing satisfies them: nothing. From one week's end to another you can't tell where they 'll unearth themselves next.'

It was becoming difficult to prevent a steadily growing distaste for my companion from showing itself in my face. But then self-pity is seldom ingratiating. Fortunately the light where we sat was by now little better than dusk. Indeed, to judge from the growing gloom in our tea-shop, the heavens at this moment were far from gracious. I determined to wait till the rain was over. Besides, though my stranger himself was scarcely winning company, and his matter was not much above the sensational newspaper order, the mere zigzagging of his narrative was interesting. Its technique, I mean, reminded me of the definition of a crab: 'The crab is a little red animal that walks backwards.'

'The fact is,' he went on, 'on that occasion—I mean about the servant—Miss Dutton and I had words. I own it. Not that she resented my taking the thing up in a perfectly open and friendly way. She knew she had put me in a fair quandary. But my own private opinion is that when you are talking to a woman it 's best not to bring in remarks about the sex in general. A woman is herself or nothing, if you follow me. What she thinks is no more than another skin. Keep her sex out of it, and she 'll be reasonable. But no further. As a matter of fact, I never argue with ladies. But I soon smoothed that over. It was only a passing cloud. And I must say, considering what a lady she *was*, she took the discomforts of having nothing but a good-for-nothing slattern in the house very generously, all things considered.

'Mind you, I worked *myself*, fit for any couple of female servants: washed up dishes, laid the table, kept the little knick-knacks going. Ay, and I 'd go into the town to fetch her out little delicacies: tinned soups and peaches, and such like; anything she might have a taste to. And I taught her to use the runabout for herself, though to hear her changing gear was like staring ruin in the face. A gallon of petrol to a hank of crimson silk—that kind of thing. Believe me, she 'd go all those miles for a shampoo-powder, or to have tea at a tea-shop—though you can't beat raw new-laid eggs and them on the premises. They got to know her there. She was a rare one for the fashions: scarves and motor-veils, and that kind of thing. But I never demurred. It wasn't for me to make objections, particularly as she'd do a little shopping on the housekeeping side as well, now and then. Though, mind you, she knew sixpence from a shilling, and particularly towards the last.

'What was the worst hindrance was that my poor sister seemed to have somehow come to know there were difficulties in the house. I mean that there had begun to be. You don't know how they do it; but they do. And it doesn't add to your patience, I grant, when what you have done at one moment is done wrong over again the next. But she meant well, poor creature: and scolding at her only made things worse. Still, we got along happily enough for a time, until'—he paused once more with mouth ajar—'until Miss Dutton took it into her head to let matters come to a crisis. Now judging from that newspaper cutting I showed you, what would you take the lady's age to be? Allowing, as you might say, for all that golden hair?'

It was an indelicate question. Though why the mere fact that Miss Dutton was now missing should intensify its indelicacy, it is not easy to say.

'Happiness makes one look younger than one really is,' I suggested.

He gaped at me, as if in wonderment that in a world of woe he himself was not possessed of a white beard as long as your arm.

'Happiness?' he echoed.

'Yes, happiness.'

'Well, what I mean is, you wouldn't say she was in the filly class; now, would you? High-spirited, easy-going, and all that; silly, too, at times: but no longer young. Not in her hey-day, I mean.'

I pushed my empty cup aside and looked at him. But he looked back at me without flinching, as if indeed it was a pleasant experience to be sharing with a stranger sentiments so naïve regarding 'the fair sex.'

'Mind you, I don't profess to be a young man either. But I can assure you, on my word of honour, that what she said to me that evening—I was doing chores in the kitchen at the time, and she was there too, arranging flowers in a vause for supper; she had a dainty taste in flowers—well, she asked me why I was so unkind to her, so unresponsive, and—it came on me like a thunderbolt.'

As if positively for exemplification, a sudden clap of thunder at that moment resounded overhead. The glasses and crockery around us softly tinkled in sympathy. We listened in silence to its reverberations dying away across the chimney-tops; though my companion seemed to be taking them in through his mouth rather than through his ears. His cheek paled a little.

'That's what she asked me, I say. And I can tell you it took me on the raw. It was my turn to flare up. We had words again; nothing much, only a storm in a tea-cup.' Instead of smiling at this metaphor in the circumstances, he seemed astonished, almost shocked, at its aptitude. But he pushed on boldly.

'And then after I had smoothed things over again, she put her cards on the table. Leap Year, and all that tomfoolery, not a bit of it! She was in dead earnest. She told me what I had guessed already, that she had scarcely a friend in the world. Never a word, mind you, of the colonel—interloping old Pepper-face! She assured me, as I say, she hadn't not only a single relative, but hardly a friend; that she was, as you might say, alone in life, and—well, that her sentiments had become engaged. In honour bound I wouldn't have breathed this to a living soul who knew the parties; but to a stranger, if I may say so, it isn't quite the same thing. What she said was—in the kitchen there, and me in an apron, mind you, tied round me—doing chores—she said—well, in short, that she wanted to make a match of it. She had taken a fancy to me, and was I agreeable.' There was no vanity in his face; only a stark unphilosophical astonishment. He seemed to think that to explain all is to forgive all; and was awaiting my concurrence.

'You mean she proposed marriage,' I interrupted him with needless pedantry, and at once, but too late, wished the word back. For vestiges of our conversation had evidently reached the counter. Our waitress, still nibbling her pencil, was gazing steadily in our direction. And for some obscure reason this heat that we were sharing with the world at large, combined with this preposterous farrago, was now irritating me almost beyond endurance. The fellow's complacency was incredible.

I beckoned to the young woman. 'You said this gentleman's bus to King's Cross was No. 18, didn't you?'

'Yes, 'ighteen,' she repeated.

'Then would you please bring him an ice.'

Mr Bleet gazed at me in stupefaction; a thick colour had mounted into his face. 'You don't mean to say,' he spluttered, 'that *I* made any such mention of such a thing. I 'm sure I never noticed it.'

My impulse had been nothing more than a protest against my own boredom and fatigue; but the way he had taken it filled me with shame. What could the creature's state of mind be like if his memory was as untrustworthy as that? The waitress retired.

'It 's so devilishly hot in here,' I explained. 'And even talking is fatiguing in this weather.'

'Ay,' he said in a low voice. 'It is. But you aren't having one yourself?'

'No, thank you,' I said, 'I daren't. I can't take ices. Indigestion—it 's a miserable handicap. . . . You were saying that at the time of Miss Dutton's proposal, you were in the kitchen.'

There was a pause. He sat looking foolishly at the little glass dishful of ice-cream: as surprising a phenomenon apparently as to an explorer from the torrid zone earth's northern snows must first appear. There was a look upon his face as if he had been 'hurt,' as if, like a child, at another harsh word he might burst out crying.

'I hardly know that it 's worth repeating,' he said at last lamely. His fine resonant voice had lost its tone. 'I suppose she intended it kindly enough. And I wouldn't say I hadn't suspected which way the wind was blowing: Willie this, and Willie that. I 've always been William to them that know me, except Bill at school. But it was always Willie with her; and a languishing look to match. Still, I never expected what came after that. It took me aback.

'There she was, hanging on my every word, looking volumes, and me not knowing what to say. In a way, too, I was attached to her. There were two sides to her, I allow that.' He turned away but not, it seemed, in order to see the less conspicuous side more clearly. 'I asked her to let me think things over, and I said it as any gentleman would. "Let me think it over, Edna," I said. "You do me honour," I said. Her hand was on my arm. She was looking at me. God being my witness, I tried to spare her feelings. I eased it over, meaning it all for the best. You see the prospect of it had no more than occurred to me. Married life wasn't

what I was after. I shouldn't be as old as I am now—and un-
married, I mean—if that had been so. It was uncomfortable
to see her carrying on like that: too early. But things having
come to such a pass, well, as you might say, we glided into an
understanding at last. And with what result? Why she made
it an occasion for putting her foot down all the way round. And
hadn't I known it of old?'

He looked at me searchingly, with those dog-bright eyes,
those high-set ears, as if to discover where precisely I now was
in relation to his confidences.

'She took the reins, as they say. All in good temper for the
most part; but there was no mistaking it. Mistress first and
Mrs after, in a manner of speaking. But when it came to speaking sharply to my poor sister on a matter which you wouldn't
expect even a full-witted person to be necessarily very quick
about at the uptake—I began to suspect I had made a mistake.
I knew it then: but forewarned isn't always forearmed. And
mistakes are easier to make than to put right It had gone
too far. . . .'

'If you really don't want that ice, I can easily ask the waitress
to take it away,' I assured him, if only to bring back that
wandering empty eye from the reverie into which he seemed to
have fallen. Or was it that he was merely absorbed in the
picture of the rain-drenched street that was reflected in the
looking-glass behind my chair?

'Thank you,' he said, taking up the spoon.

'And Miss Dutton left you at last. Did she tell you she had
any intention of going?'

'Never,' he asseverated. 'Not a word. No, not a single
word. And if you *can't* explain it, well then, why go on trying?
I say. Not at this late day. But you might as well argue
with a stone wall. The heat had come by then. Last summer,
you know: the drought. Not the great drought, I mean—but
round our parts in particular. The whole place was dried up
to a tinder; cracks in the clay; weeds dying; birds gone. Even
the trees flagging: and the oaks half eaten up by caterpillars
already. Meantime, I don't know how it was—unless, perhaps,
the heat—but there had been another quarrel. They never got
that out of me at the Inquiry, though; I can tell you. And that
was patched up, too. I apologized because she insisted. But
she had hurt me; she had hurt my feelings. And I couldn't see

that marriage was going to be a very practical experiment on those lines. But she came round; and considering what a genial woman of the world she looks like in that photograph, you wouldn't have guessed, would you, that crying, weeping, I mean, was much in her way? I found that out, too.

'And it didn't suit her, either. But she was what they call a woman made for affection. And I mean by *that*,' he broke in emphatically, 'she liked to monopolize. She wasn't a sharer. We were badly in want of a servant ourselves by that time, as you may imagine. Going from bad to worse, and me with a poisoned thumb, opening tins. But *she* was in want of a servant still more. She wanted me. Husbands often are nothing much better. What's more, I don't wish to say anything against the—against her now; but for the life of me I can't see any reason why she should have gone so far as to insult me. And not a week since we were like birds on one roost. To insult me, mind you, with my poor sister there, listening by!

'But I had learned a bit by then. I held my tongue, though there was a plenty of things to say in reply if I could have demeaned myself to utter them. Plenty. I just went on looking out of the window, easing myself with my foot—we were in the drawing-room at the time—and the very sight of the dried-up grass, and the dead vegetables, and the sun pouring down out of the sky like lava from a volcano would have been enough in themselves to finish off most people's self-restraint. But as I say, I just stood there thinking of what I might have said, but saying nothing—just let her rant on.

'Why, for instance, do you suppose she had made out weeks before that her investments were bringing in twice as much as they really did? Why all that stuff about Monte Carlo and the lady from America when it was only Boulogne and what they call a *pension*, which in plain English is nothing more than lodgings? Mind you,' he said, as if to intercept the remark I had no intention of making, 'mind you, I agree there *was* a competence, and I agree that, apart from a silly legacy to the Home for Cats and Dogs and that Belgian knacker trade, she had left all there was to leave to my sister—and long before what I told you about just now. I saw that in black and white. It was my duty. That was all settled. On the other hand, how was I to know that she wouldn't change her mind; that she hadn't been paving the way, as you may call it? And why had she deliberately deceived me? I thought it then, and I think it now, more than ever—considering what I have been through. It wasn't treating me fairly, and particularly before she was in a position when things couldn't be altered, so to speak, as between husband and wife.'

Owing to the noise of the rain—and possibly in part to his grammar—it was only with difficulty that I could now follow what the creature was mumbling. I found my attention wandering. A miniature Niagara at least eighteen inches wide was at this moment foaming along the street gutter while the rain in the middle of the street as it rebounded above the smoking asphalt was lifting into the air an exquisite mist of spray. I watched it enthralled; it was sweet as the sight of palm trees to my tired hot eyes, and its roar and motion lulled me for a moment or two into a kind of hypnotic trance. When I came back to myself and my trivial surroundings, I found my companion eyeing me as if he had eagerly taken advantage of these moments of oblivion.

'That's the real thing,' he said, as if to humour me, beckoning with his thumb over his shoulder. 'That rain. But it's waste on only stones.' He eyed it pensively, turning his head completely round on his narrow shoulders to do so. But only for a moment. He returned to the business in hand as promptly as if we gossipers had been called to order by the chairman of a committee.

'Now it says in that report there which you have just been reading, that Miss Dutton had not been seen after she left Crowstairs that afternoon of the 3rd of July. That's what it says—in so much print. And I say that's a lie. As it came out later on. And it doesn't make it any truer being in print. It's inaccurate—proved so. But perhaps I ought to tell you first exactly how the whole thing came about. Things get so confused in memory.' Once more he wearily drew his hand over his face as if to obliterate even the memory itself. 'But —quite apart from the others—it's a relief to get things clearer even in one's own mind. The fact is, the whole thing was over between us a day or two before. As I say, after the last little upset which I told you about, things were smoothed out again, as usual. At least on her side, though there was precious little in which I was really myself at fault. But my own belief is that she was an hysterical woman. What I mean is, she didn't need anything to make a fuss about; to fire up over. No foundation except just her own mood and feelings. I never was what they call a demonstrative person; it isn't in our family. My father himself was a schoolmasterish kind of man. "It hurts me more than it hurts you": that kind of man. And up to the age of ten I can honestly say that I never once heard my mother answer him back. She felt it, mind you. He thrashed me little short of savage at times. She'd look on, crying; but she kept herself in. She knew it only made matters worse; and she died when I was twelve.

'Well, what I think is this—that Miss Dutton made a mistake about me. She liked comfort. Breakfast in bed; slippers at night; hot water to wash in; that kind of thing. I'll go further: she was meant for luxury. You could see it in her habits. If she had been twice as well off, she'd have wanted three times as many luxuries: lady's maid, evening dress, tea-gowns, music in the drawing-room—that sort of thing. And maybe it only irritated her when she found that I could keep myself in and just look calm, whatever she did or said. Hesitate to say whatever came into her mind?—not she!—true or untrue. Nor actual physical violence, either. Why months before, she threw a vause full of flowers at me: snowdrops."

The expression on his face suddenly became fixed, as if at an unexpected recollection.

'I am not suggesting,' he testified earnestly, 'considering—considering what came after, that I bear her any grudge or malice on account of all that. All I mean is that I was pressed and pushed on to a point that some would say was beyond human endurance. Maybe it was. But what I say is, let'—his voice trembled—'bygones be bygones. I will say no more of that. My point is that Miss Dutton, after all, was to be, as they say, a bird of passage. There had been a final flare up and all was over between us. Insult on insult she heaped on me. And my poor sister there, in her shabby old black dress, peering out at us, from between her fingers, trembling in the corner like a dumb animal. She had called her in.

'And me at my wits' end, what with the servant trouble and the most cantankerous and unreasonable lot of tradespeople you could lay hands on, north or south. I can tell you, I was pretty hard pressed. They dragged all that up at the Inquiry. Oh, yes, bless you. Trust 'em for that. Once it's men against

man, then look to it. Not a *public* Inquiry, mind you. No
call for that. And I *will* say the police, though pressing, and
leaving no stone unturned in a manner of speaking, were gentlemen by comparison. But such things leak out. You can't
keep a penny-a-liner from gabbing, and even if there had been
nothing worse to it they 'd have made my life a hell upon
earth.'

'Nothing worse to it? How do you mean?'

His glance for the instant was entirely vacant of thought.
'I mean,' he said stubbornly, after a moment's hesitation, 'the
hurt to my private feelings. That 's what I mean. I can hear
her now. And the first thing I felt after it was all over, was
nothing but relief. We couldn't have hit it off together, not
for long: not after the first few weeks, anyhow. Better, I say,
wash your hands of the whole thing. I grant you her decision
had left me in a nasty pickle. As a matter of fact, she was to
go in a week, and me to clear up the mess. Bills all over the
place—fresh butter, mind you, olives, wine, tinned mock turtle
—that kind of thing; and all down to my account. What I
feel is, she oughtn't to have kept on at me like that right up to
the last. Wouldn't you have thought, considering all things,
any woman with an ounce of common sense—not to speak of
common caution—would have let sleeping dogs lie?'

He was waiting for an answer.

'What did her uncle, the Colonel, say to that?'

'Oh, him,' he intimated with an incredible sneer. 'In the
Volunteers! I was speaking as man to man.'

'And she didn't even wait the two or three days, then?'

'It was the 3rd of July,' he repeated. 'After tidying things
up for the day—and by that time, mind you, every drop of water
had to be brought in buckets across the burnt-up fields from a
drying-up pond half a mile away. But it was done. I did it.
After finishing, I say, all the rest of the morning chores, I was
sitting there thinking of getting a snack of lunch and then what
to do next, when I heard a cough—her door had opened; and
then her footstep on the stairs—slippers.' He held up that
forefinger as if at an auction, and he was speaking with extreme
deliberation as if, with eyes and senses fixed on the scene, he
were intent to give me the exactest of records in the clearest
of terms. 'And I said to myself, "She 's coming! and it 's all
to begin again!" I said it; I knew it. "And face it out? . . .

then—me?'" He shook his head a little like a cat tasting water, but the eyes he showed me were like the glazed windows of an empty shop. 'No, I made myself scarce. I said to myself: "Better keep your distance. Make yourself scarce; keep out of it." And heaven help me I had been doing my best to forget what had passed the night before and to face what was to come. And so—I went out.

'It was early afternoon: sultry, like now. And I wandered about the fields. I must have gone miles and never met a soul. But if you ask me to say where, then all I can say is, Isn't one field the living image of another? And what do you see when your mind isn't there? All round Winstock way—lanes, hedges, corn-fields, turnips—tramp and tramp and tramp. And it was not until about seven o'clock that evening that I got back again. Time for supper. I got out the crockery and—and raked out the fire. No sign of nobody, nor of my sister either—though there was nothing in that: she had a habit of sitting up at her bedroom window, and looking out, just with her hands in her lap. And the house as still as a—as still as a church.

'I loafed about a bit in the kitchen. Call *her*? Well, hardly! There was plenty to do. As usual. The supper, and all that. The village woman had left about eleven that morning—toothache. She owned to it. Not that that put me about. I can cook a boiled egg and a potato well enough for most Christians. But hot meals—meals for—well, anyhow, there was nothing hot that evening. It was about seven-thirty by then, I suppose; and I was beginning to wonder. Then I thought I'd go out in the yard and have a look at the runabout—an old Ford, you know—I hadn't had time then for weeks to keep it decent. When I got to the shed, there was a strange cat eating up some fish-bones; and when I looked in, it was gone.'

'You mean the Ford?'

'Yes, the Ford. There wasn't a sign of it. That froze me up, I can tell you, for there had been gipsies about a day or two before. I rushed into the house and called out, "Miss Dutton, Miss Dutton, are you there? The Ford's gone." No answer. I can tell you I was just like a frenzied man. I looked in the drawing-room—teapot and cup on a tray but empty: just sunshine streaming in as if nothing had happened. Then I looked into her little parlour: boudoir, she called it. Nothing doing. Then I went upstairs and tapped on her bedroom door. "Miss Dutton," I said, "have you seen anything of the Ford? It's gone." And then I looked in. That was the queer thing about it. They all said that. That it never occurred to me, I mean, that she was not in the car herself. But what I say is —how can you think of everything before you say it, and wasn't it I myself that *said* I had said it?

'Anyhow, I looked in: I suppose a man can do *that* in his own house and his car gone from under his very eyes! And believe me, the sight inside was shocking. I'm a great stickler myself for law and order, for neatness, I mean. I had noticed it before: it irritated me; in spite of all her finery, she was never what you would call a tidy woman. But that room beat everything. Drawers flung open, dresses hugger-mugger, slippers, bags, beadwork, boxes, gimcracks all over the place. But not a sign of her. I looked—everywhere. She wasn't there, right enough. Not—not a sign of her. She was gone. And—and I have never seen her since.'

The rain was over, and the long sigh he uttered seemed to fill the whole tea-shop as if it were a faint echo of the storm which had ceased as suddenly as it had begun. The sun was wanly shining again, gilding the street.

'You at once guessed, I suppose, the house had been broken into, while you were out?'

He kept his eyes firmly on mine. 'Yes,' he said. 'That's what I thought—at first.'

'But then, I think you said a minute or two ago that Miss Dutton *was* actually seen again?'

He nodded. 'That's just it,' he said, as if with incredulous lucidity. 'So you see, the other couldn't have been. The facts were against it. She was seen that very evening,' he said, 'and driving my Ford. By more than one, too. Our butcher happened to be outside his shop door; no friend of mine, either. It was a Saturday, cutting up pieces for the 4d. and 6d. trays, and he saw her going by: saw the number, too. It was all but broad daylight, though it's a narrow street. It was about seven then, he said, because he had only just wound his clock. There she was; and a good pace too. And who could be surprised if she looked a bit unusual in appearance? It's exactly what you'd expect. You don't bolt out of a house you have lived in comfortable for two or three years as neat as a new pin.'

'What was wrong with her?'

'Oh, the man was nothing better than a fool, though promptitude itself when it came to asking a good customer to settle up. He said he'd have hardly recognized her. There, in my car, mind you, and all but broad daylight.'

'But surely,' I said as naturally as possible, 'even if it is difficult sometimes to trace a human being, it is not so easy to dispose of a car. Wasn't that ever found?'

He smiled at me, and in a more friendly way than I should have deemed possible in a face so naturally inexpressive.

'You've hit the very nail on the head,' he assented. 'They did find the car—on the Monday morning. In fact, it was found on the Sunday by a young fellow out with his sweetheart, but they thought it was just waiting—picking flowers, or something. It had been left inside a fir-copse about a couple of hundred yards from a railway station, a mile or so out of the town.'

'Just a countrified little railway station, I suppose? Had the porter or anybody noticed a lady?'

'Countrified—ay, maybe: but the platform crowded with people going to and fro for their week's marketing, besides a garden party from the rectory.'

'The platform going into the town?'

'Yes, that's it,' said my friend. 'Covering her tracks.'

At that moment I noticed one of our waitress's bright-red 'Eighteens' whirling past the tea-shop door. It vanished.

'She had had a letter that morning—postmark Chicago,' the now far-too-familiar voice pushed on industriously. 'The postman noticed it, being foreign. It's my belief *that* caused it. But mind you, apart from that, though I'm not, and never was, complaining she'd treated me, well——' But he left the sentence unfinished while he clumsily pushed about with his spoon in the attempt to rescue a fly that had strayed in too far in pursuit of his sweet cold coffee. He was breathing gently on the hapless insect.

'And I suppose, by that time, you had given the alarm?'

'Given the alarm?' he repeated. 'Why?'

The sudden frigidity of his tone confused me a little. 'Why,' I said, 'not finding Miss Dutton in the house, didn't you let anybody know?'

'Now, my dear sir,' he said, 'I ask you. How was *I* to know what Miss Dutton was after? I wasn't Miss Dutton's keeper;

she was perfectly at liberty to do what she pleased, to come and go. How was I to know what she had taken into her head? Why, I thought for a bit it was a friendly action considering all things, that she should have borrowed the car. Mind you, I don't say I wasn't disturbed as well, her not leaving a word of explanation, as she had done once before—pinned a bit of paper to the kitchen table—"Yours with love, Edna"—that sort of thing. Though that was when everything was going smooth and pleasant. What I did first was to go off to a cottage down the lane and inquire there. All out, except the daughter in the wash-house. Not a sight or sound of car or Miss Dutton, though she did recollect the honk of a horn sounding. "Was it my horn?" I asked. But they're not very observant, that kind of young woman. Silly-like. Besides, she wasn't much more than a child.'

'And your sister: where actually was she, after all?'

He looked at me as if once more in compliment of my sagacity.

'That, I take it—to find and question *her*, I mean, was a matter of course. I went up to her room, opened the door, and I can hear myself actually saying it now: "Have you seen anything of Edna, Maria?"

'It was very quiet in her room—stuffy, too, and for the moment I thought she wasn't there; and then I saw her—I detected her there—sitting in the farthest corner out of the light. I saw her white face turn round, it must have been covered up. "Where's Edna, Maria?" I repeated. She shook her head at me, sitting there beyond the window. I could scarcely see her. And you don't seem to have realized that any kind of direct or sudden question always confused her. It didn't seem she understood what I was saying. In my belief it was nothing short of brutal the way they put her through it. I mean that Colonel, as he calls himself. Over and over and over again.

'Well, we weren't in any mood for food, as you may guess, when eight, nine, went by—and no sign of her. At last it was no use waiting any longer; but just to make sure, I went over to the farm two miles or so away—a little off the road, too, she must have taken to the town. We were still pretty friendly there. It was about half-past nine, I suppose, and they had all gone to bed. The dog yelled at me as if it was full moon and he had never seen me before. I threw a handful of gravel up at the old man's window, and I must say, considering all things, he kept his temper pretty well. Specially as he had seen nothing. Nothing whatever, he said.

'"Well," I said, speaking up at him, and they were my very words, "I should like to know what's become of her." He didn't seem to be as anxious as I was—thought she'd turn up next morning. "That kind of woman knows best what she's about," he said. So I went home and went to bed, feeling very uneasy. I didn't like the feel of it, you understand. And I suppose it must have been about three or four in the morning when I heard a noise in the house."

'You thought she had come back?'

'What?' he said.

'I say, you thought she had come back?'

'Yes, of course. Oh, yes. And I looked out of my bedroom door over the banisters. By that time there was a bit of moonlight showing, striking down on the plaster and oilcloth. It was my sister, with an old skirt thrown over her nightgown. She was as white as a sheet, and shivering.

'"Where have you been, Maria?" I asked her in as gentle a voice as I could make it. The curious thing is, she understood me perfectly well. I mean she answered at once, because often I think really and truly she did understand, only that she couldn't as quickly as most people collect her wits as they say.

'She said, mumbling her words, she had been looking for her.

'"Looking for who?" I said, just to see if she had taken me right.

'"For her," she said.

'"For Edna?" I asked. "And why should you be looking for Edna this time of night?" I spoke a little more sternly.

'She looked at me, and the tears began to roll down her face.

'"For God's sake, Maria, why are you crying?" I said.

'"Oh," she said, "she's gone. And she won't come back now."

'I put my arm round her and drew her down on to the stairs. "Compose yourself," I said to her, "don't shiver and shake like that." I forgot she had been standing barefoot on the cold oilcloth. "What do you mean, gone? Don't take on so. Who's to know she won't come back safe and sound?" I am giving you the words just as they came out of our mouths.

'"Oh," she said, "William, you know better than me—I won't

say anything more. Gone. And never knowing that I hadn't forgotten how kind she was to me!"

'"Kind, my girl!" I said. "Kind! In good part, maybe," I said, "but not surely after what she said to you that day?"

'But I could get nothing more out of her. She shrank up moaning and sobbing. She had lost herself again, her hair all draggled over her eyes, and she kept her face averted from me, and her shoulders were all humped, shaking under my hands —you know what women are. So I led her off to her room and made her as comfortable as I could. But all through the night I could hear her afterwards when I went to listen, and talking too.

'You can tell I was by now in a pretty state myself. That was a long night for me. And what do you think: when I repeated that conversation to the Colonel, and the Inspector himself standing by, he as good as told me he didn't believe me. "Friendly questions"! I could have wrung his nose. But then by that time my poor sister couldn't put two words together, he bawled at her so; until even the Inspector said it was not fair on her, and that she wouldn't be any use, anyhow, whatever happened.'

Once again there fell a pause in my stranger's disjointed story. He took two or three spoonfuls in rapid succession of his half-melted ice-cream. Even though the rain and the storm had come and gone, the air was not appreciably cooler, or rather it was no less heavy and stagnant. Our waitress had apparently given us up as lost souls, and I glanced a little deprecatingly at the notice, 'No Gratuities,' on the wall.

'How long did the drought last after that?' I inquired at last.

'The drought?' said my friend. 'The questions you ask! Why, it broke that very night. Over an inch of rain we had in less than eight hours.'

'Well, that, at any rate, I suppose, was something of a comfort.'

'I don't see quite why,' he retorted.

'And then you informed the police?'

'On the Sunday.' He took out a coloured silk handkerchief from the pocket of his neat pepper-and-salt jacket, and blew his nose. It is strange how one can actually anticipate merely from the general look of a man such minute particulars as the trumpeting of a nose. Strange, I mean, that all the parts and properties of human beings seem to hang so closely together, as if in positive collusion. Anyhow, the noise resounded through the glass-walled marbled room as sharp as cockcrow.

'Well,' he said, 'that's where I stand. Looking at me, you wouldn't suppose perhaps that everything that a man wants most in this world has been destroyed and poisoned away. I had no call perhaps to be confiding in a mere stranger. But you couldn't credit the relief. I have nothing left now. I came up here to lose myself in the noise—so shocking quiet it is, there, now. But I have to go back—can't sleep much, though: wake up shouting. But what's worst is the emptiness: it's all perished. I don't want anything now. I'd as lief die and have done with it, if I could do it undriven. I've never seen a desert, but I reckon I know what the inside of one's like now. I stop thinking sometimes, and get dressed without knowing it. You wouldn't guess that from my appearance, I dare say. But once begin living as you feel underneath living *is*, where would most of us be? They have hounded me on and they've hounded me down, and presently they'll be sealing me up, and me never knowing from one day to another what news may come of—of our friend. And my sister gone and all.'

'She isn't "missing" too, I hope?' As I reflect on it, it was a vile question to have put to the man. I don't see how anything could have justified it. His face was like a burnt-out boat. The effect on him was atrocious to witness. His swarthy cheek went grey as ashes. The hand on the marble table began to tremble violently.

'Missing?' he cried. 'She's dead. Isn't *that* good enough for you?'

At this, no doubt because I was hopelessly in the wrong, I all but lost control of myself.

'What do you mean?' I exclaimed in a low voice. 'What do you mean by speaking to me like that? Haven't I wasted the better part of a Saturday afternoon listening to a story which I could have picked up better in your own county newspaper? What's it all to me, may I ask? I want to have nothing more to do with it—or you either.'

'You didn't say that at the beginning,' he replied furiously, struggling to his feet. 'You led me on.'

'Led you on, by God! What do you mean by such a piece of impudence? I say I want nothing more to do with you.

And if that's how you accept a kindness, take my advice and keep your troubles to yourself in future. Let your bygones *be* bygones. And may the Lord have mercy on your soul.'

It was a foul outburst, due in part, I hope, to the heat; in part to the suffocating dehumanizing foetor which spreads over London when the sun has been pouring down on its bricks and mortar as fiercely as on the bones and sands of some Eastern mud village.

My stranger had sat down again abruptly, had pushed his ice away from him and covered his face with his hands. His shoulders were jumping as if with hiccups. It was fortunate perhaps that at the moment there was no other eater in the café. But the waitresses were clustered together at the counter. They must have been watching us for some little time. And the manageress was there, too, looking at us like a scandalized hen over her collar through her pince-nez. We were evidently causing a disturbance—on the brink of a 'scene.' A visionary placard flaunted across my inward eye: *Fracas in a Restaurant.*

I too sat down, and beckoned peremptorily to the young lady who had been so attentive about the bus.

'My bill, please,' I said—'this gentleman's and mine.' And then, foolishly, I added: 'It's hot, isn't it?'

She made no reply until, after damping her lead pencil, she had added up her figures and had handed me between her finger-tips the mean scrap of paper. Then she informed me crisply, in fastidious Cockney, that some people seemed to find it hotter than most, and that it was nearly closing time, and would I please pay at the desk.

My accomplice had regained a little of his self-restraint by now. He put out a wavering hand and took up his hard felt hat. It was almost incredible that so marked a change should have come over so insensitive a face in that brief space of time. Its touch of bravado, its cold clear stare as of a watchful dog, even the neatness of it, had disappeared. He looked ten years older—lost and abandoned. He put out his other hand for the check. It was a curious action for a man with an intense closeness—if not meanness—clearly visible on his features: 'I should prefer, if you don't mind, to pay my bill myself,' he said.

'Not at all,' I replied brusquely. 'It was my ice-cream. I must apologize for having been so abrupt.'

He tried to smile; and it was like the gleam of a sickly evening sunshine after heavy winter rain.

'It's broken me: that's all I can say,' he said. 'What I say is, you read such things in the newspapers, but you don't know what they mean to them as are most concerned. I don't see how you can.'

I hesitated. A furious contest—dim, spreadeagled figures silhouetted, as it were, against a background of utter black—seemed to be proceeding in some dream in my mind, a little beyond actual consciousness. 'Well,' I blurted, 'I hope time will make things better. I can guess what I should feel like myself in similar circumstances. If I were you, I should . . .' But at sight of him, the words, I am thankful to say, faded out before I could utter them. 'If I were you'—how easy! But how is that metamorphosis possible?

He looked at his hat; he looked at his ice-cream, now an insipid mush; he looked anxiously and searchingly at the table —marked over with the hieroglyphics of dark ugly marble. And at last he raised his eyes—those inexpressive balls of glass —and looked at me. He changed his hat from his right to his left hand, and still looking at me, hesitated, holding the empty hand out a little above the table. Then turning away, he drew it back.

I pretended not to have noticed the action. 'There should be another Eighteen in a few minutes,' I volunteered. 'And I think I noticed a stopping-place a few yards down.'

Nevertheless I couldn't for the moment leave him there— to the tender mercies of those censorious young waitresses in their exquisitely starched caps. 'I am going that way,' I said. 'Shall I see you into it?'

'It's the heat,' he said. 'No, thank you. You have been a . . .'

With a gasp I repelled as well as I could the distaste for him that was once more curdling as if with a few drops of vinegar my very blood. What monsters of hatred and uncharitableness we humans can be! And what will *my* little record look like, I wonder, when the secrets of all hearts are opened.

It seemed for the time being as though the whole of my right arm had become partially paralysed. But with an effort I put out my hand at last; and then he, too, his—a large green solitaire cuff-link showing itself against his wristband as he did so. We shook hands—though I doubt if a mere fleshly contact can express much while the self behind it is dumb with instinctive distaste.

Besides, the effect on him even of a friendly action as frigid as this was horribly disconcerting. It reminded me of ice pitted and crumbling in a sudden thaw. He seemed to have been reduced to a state of physical and spiritual helplessness, as if by an extremity of emotion, or by a drug. It was nauseating. It confused me and made me ashamed and miserable. I turned away abruptly; paid our bill at the desk, and went out. And London enveloped me.

From *The Connoisseur*.

THE GREEN ROOM

ONLY Mr Elliott's choicer customers were in his own due season let into his little secret—namely, that at the far end of his shop —beyond, that is, the little table on which he kept his account books, his penny bottle of ink, and his rusty pen, there was an annexe. He first allowed his victims to ripen; and preferred even to see their names installed in the pages of his fat, dumpy ledger before he decided that they were really worthy of this little privilege.

Alan, at any rate, though a young man of ample leisure and moderate means, had been browsing and pottering about on and off in the shop for weeks before he even so much as suspected there *was* a hidden door. He must, in his innocence, have spent pounds and pounds on volumes selected from the vulgar shelves before his own initiation.

This was on a morning in March. Mr Elliott was tying up a parcel for him. Having no scissors handy he was burning off the ends of the string with a lighted match. And as if its small flame had snapped at the same moment both the string and the last strands of formality between them, he glanced up almost roguishly at the young man through his large round spectacles with the remark: 'P'r'aps, sir, you would like to take a look at the books in the parlour?' And a birdlike jerk of his round bald head indicated where the parlour was to be found.

Alan had merely looked at him for a moment or two out of his blue eyes with his usual pensive vacancy. 'I didn't know there *was* another room,' he said at last. 'But then, I suppose it wouldn't have occurred to me to think there might be. I fancied these books were all the books you had.' He glanced over the dingy hugger-mugger of second-hand literature that filled the shelves and littered the floor—a mass that would have twenty-fold justified the satiety of a Solomon.

'Oh, dear me, no, sir!' said Mr Elliott, with the pleasantest confidentiality. 'All this is chiefly riff-raff. But I don't mention it except to those gentlemen who are old clients, in a manner of speaking. What's in there is all in the printed catalogue and I can always get what's asked for. Apart from that, there's some who—well, at any rate, I *don't*, sir. But if by any chance you should care to take a look round at any time, you would, I'm sure, be very welcome. This is an oldish house, as you may have noticed, sir, and out there is the oldest parts of it. We call it the parlour—Mrs Elliott and me; we got it from the parties that were here before we came. Take a look now, sir, if you please; it's a nice little place.'

Mr Elliott drew aside. Books—and particularly old books—tend to be dusty company. This may account for the fact that few antiquarian booksellers are of Falstaffian proportions. They are more usually lean, ruminative, dryish spectators of life. The gnawing of the worm in the tome is among the more melancholy of nature's lullabies; and the fluctuations in price of 'firsts' and of 'mint states' must incline any temperament, if not towards cynicism, at least towards the philosophical. Herodotus tells of a race of pygmies whose only diet was the odour of roses; and though morocco leather is sweeter than roses, it is even less fattening.

Mr Elliott, however, flourished on it. He was a rotund little man with a silver watch-chain from which a gold locket dangled, and he had uncommonly small feet. He might have been a ballet-master. 'You make your way up those four stairs, sir,' he went on, as he ushered his customer beneath the curtain, 'turn left down the passage, and the door's on the right. It's quiet in there, but that's no harm done. No hurry, sir.'

So Alan proceeded on his way. The drugget on the passage floor showed little trace of wear. The low panelled walls had been whitewashed. He came at last to the flowered china handle of the door beyond the turn of the passage, then stood for a moment lost in surprise. But it was the trim cobbled garden beyond the square window on his right that took his glance rather than the room itself. Yellow crocuses, laden with saffron pollen, stood wide agape in the black mould, and the greening buds of a bush of lilac were tapping softly against the glass. And above was a sky of the gentlest silken blue; wonderfully still.

He turned and looked about him. The paint on wainscot and cornice must once have been of a bright apple green. It had faded now. A gate-leg table was in the far corner beyond the small-paned window; and on his left, with three shallow steps up to it, was another door. And the shelves were lined from floor to ceiling with the literary treasures which Mr Elliott kept solely for his elect. So quiet was the room that even the flitting of a clothes-moth might be audible, though the brightness of noonday now filled it to the brim. For the three poplars beyond the lilac bush were still almost as bare as the frosts of winter had made them.

In spite of the flooding March light, in spite of this demure sprightliness after the gloom and disorder of the shop he had left behind him, Alan—as in his languid fashion he turned his head from side to side—became conscious first and foremost of the *age* of Mr Elliott's pretty parlour. The paint was only a sort of 'Let 's pretend.' The space between its walls seemed, indeed, to be as much a reservoir of time as of light. The panelled ceiling, for example, was cracked and slightly discoloured; so were the green shutter-cases to the windows; while the small and beautiful chimney-piece—its carved marble lintel depicting a Cupid with pan pipes dancing before a smiling goddess under a weeping willow—enshrined a grate that at this moment contained nothing, not even the ashes of a burnt-out fire. Its bars were rusty, and there were signs of damp in the moulded plaster above it.

A gentle breeze was now brisking the tops of the poplar trees, but no murmur of it reached Alan where he stood. With his parcel tucked under his arm, he edged round softly from shelf to shelf, and even after so cursory an examination as this—and it was one of Mr Elliott's principles to mark all his books in plain figures—he realized that his means were much too moderate for his appetite. He came to a standstill, a little at a loss. What was he to do next? He stifled a yawn. Then, abstracting a charming copy of *Hesperides*, by that 'Human and divine,' poet, Robert Herrick, he seated himself idly on the edge of the table and began to turn over its leaves. They soon became vocal:

> Aske me, why I do not sing
> To the tension of the string,
> As I did, not long ago,
> When my numbers full did flow?
> Griefe (ay me!) hath struck my Lute,
> And my tongue—at one time—mute.

His eye strayed on, and he read slowly—muttering the words to himself as he did so—'*The departure of the good* Daemon':

> What can I do in Poetry,
> Now the good Spirit's gone from me?
> Why nothing now, but lonely sit,
> And over-read what have I writ.

Alan's indolence was even more extreme; he was at this moment merely over-reading what he had *read*—and what he had read again and again and again. For the eye may be obedient while the master of the mind sits distrait and aloof. His wits had gone wool-gathering. He paused, then made yet another attempt to fix his attention on the sense of this simple quatrain. But in vain. For in a moment or two his light, clear eyes had once more withdrawn themselves from the printed page and were once more, but now more intently, exploring the small green room in which he sat.

And as he did so—though nothing of the bright external scene around him showed any change—out of some day-dream, it seemed, of which until then he had been unaware, there had appeared to him from the world of fantasy the image of a face.

No known or remembered face—a phantom face, as alien and inscrutable as are the apparitions that occasionally visit the mind in sleep. This in itself was not a very unusual experience. Alan was a young man of an imaginative temperament, and possessed that inward eye which is often, though not unfailingly, the bliss of solitude. And yet there was a difference. This homeless image was at once so real in effect, so clear, and yet so unexpected. Even the faint shadowy colours of the features were discernible—the eyes dark and profound, the hair drawn back over the rather narrow temples of the oval head; a longish, quiet, intent face, veiled with reverie and a sort of vigilant sorrowfulness, and yet possessing little of what at first sight might be called beauty—or what at least is usually accepted as beauty.

So many and fleeting, of course, are the pictures that float into consciousness at the decoy of a certain kind of poetry that one hardly heeds them as they pass and fade. But this, surely, was no after-image of one of Herrick's earthly yet ethereal Electras or Antheas or Dianemes, vanishing like the rainbows in a fountain's falling waters. There are degrees of realization. And, whatever 'good Spirit' this shadowy visitant may have represented, and whatever its origin, it had struck *some* 'observer' in Alan's mind mute indeed, and had left him curiously disquieted. It was as if in full sight of a small fishing smack peacefully becalmed beneath the noonday blue, the spars and hulk of some such phantom as the *Flying Dutchman* had suddenly appeared upon the smooth sea green; though this perhaps was hardly a flattering account of it. Anyhow, it had come, and now it was gone—except out of memory—as similar images do come and go.

Mere figment of a day-dream, then, though this vision must have been, Alan found himself vacantly searching the room as if for positive corroboration of it, or at least for some kind of evidence that would explain it away. Faces are but faces, of course, whether real or imaginary, and whether they appear in the daytime or the dark, but there is at times a dweller behind the eye that looks out, though only now and again, from that small window. And *this* looker-out—unlike most—seemed to be innocent of any attempt at concealment. 'Here am I. . . . And you?' *That* had seemed to be the mute question it was asking; though with no appearance of needing an answer; and, well, Alan distrusted feminine influences. He had once or twice in his brief career loved not wisely but too idealistically, and for the time being he much preferred first editions. Besides, he disliked mixing things up—and how annoying to be first slightly elated and then chilled by a mere fancy!

The sun in his diurnal round was now casting a direct beam of light from between the poplars through one of the little panes of glass in Mr Elliott's parlour. It limned a clear-cut shadow-pattern on the fading paint of the frame and on the floor beneath. Alan watched it and was at the same time listening—as if positively in hope of detecting that shadow's indetectable motion!

In the spell of this reverie, time seemed to have become of an almost material density. The past hung like cobwebs in the air. He turned his head abruptly; he was beginning to feel a little uneasy. And his eyes now fixed themselves on the narrow panelled door above the three stairs on the other side of the room. When consciousness is thus unusually alert it is more easily deceived by fancies. And yet so profound was the quiet around him it seemed improbable that the faint sound he had heard as of silk very lightly brushing against some material obstacle was imaginary. Was there a listener behind that door?

Or was there not? If so, it must be one as intent as himself, but far more secret.

For a full minute, and as steadily as a cat crouching over a mouse's hole—though there wasn't the least trace of the predatory on his mild fair features, he scrutinized the key in the lock. He breathed again; and then with finger in book to keep his place tiptoed across the room and gently—by a mere finger's breadth—opened the door. Another moment and he had pushed it wider. Nothing there. Exactly as he had expected, of course, and yet—why at the same moment was he both disappointed and relieved?

He had exposed a narrow staircase—unstained, uncarpeted. Less than a dozen steep steps up was another door—a shut door, with yet another pretty flowered china handle and china fingerplates to it. A rather unusual staircase, too, he realized, since, unless one or other of its two doors were open, it must continually be in darkness. But you never know what oddity is going to present itself next in an old rambling house. How many human beings, he speculated, as he scanned this steep and narrow vacancy, must in the two or three centuries gone by have ascended and descended that narrow ladder—as abrupt as that of Jacob's dream. They had come, disguised in the changing fashions of their time; they had gone, leaving apparently not a wrack behind.

Well, that was that. This March morning might be speciously bright and sunny, but in spite of its sunshine it was cold. Books, too, may cheer the mind, but even when used as fuel they are apt to fail to warm the body, and rust on an empty grate diminishes any illusion of heat its bars might otherwise convey. Alan sighed, suddenly aware that something which had promised to be at least an arresting little experience had failed him. The phantasmal face so vividly seen, and even watched for a moment, had already become a little blurred in memory. And now there was a good deal more disappointment in his mind than relief. He felt like someone who has been cheated at a game he never intended to play. A particularly inappropriate simile, none the less, for he hadn't the smallest notion what the stakes had been, or, for that matter, what the game. He took up his hat and walking-stick, and still almost on tiptoe, and after quietly but firmly shutting both doors behind him, went back into the shop.

'I think I will take *this*, please,' he said almost apologetically to the old bookseller, who with his hands under his black coat-tails was now surveying the busy world from his own doorstep.

'Certainly, sir.' Mr Elliott wheeled about and accepted the volume with that sprightly turn of his podgy wrist with which he always welcomed a book that was about to leave him for ever. 'Ah, the *Hesperides*, sir. I'll put the three into one parcel. A nice tall clean copy, I see. It came, if memory serves me right, from the library of Colonel Anstey, sir, who purchased the Talbot letters—and at a very reasonable price, too. Now if I had a *first* in this condition! . . .'

Alan dutifully smiled. 'I found it in the parlour,' he said. 'What a charming little room—and garden too; I had no idea the house was so old. Who lived in it before you did? I suppose it wasn't always a bookshop?'

He tried in vain to speak naturally and not as if he had plums in his mouth.

'Lived here before me, now?' the bookseller repeated ruminatively. 'Well, sir, there was first, of course, my immediate predecessor. *He* came before me; and *we* took over his stock. Something of a disappointment, too, when I came to go through with it.'

'And before *him*?' Alan persisted.

'Before him, sir? I fancy this was what might be called a *private* house. You could see if you looked round a bit how it has been converted. It was a doctor's, I understand—a Dr Marchmont's. And what we call the parlour, sir, from which you have just emerged, was always, I take it, a sort of book room. Leastways some of the books there now were there then —with the book-plate and all. You see, the Mr Brown who came before me and who, as I say, converted the house, *he* bought the doctor's library. Not merely medical and professional works neither. There was some choice stuff besides; and a few moderate specimens of what is known in the trade as the curious, sir. Not that I go out of my way for it, myself.'

Alan paused in the doorway, parcel in hand.

'A bachelor, I suppose?'

'The doctor, sir, or Mr Brown?'

'The doctor.'

'Well, now, that I couldn't rightly say,' replied Mr Elliott cheerfully. 'Let us hope *not*. They tell me, sir, it makes things seem more homely-like to have a female about the house. And'—

he raised his voice a little—'I'll warrant that Mrs Elliott, sir, if she were here to say so, would bear me out.'

Mrs Elliott, in fact, a pasty-looking old woman, with a mouth like a cod's and a large marketing basket on her arm, was at this moment emerging out from behind a curtained doorway. Possibly her husband had caught a glimpse of her reflection in his spectacles. She came on with a beetle-like deliberation.

'What's that you were saying about me, Mr Elliott?' she said.

'This gentleman was inquiring, my love, if Dr Marchmont-as-was lived in a state of single blessedness or if there was a lady in the case.'

Mrs Elliott fixed a slow, flat look on her husband, and then on Alan.

'There was a sister or niece or something, so they say. But I never knew anything about them, and don't want to,' she declared. And Alan, a little chilled by her demeanour, left the shop.

Not that that one fish-like glance of Mrs Elliott's censorious eye had by any means freed his fancy of what had passed. In the days that followed he could never for an instant be sure when or where the face that reverie had somehow conjured up out of the recesses of his mind on his first visit to the old bookseller's parlour was not about to reappear. And it chose the oddest of moments. Even when his attention was definitely fixed on other things it would waft itself into his consciousness again—and always with the same serene yet vivid, naïve yet serious question in the eyes—a question surely that only life itself could answer, and that not always with a like candour or generosity. Alan was an obstinate young man in spite of appearances. But to have the rudiments of an imagination is one thing, to be at the beck and call of every passing fancy is quite another. He was not, he reassured himself, as silly as all that. He held out for days together; and then when he had been left for twenty-four hours wholly at peace—he suddenly succumbed.

A westering sun was sharply gilding its windows when he once more made his way into Mr Elliott's parlour. It was empty. And almost at the same instant he realized how anxious he had been that this *should* be so, and how insipid a bait as such the little room now proved to be. He hadn't expected that. And yet—not exactly insipid; its flavour had definitely soured. He wished he had never come; he tried to make up his mind to go. Ill at ease, angry with himself, and as if in open defiance of some inward mentor, he took down at random a fusty old quarto from its shelf and seating himself on a chair by the table, he began, or rather attempted, to read.

Instead, with downcast eyes shelled in by the palm of his hand, and leaning gently on his elbow in an attitude not unlike that of the slippered and pensive Keats in the portrait, he found himself listening again. He did more than listen. Every nerve in his body was stretched taut. And time ebbed away. At this tension his mind began to wander off again into a dreamlike vacuum of its own, when, 'What was that?' a voice within whispered at him. A curious thrill ebbed through his body. It was as though unseen fingers had tugged at a wire—with no bell at the end of it. For this was no sound he had heard—no stir of the air. And yet in effect it so nearly resembled one that it might have been only the sigh of the blast of the east wind at the window. He waited a minute, then, with a slight shiver, glanced up covertly but steadily through his fingers.

He was shocked—by what he saw—yet not astonished. It seemed as if his whole body had become empty and yet remained as inert and heavy as lead. He was no longer alone. The figure that stood before him in the darker corner there, and only a few paces away, was no less sharply visible and even more actual in effect than the objects around her. One hand, from a loose sleeve, resting on the edge of the door to the staircase, she stood looking at him, her right foot with its high-heeled shoe poised delicately on the lowest of the three steps. With head twisted back sidelong over her narrow shoulder, her eyes were fixed on this earthly visitor to her haunts—as he sat, hand to forehead, drawn up stiff and chill at the table. She was watching Alan. And the face, though with even fewer claims to be beautiful, and none to be better than knowing and wide-awake, was without any question the face he had shared with Herrick's *Hesperides*.

A peculiar vacancy—like a cold mist up from the sea—seemed to have spread over his mind, and yet he was alert to his very finger-tips. Had she seen he had seen her? He couldn't tell. It was as cold in the tiny room as if the windows were wide open and the garden beyond them full of snow. The late afternoon light, though bleakly clear, was already thinning away, and, victim of this silly decoy, he was a prisoner who in order to regain his freedom must pass *her* way out. He stirred in his chair, his eyes now fixed again on the book beneath them.

And then at last, as if with confidence restored, he withdrew his hand from his face, lifted his head, and affecting a boldness he far from felt, deliberately confronted his visitor. At this the expression on her features—her whole attitude—changed too. She had only at this moment seen that he had seen her, then? The arm dropped languidly to her side. Her listless body turned a little, her shoulders slightly lifted themselves, and a faint provocative smile came into her face, while the dark jaded eyes resting on his own remained half mocking, half deprecatory—almost as if the two of them, he and she, were old cronies who had met again after a long absence from one another, with ancient secrets awaiting discreet discussion. With a desperate effort Alan managed to refrain from making any answering signal of recognition. He stared back with a face as blank as a turnip. How he knew with such complete assurance that his visitor was not of this world he never attempted to explain to himself. Real! She was at least as real as a clearly lit reflection of anything seen in a looking-glass, and in *effect* on his mind was more positive than the very chair on which he was sitting and the table beneath his elbow to which that chair was drawn up. For this was a reality of the soul, and not of the senses. Indeed, he himself might be the ghost and she the dominating pervasive actuality.

But even if he had been able to speak he had no words with which to express himself. He was shuddering with cold and had suddenly become horribly fatigued and exhausted. He wanted to 'get out' of all this and yet knew not only that this phantasm must have been lying in wait for him, but that sooner or later she would compel him to find out what she wanted of him, that she meant to be satisfied. Her face continued to change in expression even while he watched her. Its assurance seemed to intensify. The head stooped forward a little; the narrow, pallid, slanting eyelids momentarily closed; and then, with a gesture not merely of arm or shoulder but of her whole body, she once more fixed him with a gaze more intense, more challenging, more crammed with meaning than he had supposed possible in any human eye. It was as if some small wicket gate into the glooms of Purgatory had suddenly become thronged with bright-lit faces.

Until this moment they had been merely eyeing one another while time's sluggish moments ebbed away. They had been merely 'looking at' one another. Now there had entered those glazed dark fixed blue eyes the very self within. It stayed there gazing out at him transfixed—the pleading, tormented, dangerous spirit within that intangible husk. And then the crisis was over. With a slow dragging movement of his head Alan had at last succeeded in breaking the spell—he had turned away. A miserable disquietude and self-repulsion possessed him. He felt sick, body and soul. He had but one thought—to free himself once and for all from this unwarranted ordeal. Why should *he* have been singled out? What hint of any kind of 'encouragement' had he been responsible for? Or was this ghostly encounter an experience that had been shared by other visitors to the old bookseller's sanctum—maybe less squeamish than himself? His chilled, bloodless fingers clenched on the open page of the book beneath them. He strove in vain to master himself, to fight the thing out. It was as if an icy hand had him in its grip, daring him to stir.

The evening wind had died with the fading day. The three poplars, every budded double-curved twig outlined against the glassy grey of the west, stood motionless. Daylight, even dusk, was all very well, but supposing this presence, as the dark drew on, ventured a little nearer? And suddenly his alarms—as much now of the body as of the mind—were over. She had been interrupted.

A footstep had sounded in the corridor. Alan started to his feet. The handle of the door had turned in the old brass lock; he watched it. With a jerk he twisted his head on his shoulders. He was alone. Yet again the interrupter had rattled impatiently with the door handle. Alan at last managed to respond to the summons. But even as he grasped the handle on his own side of it, the door was pushed open against him and a long-bearded face peered through.

'Pardon,' said this stranger, 'I didn't realize you had locked yourself in.'

In the thin evening twilight that was now their only illumination Alan found himself blushing like a schoolgirl.

'But I hadn't,' he stammered. 'Of course not. The catch must have jammed. I came in here myself only a few minutes ago.'

The long face with its rather watery blue-grey eyes placidly continued to survey him in the dusk. 'And yet, you know,' its owner drawled, with a soupçon of incredulity, 'I should have guessed myself that I have been poking about in our patron's shop out there for at least the best part of half an hour. But that, of course, is one of the charms of lit-er-a-ture. You haven't chanced, I suppose, on a copy of the *Vulgar Errors*— Sir Thomas Browne?'

Alan shook his head. 'The B's, I think, are in that corner,' he replied, '—alphabetical. But I didn't notice the *Errors*.'

Nor did he stay to help his fellow-customer find the volume. He hurried out, and this time he had no spoil to present to the old bookseller in recognition of the rent due for his occupation of the parlour.

A whole week went by, its last few days the battleground of a continuous conflict of mind. He hadn't, he assured himself with the utmost conviction, the faintest desire in the world to set eyes again on—on what he *had* set eyes on. That was certain. It had been the oddest of shocks to what he had thought about things, to what had gone before, and, yes, to his vanity. Besides, the more he occupied himself with and pondered over his peculiar little experience the more probable it seemed that it and she and everything connected with her had been nothing but a cheat of the senses, a triumph of self-deception—a pure illusion, induced by the quiet, the solitude, the stirrings of springtime at the window, the feeling of age in the room, the romantic associations—and last, to the Herrick!

All this served very well in the middle of the morning or at two o'clock in the afternoon. But a chance waft of the year's first waxen hyacinths, the onset of evening, a glimpse of the waning moon—at any such oblique reminder of what had happened, these pretty arguments fell flat as a house of cards. Illusion! Then why had everything else in his life become by comparison so empty of interest and himself at a loose end? The thought of Mr Elliott's bookshop at such moments was like an hypnotic lure. Cheat himself as he might, he knew it was only cheating. Distrust the fowler as he might, he knew what nets he was in. How gross a folly to be at the mercy of one vehement coupling of glances. If only it had been that other face! And yet, supposing he were wrong about all this; supposing this phantasm really was in need of help, couldn't rest, had come back for something—there *were* things one might want to come back for—and even for something which he alone could give?

What wonder this restless conflict of mind reacted on his body and broke his sleep? Naturally a little invalidish in his appetite, Alan now suffered the pangs of a violent attack of indigestion. And at last he could endure himself no longer. On the following Tuesday he once more pushed open the outer door of Mr Elliott's bookshop, with its jangling bell, and entered, hot and breathless, from out of the pouring rain.

'There was a book I caught sight of,' he panted out to the old gentleman as he came in, 'when I was here last, you know. In the other room. I won't keep you a minute.'

At this, the bookseller's bland eye fixed itself an instant on the fair flushed face, almost as if he too could a tale unfold.

'Let me take your umbrella, sir,' he entreated. 'Sopping! A real downpour. But very welcome to the farmers, I'll be bound—if for once in a while they'd only *say* so. No hurry whatever, sir.'

Downpour indeed it was. As Alan entered the parlour the cold, sullen gush of rain on the young lilac buds and cobblestones of the little yard in the dreary leaden light at the window resounded steadily on. He had set out in the belief that his one desire was to prove that his 'ghost' was no ghost at all, that he had been the victim of a pure hallucination. Yet throughout his journey, with only his umbrella for company, he had been conscious of a thrill of excitement and expectation. And now that he had closed the door behind him, and had shut himself in, the faded little room in this obscurity at once began to influence his mind in much the same fashion as the livid gloom of an approaching thunderstorm affects the scenery of the hills and valleys over which it broods.

And this, it soon seemed, was to be his sole reward! His excitement fizzled out. With every passing moment his heart fell lower. He had gone away filled with a stark irrational hatred of the poor, restless, phantasmal creature who had intruded on his solitude. He had come back only to realize not only that she herself had been his lodestone, but that, even though any particular spot may undoubtedly be 'haunted,' it by no means follows that its ghost is always at home. Everything about him seemed to have changed a little. Or was the change only in himself? In this damp air the room smelt of dry-rot and mouldering leather. Even the pretty grate looked thicklier scurfed with rust. And the books on the shelves had now taken to themselves the leaden livery of the weather. 'Look not too closely on us,' they seemed to cry. 'What are we all but memorials of the dead? And we too are swiftly journeying towards the dust.'

The prospect from the window was even more desolating. None the less Alan continued to stare stupidly out of it. By the time he had turned away again he had become certain—though how he couldn't tell—that he need have no apprehension whatever of intangible company to-day. Mr Elliott's 'parlour' was emptier than he supposed a room could be. It seemed as if by sheer aversion for its late inmate he had exorcised it, and, irrational creature that he was, a stab of regret followed.

He turned to go. He gave a last look round—and paused. Was it that the skies had lightened a little or had he really failed to notice at his entry that the door at which his visitor had appeared was a few inches open? He stepped across softly and glanced up the staircase. Only vacancy there too. But that door was also ajar. The two faint daylights from above and below mingled midway. For a moment or two he hesitated. The next he had stolen swiftly and furtively up the staircase and had looked in.

This room was not only empty but abandoned. It was naked of any stick of furniture and almost of any trace of human occupation. Yet with its shallow bow window, low ceiling, and morning sun it must once in its hey-day have blossomed like the rose. The flowered paper on its walls was dingy now; a few darker squares and oblongs alone showed where pictures had once hung. The brass gas bracket was green with verdigris, and a jutting rod was the only evidence of the canopy where once a bed had been.

But even vacancy may convey a sense of age and tell its tale. Alan was looking into the past. Indeed, the stale remnant of some once pervasive perfume still hung in the musty atmosphere of the room, though its sole refuse consisted of a few dust-grimed books in a corner and—on a curved white narrow shelf that winged the minute fireplace—a rusty hairpin.

Alan stooped, and very gingerly, with gloved finger and

thumb, turned the books over—a blistered green-bound *Enoch Arden*, a small thick copy of *The Mysteries of Paris*, Dante Gabriel Rossetti's *House of Life*, a *Nightingale Valley*, a few damp, fly-blown shockers, some of them in French and paper-bound; and last, a square black American cloth-bound exercise book with *E.F.* cut out with a clumsy penknife at one of the top corners. The cockled cloth was slightly greened.

He raised the cover with the extreme tips of his fingers, stooped forward a little, and found himself in the window-light scanning with peculiar intensity the vanishing lineaments of a faded photograph—the photograph of a young woman in clothes somehow made the more old-fashioned in appearance by the ravages of time and light on the discoloured cardboard. He knew this face; and yet not *this* face. For days past it had not been out of his mind for more than a few hours together. But while his first impression had been that of the vivid likeness of the one to the other, what next showed clearest were the differences between them. Differences that stirred his heart into a sudden tumult.

The hair in the photograph was dressed in pretty much the same fashion—drawn up and back from the narrow temples across the widening head. The lips were, possibly, not so full; certainly not so dark. And though the cheek even of this much younger face was a little sunken, these faded eyes—a fading only of the paper depicting them and not of age—looked out at him without the faintest trace of boldness or effrontery. They were, it is true, fixed profoundly on his own. But they showed no interest in him, little awareness, no speculation—only a remote settled melancholy. What strange surmises, the young man reflected, must the professional photographer at times indulge in when from beneath his ink-black inquisitorial velvet cowl he peers into his camera at a face as careless of human curiosity as this had been. The young woman in the photograph had made, if any, a more feeble attempt to conceal her secret sorrows than a pall to conceal its bier or a broken sepulchre its bones.

At a breath the young man's aversion had died away. A shame-stricken compassion of which he had never dreamed himself capable had swept over him in its stead. He gazed on for a minute or two at the photograph—this withering memento which not even the removing men seemed to have considered

worth flinging into a dustbin; then he opened the book at random—towards the middle of it—and leaning into the light at
the window read these lines:

> My midnight lamp burns dim with shame,
>   In Heaven the moon is low;
> Sweet sharer of its secret flame,
>   Arise, and go!
>
> Haste, for dawn's envious gaping grave
>   Bids thee not linger here;
> Though gone is all I am, and have—
>   Thy ghost once absent, dear.

He read them over again, then glanced stealthily up and out.
They were a voice from the dead.   It was as if he had trespassed
into the echoing cold of a vault.   And as he looked about him
he suddenly realized that at any moment he might be interrupted,
caught—prying.   With a swift glance over his shoulder he
pushed the photograph back into the old exercise book, and
tucking this under his arm beneath his coat, tiptoed down the
unlighted stairs into the parlour.

It had been a bold venture—at least for Alan.   For, of all
things in this world he disliked, he disliked by far the most being
caught out in any little breach of the conventions.   Suppose that
old, cod-like Mrs Elliott had caught him exploring this abandoned
bedroom?   After listening yet again for any rumour either of
herself or of her husband, he drew out from the lowest shelf
near by two old sheepskin folios, seated himself in full view of
the door that led into the shop, and having hidden the exercise
book well within cover of these antiquated tomes he began to
turn over its pages.   The trick took him back to his early
schooldays—the sun, the heat, the drone of bees at the window,
a settling wayward fly, the tick of the clock on the wall, and the
penny 'blood' half concealed in his arithmetic book.   He smiled
to himself.   Wasn't he being kept in now?   And how very odd
he should be minding so little what, only an hour before, he
had foreseen he would be minding so much.   How do ghosts
show that you needn't expect them?   Not even in their chosen
haunts?

The book he was now examining was not exactly a penny
'blood.'   In spite of appearances it must have cost at least sixpence.   The once black ink on its pages had faded, and mildew
dappled the leaves.   The handwriting was irregular, with pro-

tracted loops. And what was written in the book consisted of
verses, interlarded with occasional passages in prose, and a day
or a date here and there, and all set down apparently just as it
had taken the writer's fancy. And since many of the verses
were heavily corrected and some of them interlined, Alan concluded—without any very unusual acumen!—that they were
home made. Moreover, on evidence as flimsy as this, he had
instantly surmised who this E.F. was, and that here was not
only her book but a book of her own authorship. So completely,
too, had his antipathy to the writer of it now vanished out of
memory, so swiftly had the youthful, tragic face in the photograph secreted itself in his sentiments, that he found himself
reading these scribbled 'effusions' with a mind all but bereft of
its critical faculties. And of these the young man had hitherto
rather boasted himself.

Still, poetry, good or bad, depends for its very life on the
hospitable reader, as tinder awaits the spark. After that, what
else matters? The flame leaps, the bosom glows! And as
Alan read on he never for an instant doubted that here, however
faultily expressed, was what the specialist is apt to call 'a tran-
script of life.' He knew of old—how remotely of old it now
seemed—what feminine wiles are capable of; but here, surely,
was the truth of self to self. He had greedily and yet with real
horror looked forward to his reappearance here, as if Mr Elliott's
little parlour was the positive abode of the Evil One. And yet
now that he was actually pecking about beneath the very
meshes of his nets, he was drinking in these call-notes as if they
were cascading down upon him out of the heavens from the
throat of Shelley's skylark itself. For what is Time to the arti-
fices of Eros? Had he not (with Chaucer's help) once fallen
head over ears in love with the faithless Criseyde? He drank in
what he had begun to read as if his mind were a wilderness
thirsty for rain, though the pall of cloud that darkened the
window behind him was supplying it in full volume. He was
elated and at the same time dejected at the thought that he
was perhaps the very first human creature, apart from the
fountain head, to sip of these secret waters.

And he had not read very far before he realized that its
contents referred to an actual experience as well as to one of
the imagination. He realized too that the earlier poems had
been written at rather long intervals; and, though he doubted

very much if they were first attempts, that their technique tended to improve as they went on—at least, that of the first twenty poems or so. With a small ivory pocket paper-knife which he always carried about with him he was now delicately separating page 12 from page 13, and he continued to read at random:

> There was sweet water once,
> Where in my childhood I
> Watched for the happy innocent nonce
> Day's solemn clouds float by.
>
> O age blur not that glass;
> Kind Heaven still shed thy rain;
> Even now sighs shake me as I pass
> Those gentle haunts again.

He turned over the page:

> Lullay, my heart, and find thy peace
> Where thine old solitary pastures lie;
> Their light, their dews need never cease,
> Nor sunbeams from on high.
>
> Lullay, and happy dream, nor roam,
> Wild though the hills may shine,
> Once there, thou soon would'st long for home,
> As I for mine!

and then:

> Do you see; O, do you see?—
> Speak—and some inward self that accent knows,
> Bidding the orient East its rose disclose—
> And daybreak wake in me.
>
> Do you hear? O, do you hear?—
> This heart whose pulse like menacing night-bird cries?
> Dark, utter dark, my loved, is in these eyes
> When gaunt good-bye draws near.

and then, after a few more pages:

> 'There is a garden in her face':
> *My* face! Woe 's me were *that* my all!—
> Nay, but my *self*, though thine its grace,
> Thy fountain is, thy peach-bloomed wall.
>
> Come soon that twilight dusky hour,
> When thou thyself shalt enter in
> And take thy fill of every flower,
> Since thine they have always been.

No rue? No myrrh? No nightshade? Oh,
Tremble not, spirit! All is well.
For Love's is that lovely garden; and so,
There only pleasures dwell.

Turning over the limp fusty leaves, one by one, he browsed on:

When you are gone, and I'm alone,
From every object that I see
Its secret source of life is flown:
All things look cold and strange to me.

Even what I use—my rings, my gloves,
My parasol, the clothes I wear—
'Once she was happy; now she loves!
Once young,' they cry, 'now carked with care!'

I wake and watch when the moon is here—
A shadow tracks me on. And I—
Darker than any shadow—fear
Her fabulous inconstancy.

That sphinx, the Future, marks its prey;
I who was ardent, sanguine, free,
Starve now in fleshly cell all day—
And yours the rusting key.

and then:

Your maddening face befools my eyes,
Your hand—I wake to feel—
Lost in deep midnight's black surmise—
Its touch my veins congeal.

What peace for me in star or moon?
What solace in nightingale!
They tell me of the lost and gone—
And dawn completes the tale.

A note in pencil—the point of which must have broken in use
—followed at the foot of the page:

All this means all but *nothing* of what was in my mind when I
began to write it. *Dawn ! !* I look at it, read it—it is like a saucer
of milk in a cage full of asps. I didn't *know* one's mind could dwell
only on one thought, one face, one longing, on and on without any
respite, and yet remain sane. I didn't even know—until when?—
it was possible to be happy, unendurably happy, and yet as miserable
and as hopeless as a devil in hell. It is as if I were sharing my own
body with a self I hate and fear and shake in terror at, and yet am
powerless to be rid of. Well, never mind. If I *can* go on, that's
my business. They mouth and talk and stare and sneer at me.
What do I care! The very leaves of the trees whisper against me,

and last night came thunder. I see my haunted face in every stone. And what cares *he*! Why should he? Would *I*, if I were a man? I sit here alone in the evening—waiting. My heart is a quicksand biding its time to swallow me up. Yet it isn't even that I question now whether he ever loved me or not—I only thirst and thirst for him to come. One look, a word, and I am at peace again. At peace! And yet I wonder sometimes, if I—if it is even *conceivable* that I still love him. Does steel *love* the magnet? Surely that moon which shone last night with her haggard glare in both our faces *abhors* the earth from which, poor wretch, she parted to perish and yet from which she can never, never, never utterly break away? Never, never, never. O God, how tired I am!—knowing as I do— as if my life were all being lived over again—that only worse lies in wait for me, that the more I feel the less I am able to please him. I *see* myself dragging on and on—and that other sinister mocking one within rises up and looks at me—'What? And shall *I* never come into my own!'

Alan had found some little difficulty in deciphering the faint, blurred, pencilled handwriting—he decided to come back to this page again, then turned it over and read on:

Your hate I see, and can endure, nay, *must*—
Endure the stark denial of your love;
It is your *silence*, like a cankering rust,
That I am perishing of.

What reck you of the blinded hours I spend
Crouched on my knees beside a shrouded bed?
Grief even for the loveliest has an end;
No end in one whose soul it is lies dead.

I watch the aged who 've dared the cold slow ice
That creeps from limb to limb, from sense to sense,
Yet never dreamed this also is the price
Which youth must pay for a perjured innocence.

Yours that fond lingering lesson. Be content!
Not one sole moment of its course I rue.
The all I had was little. Now it 's spent.
Spit on the empty purse: 'tis naught to you.

And then these *Lines on Ophelia*:

She found an exit from her life;
She to an earthly green-room sped
Where parched-up souls distraught with strife
Sleep and are comforted.

Hamlet! I know that dream-drugged eye,
That self-coiled melancholic mien!
Hers was a happy fate—to die:
Mine—her foul Might-have-been.

and then:

> To-morrow waits me at my gate,
> While all my yesterdays swarm near;
> And one mouth whines, Too late, too late:
> And one is dumb with fear.
>
> Was this the all that life could give
> Me—who from cradle hungered on,
> Body and soul aflame, to *live*—
> Giving my all—and then be gone?
>
> O sun, in heaven, to don that shroud,
> When April's cuckoo thrilled the air!
> Light thou no more the fields I loved,
> Be only winter there!

and then:

> Have *done* with moaning, idiot heart;
> If it so be that Love has wings
> I with my shears will find an art
> To still his flutterings.
>
> Wrench off that bandage too will I,
> And show the imp he is blind indeed;
> Hot irons will prove my mastery;
> He shall not weep, but bleed.
>
> And when he is dead, and cold as stone,
> Then in his Mother's book I'll con
> The lesson none need learn alone,
> And, callous as she, play on.

He raised his eyes. The heavy rain had ebbed into a drifting drizzle; the day had darkened. He stared vacantly for a moment or two out of the rain-drenched window, and then, turning back a few of the damp cockled leaves, once more resumed his reading:

> And when at last I journey where
> All thought of you I must resign,
> Will the least memory of me be fair,
> Or will you even my ghost malign?
>
> I plead for nothing. Nay, Time's tooth—
> That frets the very soul away—
> May prove at last your slanders *truth*,
> And me the Slut you say.

There followed a series of unintelligible scrawls. It was as if the writer had been practising a signature in various kinds of more or less affected handwritings: 'Esther de Bourgh, Esther de Bourgh, Esther De Bourgh, E. de Bourgh, E de B, E de B, E. de Ice Bourgh, Esther de la Ice Bourgh, Esther de Borgia, Esther Césarina de Borgia, Esther de Bauch, Esther de Bausch, E. de Bosh.' And then, this unfinished scrap:

> Why cheat the heart with old deceits?—
> Love—was it *love* in thine
> Could leave me thus grown sick of sweets
> And . . .

The words sounded on—forlornly and even a little self-pityingly —in Alan's mind. Sick of sweets, sick of sweets. He had had enough for to-day. He shut the book, lifted his head, and with a shuddering yawn and a heavy frown on his young face, once more stared out of the window.

This E.F., whoever she was, had often sat in this room, alert, elated, drinking in its rosily reflected morning sunshine from that wall, happy in being merely herself, young, alone, and alive. He could even watch in fancy that intense lowered face as she stitched steadily on, lost in a passionate reverie, while she listened to as dismal a downpour as that which had but lately ceased on the moss-grown cobbles under the window. 'It 's only one's inmost *self* that matters,' she had scribbled at the end of one of her rhymes. And then—how long afterwards?—the days, empty of everything but that horror and dryness of the heart, when desire had corrupted and hope was gone, and every hour of solitude must have seemed to be lying in wait only to prove the waste, the bleakness, the desolation to which the soul within can come. No doubt in time they would learn even a bookworm to be a worm. 'That is one of the charms of lit-er-a-ture,' as the bland, bearded, supercilious gentleman had expressed it. But he wouldn't have sentimentalized about it.

Oddly enough, it hadn't yet occurred to Alan to speculate what kind of human being it was to whom so many of these poems had been addressed, and to whom seemingly every one of them had clearer or vaguer reference. There are ghosts for whom spectre is the better word. In this, the gloomiest hour of an English spring, he glanced again at the door he had shut behind him in positive hope that it might yet open once more—that he was not so utterly alone as he seemed. Sick: sick: surely, surely a few years of life could not have wreaked such horrifying changes in any human face and spirit as that!

But the least promising method apparently of evoking a visitant from another world is to wait on to welcome it. Better, perhaps, postpone any little experiment of this kind until after the veils of nightfall have descended. Not that he had failed to notice how overwhelming is the evidence that when once you have gone from this world you have gone for ever. Still, even if he *had* been merely the victim of an illusion, it would have been something just to smile or to nod in a common friendly human fashion, to lift up the dingy little black exercise book in his hand, merely to show that its owner had not confided in him in vain.

He was an absurdly timid creature—tongue-tied when he wanted most to express himself. And yet, if only . . . His glance strayed from door to book again. It was curious that the reading of poems like these should yet have proved a sort of solace. They had triumphed even over the miserable setting destiny had bestowed on them. Surely lit-er-a-ture without any vestige of merit in it couldn't do that. A veil of day-dream drew over the fair and rather effeminate face. And yet the young man was no longer merely brooding; he was beginning to make plans. And he was making them without any help from the source from which it might have been expected.

Seeming *revenants*, of course, in this busy world are not of much account. They make indelible impressions if they do chance to visit one, though it is imprudent, perhaps, to share them with the sceptic. None the less at this moment he was finding it almost impossible to recall the face not of the photograph but of his phantasm. And though there was nothing in the earlier poems he had read to suggest that they could not have been the work of the former, was it conceivable that they could ever have been the work of—that other one? But why not! To judge from some quite famous poets' faces their owners would have flourished at least as successfully in the pork-butchering line. Herrick himself—well, he was not exactly ethereal in appearance. But what need for these ridiculous unanswerable questions? Whoever *E.F.* had been, and whatever the authorship of the poems, he himself could at least claim now to be their only re-begetter.

At this thought a thrill of excitement had run through Alan's veins. Surely the next best thing to publishing a first volume of verse of one's own—and that he had now decided never to attempt—is to publish someone else's. He had seen worse stuff than this in print, and on hand-made paper, too. Why shouldn't he turn editor? How could one tell for certain that it is impossible to comfort—or, for that matter, to soothe the vanity—of some poor soul simply because it has happened to set out on the last long journey a few years before oneself? Mere initials are little short of anonymity, and even kindred spirits may be all the kinder if kept at the safe distance which anonymity ensures. But what about the old bookseller? An Englishman's shop is his castle, and this battered old exercise book, Alan assumed, must fully as much as any other volume on the shelves around him be the legal property of the current tenant of the house. Or possibly the ground-landlord's? He determined to take Mr Elliott into his confidence—but very discreetly.

With this decision, he got up—dismayed to discover that it was now a full half-hour after closing time. None the less he found the old bookseller sitting at his table and apparently lost to the cares of business beneath a wire-protected gas bracket now used for an electric bulb. The outer door was still wide open, and the sullen clouds of the last of evening seemed to have descended even more louringly over the rain-soaked streets. A solitary dog lopped by the shrouded entrance. Not a sound pierced the monotony of the drizzle.

'I wonder,' Alan began, keeping the inflexions of his voice well in check, 'I wonder if you have ever noticed *this* particular book? It is in manuscript. . . . Verse.'

'Verse, sir?' said the bookseller, fumbling in a tight waistcoat pocket for the silver case of his second pair of spectacles. 'Well, now, verse—in manuscript. *That* doesn't sound as if it's likely to be of much value, though finds there have been, I grant you. Poems and sermons—we are fairly glutted out with them nowadays; still, there was this Omar Khayyám fuss, sir, so you never know.'

He adjusted his spectacles and opened the book where the book opened itself. Alan stooped over the old man's shoulder and read with him:

> Once in kind arms, alas, you held me close;
> Sweet to its sepals was the unfolding rose.
> Why, then—though wind-blown, hither, thither,
> I languish still, rot on, and wither
> Yet *live*, God only knows.

A queer, intent, an almost hunted expression drew over Mr Elliott's greyish face as he read on.

'Now I wonder,' he said at last, firmly laying the book down again and turning an eye as guileless as an infant's to meet Alan's scrutiny, 'I wonder now who could have written that? Not that I flatter myself to be much of a judge. I leave that to my customers, sir.'

'There is an *E.F.* cut out on the cover,' said Alan, 'and'—the words came with difficulty—'there is a photograph inside. But then, I suppose,' he added hastily, automatically putting out his hand for the book and withdrawing it again, 'I suppose just a loose photograph doesn't prove anything. Not at least to whom it belonged—the book, I mean.'

'No, sir,' said the bookseller, as if he thoroughly enjoyed little problems of this nature; 'in a manner of speaking I suppose it don't.' But he made no attempt to find the photograph, and a rather prolonged pause followed.

'It's quiet in that room in there,' Alan managed to remark at last. 'Extraordinarily quiet. You haven't yourself, I suppose, ever noticed the book before?'

Mr Elliott removed both pairs of spectacles from the bridge of his nose. 'Quiet is the word, sir,' he replied, in a voice suiting the occasion. 'And it's quieter yet in the two upper rooms above it. Especially of a winter's evening. Mrs Elliott and me don't use that part of the house much, though there is a good bit of lumber stowed away in the nearest of 'em. We can't sell more than a fraction of the books we get, sir, so we store what's over up there for the pulpers. I doubt if I have even so much as seen the inside of the other room these six months past. As a matter of fact'—he pursed his mouth and nodded—'what with servant-girls and the like, and not everybody being as common-sensical as most, we don't mention it much.'

The bookseller's absent eye was now fixed on the rain-soaked street, and Alan waited, leaving his 'What?' unsaid.

'You see, sir, the lady that lived with Dr Marchmont here—his niece, or ward, or whatever it may be—well, they say she came to what they call an untimely end. A love affair. But there, for the matter of that you can't open your evening news-paper without finding more of such things than you get in a spring season's fiction. Strychnine, sir—that was the way of it; and it isn't exactly the poison I myself should choose for the purpose. It erects up the body like an arch, sir. So.' With a gesture of his small, square hand Mr Elliott pictured the effect in the air. 'Dr Marchmont hadn't much of a practice by that time, I understand; but I expect he came to a pretty sudden standstill when he saw *that* on the bed. A tall man, sir, with a sharp nose.'

Alan refrained from looking at the bookseller. His eyes stayed fixed on the doorway which led out into the world beyond, and they did not stir. But he had seen the tall dark man with the sharp nose as clearly as if he had met him face to face, and was conscious of a repulsion far more deadly than the mere features would seem to warrant. And yet; *why* should he have come to a 'standstill' quite like that if . . .? But the bookseller had opened the fusty, mildewed book at another page. He sniffed, then having rather pernicketily adjusted his spectacles, read over yet another of the poems:

> *Esther !* came whisper from my bed.
> *Answer me, Esther—are you there ?*
> 'Twas waking self to self that 's dead
> Called on the empty stair.
>
> Stir not that pit; she is lost and gone
> A Jew decoyed her to her doom.
> Sullenly knolls her passing bell
> Mocking me in the gloom.

The old man gingerly turned the leaf, and read on:

> Last evening, as I sat alone—
> Thimble on finger, needle and thread—
> Light dimming as the dusk drew on,
>   I dreamed that I was dead.
>
> Like wildering timeless plains of snow
> Which bitter winds to ice congeal
> The world stretched far as sight could go
>   'Neath skies as hard as steel.
>
> Lost in that nought of night I stood
> And watched my body—brain and breast
> In dreadful anguish—in the mould
>   Grope to'rd its final rest.
>
> Its craving dreams of sense dropped down
> Like crumbling maggots in the sod:
> Spectral, I stood; all longing gone,
>   Exiled from hope and God.

And you I loved, who once loved me,
And shook with pangs this mortal frame,
Were sunk to such an infamy
   That when I called your name,

Its knell so racked that sentient clay
That my lost spirit lurking near,
Wailed, liked the damned, and fled away—
   And woke me, stark with *Fear*.

He pondered a moment, turned back the leaf again, and
holding the book open with his dumpy forefinger, 'A *Jew*, now,'
he muttered to himself, 'I never heard any mention of a Jew.
But what, if you follow me,' he added, tapping on the open page
with his spectacles, 'what I feel about such things as these is
that they 're not so much what may be called mournful as *morbid*,
sir. They rankle. I don't say, mind you, there isn't a ring of
truth in them—but it 's so *put*, if you follow me, as to make it
worse. Why, if all our little mistakes were dealt with in such a
vengeful spirit as this—as *this*, where would any of us be? And
death. . . . Say things out, sir, by all means. But what
things? It isn't human nature. And what 's more,' he finished
pensively, 'I haven't noticed that the stuff *sells* much the better
for it.'

Alan had listened but had not paid much attention to these
moralizings. 'You mean,' he said, 'that you think the book *did*
actually belong to the lady who lived here, and that—that it
was she herself who wrote the poems? But then, you see, it 's
E.F. on the cover, and I thought you said the name was
Marchmont?'

'Yes, sir, Marchmont. Between you and me, there *was* a
Mrs, I understand; but she went away. And who this young
woman was I don't rightly know. Not much good, I fancy.
At least——' He emptily eyed again the blurred lettering of the
poem. 'But there, sir,' he went on with decision, 'there 's no
need that I can see to worry about that. The whole thing 's a
good many years gone, and what consequence is it now? You 'd
be astonished how few of my customers really care who wrote
a book so long as wrote it was. Which is not to suggest that if
we get someone—someone with a name, I mean—to lay out the
full story of the young woman as a sort of foreword, there might
not be money in it. There *might* be. It doesn't much signify
nowadays what you say about the dead, not legally, I mean.

And especially these poets, sir. It all goes in under "biography.'
Besides, a suicide's a suicide all the world over. On the other
hand'—and he glanced over his shoulder—'I rather fancy
Mrs E. wouldn't care to be mixed up in the affair. What she
reads she never much approves of, though that's the kind of
reading she likes best. The ladies can be so very scrupulous.'

Alan had not seen the old bookseller in quite so bright a light
as this before.

'What I was wondering, Mr Elliott,' he replied in tones so
frigid they suggested he was at least twenty years older than he
appeared to be, 'is whether you would have any objection to my
sending the book myself to the printers. It's merely an idea.
One can't tell. It could do no harm. Perhaps who*ever* it was
who wrote the poems may have hoped some day to get them
printed—you never know. It would be at my expense, of course.
I shouldn't dream of taking a penny piece and I would rather
there were no introduction—by *any* one. There need be no
name or address on the title-page, need there? But this is, of
course, only if you see no objection?'

Mr Elliott had once more lifted by an inch or two the back
cover of the exercise book, as if possibly in search of the photograph. He found only this pencilled scrawl:

Well, well, well! squeaked the kitten to the cat;
Mousie refuses to play any more! so that's the end of that!

He shut up the book and rested his small plump hand on it.

'I suppose, sir,' he inquired discreetly, 'there *isn't* any risk of
any infringement of copyright? I mean,' he added, twisting
round his unspectacled face a little in Alan's direction, 'there
isn't likely to be anybody who would *recognize* what's in here?
I am not, of course, referring to the photograph, but a book,
even nowadays, may be what you may call *too* true-spoken—
when it's new, I mean. And it's not so much Mrs E. I
have in mind now as the police'—he whispered the word—'the
police.'

Alan returned his blurred glance without flinching.

'Oh, no . . .' he said. 'Besides, I should merely put *E.F.* on
the title-page and say it had been printed privately. I am quite
prepared to take the risk.'

The cold tones of the young man seemed to have a little
daunted the old bookseller.

'Very well, sir. I will have just a word with a young lawyer friend of mine, and if that 's all right, why, sir, you are welcome.'

'And the books could be sold from here?'

'Sold? Why, yes, sir—they 'll have plenty of respectable company, at any rate.'

But if Alan had guilelessly supposed that the mere signing of a cheque for £33 10s. in settlement of a local printer's account would finally exile a ghost that now haunted his mind far more persistently than it could ever have haunted Mr Elliott's green parlour, he soon discovered his mistake. He had kept the photograph, but had long since given up any attempt to find his way through the maze in which he found himself. Why, why, should he concern himself with what an ill-starred life had done to that young face? If the heart, if the very soul is haunted by a ghost, need one heed the frigid dictates of the mind? Infatuated young man, he was in servitude to one who had left the world years before he was born, and had left it, it seemed, only the sweeter by her exit. He was sick for love of one who was once alive but was now dead, and—why should he deny it? Mrs E. wouldn't!—damned.

Still, except by way of correspondence he avoided Mr Elliott and his parlour for weeks, until, in fact, the poems were finally in print, until their neat grey deckled paper covers had been stitched on, and the copies were ready for a clamorous public! So it was early one morning in the month of June before he once more found himself in the old bookseller's quiet annexe. The bush of lilac, stirred by the warm, languid breeze at the window, was shaking free its faded once-fragrant tassels of bloom and tapering heart-shaped leaves from the last dews of night. The young poplars stood like gold-green torches against the blue of the sky. A thrush was singing somewhere out of sight. It was a scene worthy of Arcady.

Alan had trailed through life without any positive need to call on any latent energy he might possess. And now that he had seen through the press his first essay in publishing a reaction had set in. A cloud of despondency shadowed his young features as he stared out through the glass of the window. Through the weeks gone by he had been assuring himself that it was no more than an act of mere decency to get the poems into print. A vicarious thirty pounds or so, just to quiet his conscience. What reward was even thinkable? And yet but a few nights

before he had found himself sitting up in bed in the dark of the
small hours just as if there had come a tap upon the panel of
his door or a voice had summoned him out of dream. He had
sat up, leaning against his bed-rail, exhausted by his few hours'
broken sleep. And in the vacancy of his mind had appeared yet
again in silhouette against the dark the living presentment of
the young face in the photograph. Merely the image of a
face floating there, with waxen downcast lids, the features
passive as those of a death-mask—as unembodied an object
as the after-image of a flower. There was no speculation in
the downcast eyes, and in that lovely, longed-for face; no,
nothing whatever for *him*—and it had faded out as a mirage of
green-fronded palm trees and water fades in the lifeless sands
of the desert.

He hadn't any desire to sleep again that night. Dreams might
come; and wakeful questions pestered him. How old was she
when the first of the poems was written? How old when no more
came, and she herself had gone on—gone on? That barren
awful road of disillusionment, satiety, self-disdain. Had she
even when young and untroubled ever been happy? Was what
she had written even true? How far are poems *true*? What
had really happened? What had been left out? You can't
even tell—yourself—what goes on in the silent places of your
mind when you have swallowed, so to speak, the dreadful *out*side
things of life. What, for example, had *Measure for Measure* to
do with the author of *Venus and Adonis*, and what *Don Juan*
with Byron as a child? One thing, young women of his own
day didn't take their little affairs like that. They kept life in
focus. But that ghost! The ravages, the paint, the insidious-
ness, the very clothes!

Coming to that, then, who the devil had he been taking such
pains over? The question kept hammering at his mind day
after day; it was still unanswered, showed no promise of an
answer. And the Arcadian scene beyond the windows suddenly
became an irony and a jeer. The unseen bird itself sang on in
vulgar mockery: 'Come *off* of it! Come off of it! Come off of
it! Dolt, dolt, dolt!'

He turned away out of the brightness of the light, and fixed
his eyes on the bulky brown-paper package that contained the
printed volumes. It was useless to stay here any longer. He
would open the package, but merely to take a look at a copy and

assure himself that no ingenuity of the printer had restored any little aberration of spelling or punctuation which he himself had corrected three times in the proofs. He knew the poems—or some of them—by heart now.

With extreme reluctance he had tried one or two of them on a literary friend: 'An anonymous thing, you know, I came across it in an old book.'

The friend had been polite rather than enthusiastic. After, cigarette between fingers, idly listening to a few stanzas, he had smiled and asked Alan if he had ever read a volume entitled *Poems of Currer, Ellis, and Acton Bell.*

'Well, there you are! A disciple of Acton's, dear boy, if you ask *me*. Stuff as common as blackberries!'

And Alan had welcomed the verdict. He didn't want to share the poems with anybody. If nobody bought them and nobody cared, what matter? All the better. And he wasn't being sentimental about them now either. He didn't care if they had any literary value or not. He had entrusted himself with them, and that was the end of the matter. What was Hecuba to him, or he to Hecuba? What?

And what did it signify that he had less right to the things even than Mrs Elliott—who fortunately was never likely to stake out any claim. The moral ashbins old women can be, he thought bitterly. Simply because this forlorn young creature of the exercise book had been forced at last to make her exit from the world under the tragic but hardly triumphant arch of her own body this old woman had put her hand over her mouth and looked 'volumes' at that poor old hen-pecked husband of hers even at mention of her name. Suicides, of course, are a nuisance in any house. But all those years gone by! And what did they *know* the poor thing had done to merit insults? *He* neither knew nor cared, yet for some obscure reason steadily wasted at least five minutes in untying the thick, knotted cord of the parcel instead of chopping it up with his pocket-knife in the indignant fashion which he had admired when he visited the printers.

The chastest little pile of copies was disclosed at last in their grey-blue covers and with their enrichingly rough edges. The hand-made paper had been an afterthought. A further cheque was due to the printer, but Alan begrudged not a farthing. He had even incited them to be expensive. He believed in turning things out nicely—even himself. He and his pretty volumes were 'a pair'!

Having opened the parcel, having neatly folded up its prodigal wrappings of brown paper, and thrown away the padding and hanked the string, there was nothing further to do. He sat back in Mr Elliott's old Windsor chair, leaning his chin on his knuckles. He was waiting, though he didn't confess it to himself. What he did confess to himself was that he was sick of it all. Age and life's usage may obscure, cover up, fret away a fellow-creature at least as irrevocably as six feet of common clay.

When, then, he raised his eyes at some remote inward summons he was already a little hardened in hostility. He was looking clean across the gaily lit room at its other occupant standing there in precisely the same attitude—the high-heeled shoe coquettishly arched on the lowest of the three steps, the ridiculous flaunting hat, the eyes aslant beneath the darkened lids casting back on him their glitter from over a clumsy blur that was perfectly distinct on the cheek-bone in the vivid light of this June morning. And even this one instant's glimpse clarified and crystallized all his old horror and hatred. He knew that she had seen the tender firstfruits on the table. He knew that he had surprised a gleam of triumph in her snakish features, and he knew that she no more cared for that past self and its literary exercises than she cared for his silly greenhorn tribute to them. What then was she after?

The darkening, glittering, spectral eyes were once more communicating with him with immense rapidity, and yet were actually conveying about as empty or as mindless a message as eyes can. If half-extinguished fires in a dark room can be said to look coy, these did. But a coyness practised in a face less raddled and ravaged by time than by circumstance is not an engaging quality. 'Arch!' My God, 'arch' was the word!

Alan was shivering. How about the ravages that life's privy paw had made in his *own* fastidious consciousness? Had his own heart been a shade more faithful would the horror which he knew was now distorting his rather girlish features and looking out of his pale blue eyes have been quite so poisonously bitter?

Fortunately his back was turned to the window, and he could in part conceal his face with his hand before this visitor had had time to be fully aware what that face was saying. She had stirred. Her head was trembling slightly on her shoulders. Every tinily exquisite plume in the mauve ostrich feathers on her drooping hat trembled as if in sympathy. Her ringed fingers slipped down from the door to her narrow hip; her painted eyelids narrowed, as if she were about to speak to him. But at this moment there came a sudden flurry of wind in the lilac tree at the window, ravelling its dried-up flowers and silky leaves. She stooped, peered; and then, with a sharp, practised, feline, seductive nod, as bold as grass-green paint, she was gone. An instant or two, and in the last of that dying gust, the door above at the top of the narrow staircase, as if in a sudden access of bravado, violently slammed: 'Touch me, tap at me, force me, if you dare!'

The impact shook the walls and rattled the windows of the room beneath. It jarred on the listener's nerves with the force of an imprecation. As abrupt a silence followed. Nauseated and slightly giddy he got up from his chair, resting his fingers automatically on the guileless pile of books, took up his hat, glanced vacantly at the gilded Piccadilly maker's name on the silk lining, and turned to go. As he did so, a woeful, shuddering fit of remorse swept over him, like a parched-up blast of the sirocco over the sands of a desert. He shot a hasty strangulated look up the narrow empty staircase as he passed by. Then, 'O God,' he groaned to himself, 'I wish—I *pray*—you poor thing, you could only be a little more at peace—whoever, wherever you are—whatever *I* am.'

And then he was with the old bookseller again, and the worldly-wise old man was eyeing him as ingenuously as ever over his steel-rimmed glasses.

'He isn't looking quite himself,' he was thinking. 'Bless me, sir,' he said aloud, 'sit down and rest a bit. You must have been overdoing it. You look quite het up.'

Alan feebly shook his head. His cheek was almost as colourless as the paper on which the poems had been printed; small beads of sweat lined his upper lip and damped his hair. He opened his mouth to reassure the old bookseller, but before he could utter a word they were both of them caught up and staring starkly at one another—like conspirators caught in the act. Their eyes met in glassy surmise. A low, sustained, sullen rumble had come sounding out to them from the remoter parts of the shop which Alan had but a moment before left finally behind him.   The whole house shuddered as if at the menace of an earthquake.

'Bless my soul, sir!' cried the old bookseller. 'What in merciful heaven was that!'

He hurried out, and the next instant stood in the entry of his parlour peering in through a dense fog of dust that now obscured the light of the morning.   It silted softly down, revealing the innocent cause of the commotion.   No irreparable calamity. It was merely that a patch of the old cracked plaster ceiling had fallen in, and a mass of rubble and plaster was now piled up, inches high, on the gate-leg table and the chair beside it, while the narrow laths of the ceiling above them, a few of which were splintered, lay exposed like the bones of a skeleton.   A thick film of dust had settled over everything, intensifying with its grey veil the habitual hush of the charming little room.   And almost at one and the same moment the old bookseller began to speculate first, what damages he might have been called upon to pay if his young customer had not in the nick of time vacated that chair, and next, that though perhaps his own little stock of the rare and the curious would be little the worse for the disaster, Alan's venture might be very much so.   Indeed, the few that were visible of the little pile of books—but that morning come virgin and speckless from the hands of the binders—were bruised and scattered.   And as Mr Elliott eyed them, his conscience smote him: 'Softly now, softly,' he muttered to himself, 'or we shall have Mrs E. down on this in pretty nearly no time!'

But Mrs E. had not heard.   No footfall sounded above; nothing stirred; all remained as it might be expected to remain. And Alan, who meanwhile had stayed motionless in the outer shop, at this moment joined the old bookseller, and looked in on the ruins.

'Well, there, sir,' Mr Elliott solemnly assured him, 'all I can say is, it's a mercy you had come out of it.   And by no more than a hair's breadth!'

But Alan made no answer.   His mind was a void.   He was listening again—and so intently that it might be supposed the faintest stirrings even on the uttermost outskirts of the unseen might reach his ear.   It was too late now—and in any case it hadn't occurred to him—to add to the title-page of his volume that well-worn legend: 'The heart knoweth his own bitterness;

and a stranger doth not intermeddle with his joy.' But it might at least have served for his own brief *apologia*. He had meant well—it would have suggested. You never can tell.

As they stood there, then, a brief silence had fallen on the ravaged room. And then a husky, querulous, censorious voice had broken out behind the pair of them: 'Mr E., where are you?'

From *On the Edge*.

THE RIDDLE

So these seven children, Ann and Matilda, James, William, and Henry, Harriet and Dorothea, came to live with their grandmother. The house in which their grandmother had lived since her childhood was built in the time of the Georges. It was not a pretty house, but roomy, substantial, and square; and an elm tree outstretched its branches almost to the windows.

When the children were come out of the cab (five sitting inside and two beside the driver), they were shown into their grandmother's presence. They stood in a little black group before the old lady, seated in her bow-window. And she asked them each their names, and repeated each name in her kind, quavering voice. Then to one she gave a work-box, to William a jack-knife, to Dorothea a painted ball; to each a present according to age. And she kissed all her grandchildren to the youngest.

'My dears,' she said, 'I wish to see all of you bright and gay in my house. I am an old woman, so that I cannot romp with you; but Ann must look to you, and Mrs Fenn too. And every morning and every evening you must all come in to see your granny; and bring me smiling faces, that call back to my mind my own son Harry. But all the rest of the day, when school is done, you shall do just as you please, my dears. And there is only one thing, just one, I would have you remember. In the large spare bedroom that looks out on the slate roof there stands in the corner an old oak chest; aye, older than I, my dears, a great deal older; older than my grandmother. Play anywhere else in the house, but not there.' She spoke kindly to them all, smiling at them; but she was very aged, and her eyes seemed to see nothing of this world.

And the seven children, though at first they were gloomy and strange, soon began to be happy and at home in the great house. There was much to interest and to amuse them there; all was new to them. Twice every day, morning and evening, they came in to see their grandmother, who every day seemed more feeble; and she spoke pleasantly to them of her mother, and her childhood, but never forgetting to visit her store of sugar-plums. And so the weeks passed by.

It was evening twilight when Henry went upstairs from the nursery by himself to look at the oak chest. He pressed his fingers into the carved fruit and flowers, and spoke to the dark-smiling heads at the corners; and then, with a glance over his shoulder, he opened the lid and looked in. But the chest concealed no treasure, neither gold nor baubles, nor was there anything to alarm the eye. The chest was empty, except that it was lined with silk of old-rose, seeming darker in the dusk, and smelling sweet of pot-pourri. And while Henry was looking in, he heard the softened laughter and the clinking of the cups downstairs in the nursery; and out at the window he saw the day darkening. These things brought strangely to his memory his mother who in her glimmering white dress used to read to him in the dusk; and he climbed into the chest; and the lid closed gently down over him.

When the other six children were tired with their playing, they filed into their grandmother's room as usual for her good night and her sugar-plums. She looked out between the candles at them as if she were unsure of something in her thoughts. The next day Ann told her grandmother that Henry was not anywhere to be found.

'Dearie me, child. Then he must be gone away for a time,' said the old lady. She paused. 'But remember all of you, do not meddle with the oak chest.'

But Matilda could not forget her brother Henry, finding no pleasure in playing without him. So she would loiter in the house thinking where he might be. And she carried her wood doll in her bare arms, singing under her breath all she could make up about him. And when in a bright morning she peeped in on the chest, so sweet-scented and secret it seemed that she took her doll with her into it—just as Henry himself had done.

So Ann, and James, and William, Harriet and Dorothea were left at home to play together. 'Some day maybe they will come back to you, my dears,' said their grandmother, 'or maybe you will go to them. Heed my warning as best you may.'

Now Harriet and William were friends together, pretending to be sweethearts; while James and Dorothea liked wild games of hunting, and fishing, and battles.

On a silent afternoon in October, Harriet and William were talking softly together, looking out over the slate roof at the green fields, and they heard the squeak and frisking of a mouse behind them in the room. They went together and searched for the small, dark hole from whence it had come out. But finding no hole, they began to finger the carving of the chest, and to give names to the dark-smiling heads, just as Henry had done. 'I know! let's pretend you are Sleeping Beauty, Harriet,' said William, 'and I'll be the Prince that squeezes through the thorns and comes in.' Harriet looked gently and strangely at her brother; but she got into the box and lay down, pretending to be fast asleep; and on tiptoe William leaned over, and seeing how big was the chest he stepped in to kiss the Sleeping Beauty and to wake her from her quiet sleep. Slowly the carved lid turned on its noiseless hinges. And only the clatter of James and Dorothea came in sometimes to recall Ann from her book.

But their old grandmother was very feeble, and her sight dim, and her hearing extremely difficult.

Snow was falling through the still air upon the roof; and Dorothea was a fish in the oak chest, and James stood over the hole in the ice, brandishing a walking-stick for a harpoon, pretending to be an Esquimaux. Dorothea's face was red, and her wild eyes sparkled through her tousled hair. And James had a crooked scratch upon his cheek. 'You must struggle, Dorothea, and then I shall swim back and drag you out. Be quick now!' He shouted with laughter as he was drawn into the open chest. And the lid closed softly and gently down as before.

Ann, left to herself, was too old to care overmuch for sugar-plums, but she would go solitary to bid her grandmother good night; and the old lady looked wistfully at her over her spectacles. 'Well, my dear,' she said with trembling head; and she squeezed Ann's fingers between her own knuckled finger and thumb. 'What lonely old people we are, to be sure!' Ann kissed her grandmother's soft, loose cheek. She left the old lady sitting in her easy chair, her hands upon her knees, and her head turned sidelong towards her.

When Ann was gone to bed she used to sit reading her book by candlelight. She drew up her knees under the sheets, resting her book upon them. Her story was about fairies and gnomes, and the gently-flowing moonlight of the narrative seemed to illumine the white pages, and she could hear in fancy fairy voices, so silent was the great many-roomed house, and so mellifluent were the words of the story. Presently she put out her candle, and, with a confused babel of voices close to her ear, and faint swift pictures before her eyes, she fell asleep.

And in the dead of night she arose out of bed in dream, and with eyes wide open yet seeing nothing of reality, moved silently through the vacant house. Past the room where her grandmother was snoring in brief, heavy slumber, she stepped light and surely, and down the wide staircase. And Vega the far-shining stood over against the window above the slate roof. Ann walked in the strange room as if she were being guided by the hand towards the oak chest. There, just as if she was dreaming it was her bed, she laid herself down in the old rose silk, in the fragrant place. But it was so dark in the room that the movement of the lid was indistinguishable.

Through the long day, the grandmother sat in her bow-window. Her lips were pursed, and she looked with dim, inquisitive scrutiny upon the street where people passed to and fro, and vehicles rolled by. At evening she climbed the stair and stood in the doorway of the large spare bedroom. The ascent had shortened her breath. Her magnifying spectacles rested upon her nose. Leaning her hand on the doorpost she peered in towards the glimmering square of window in the quiet gloom. But she could not see far, because her sight was dim and the light of day feeble. Nor could she detect the faint fragrance, as of autumnal leaves. But in her mind was a tangled skein of memories—laughter and tears, and little children now old-fashioned, and the advent of friends, and long farewells. And gossiping fitfully, inarticulately, with herself, the old lady went down again to her window-seat.

From *The Riddle.*

THE ORGY: AN IDYLL

It was a Wednesday morning, and May Day, and London—its West End too, crisp, brisk, scintillating. Even the horses had come out in their Sunday best. With their nosegays and ribbons and rosettes they might have been on their way to a wedding—the nuptials of Labour and Capital, perhaps. As for people, the wide pavements of the great street were packed with them. Not so many busy idlers of the one sex as of the other, of course, at this early hour—a top-hat here, a pearl-grey Homburg there; but of the feminine a host as eager and variegated as the butterflies in an Alpine valley in mid-summer; some stepping daintily down from their landaulettes like 'Painted Ladies' out of the chrysalis, and thousands of others, blues and browns and speckleds and sables and tawnies and high-fliers and maiden's blushes, from all parts of the world and from most of the suburbs, edging and eddying along, this way, that way, their eyes goggling, their tongues clacking, but most of them, their backs to the highway, gazing, as though mesmerized, in and in through the beautiful plate-glass windows at the motley merchandise on the other side. And much of that on the limbs and trunks of beatific images almost as life-like but a good deal less active than themselves.

The very heavens, so far as they could manage to peep under the blinds, seemed to be smiling at this plenty. Nor had they any need for care concerning the future, for nursemaids pushing their baby-carriages before them also paraded the pavements, their infant charges laid in dimpled sleep beneath silken awning and coverlet, while here and there a tiny tot chattered up into the air like a starling.

A clock, probably a church clock, and only just audible, struck ten. The sun from its heights far up above the roof-tops blazed down upon the polished asphalt and walls with such an explosion of splendour that it looked as if everything had been repainted overnight with a thin coat of crystalline varnish and then sprinkled with frozen sea-water. And every human creature within sight seemed to be as heart-free and gay as this beautiful weather promised to be brief. With one exception only—poor Philip Pim.

And why not? He was young—so young in looks, indeed, that if Adonis had been stepping along at his side they might have been taken for cousins. He was charmingly attired, too, from his little, round, hard felt hat—not unlike Mercury's usual wear, but without the wings—to his neat brogue shoes; and he was so blond, with his pink cheeks and flaxen hair, that at first you could scarcely distinguish his silken eyebrows and eyelashes, though they made up for it on a second glance. Care seemed never to have sat on those young temples. Philip looked as harmless as he was unharmed.

Alas! this without of his had no resemblance whatever to his within. He eyed vacantly a buzzing hive-like abandonment he could not share; first, because though he had had the whole long day to himself he had no notion of what to do with it; and next, because only the previous afternoon the manager of the bank in which until then he had had a stool specially reserved for him every morning, had shaken him by the hand and had wished him well—for ever. He had said how deeply he regretted Philip's services could not be indulged in by the bank any longer. He would miss him. Oh, yes, very much indeed —but missed Philip must be.

The fact was that Philip had never been able to add up pounds, shillings, and pence so that he could be certain the total was correct. His 9's, too, often looked like 7's, his 5's like 3's. And as 'simple addition' was all but his sole duty in the bank, he would not have adorned its premises for a week, if his uncle, Colonel Crompton Pim, had not been acquainted with one of its most stylish directors, and was not in the habit of keeping a large part of his ample fortune in its charge. He had asked Mr Bumbleton to give Philip a chance. But chances—some as rapidly as Manx cats—come to an end. And Philip's had.

Now, if Colonel Pim had sent his nephew when he was a small boy to a nice public school, he might have been able by this time to do simple sums very well indeed. Philip might have become an accurate adder-up. It is well to look on the bright side of things. Unfortunately when Philip was an infant, his health had not been very satisfactory—at least to his widowed mother—and he had been sent instead to a private academy.

There a Mr Browne was the mathematical master—a Mr Browne so much attached to algebra and to reading *The Times* in school hours that he hadn't much patience with the rudiments of arithmetic. 'Just add it up,' he would say, 'and look up the answer. And if it isn't right, do it again.'

It was imprudent of him, but in these early years poor Philip had never so much as dreamed that some day he was going to be a clerk on a stool. If he had, he might not perhaps have been so eager to look up the answers. But then, his uncle was fabulously rich and yet apparently unmarriageable, and Philip was his only nephew. Why, then, should he ever have paid any attention to banks, apart from the variety on which the wild thyme grows?

Term succeeded term, and still, though 'a promising boy,' he remained backward—particularly in the last of the three R's. And his holidays, so called, would be peppered with such problems as (*a*) if a herring and a half cost three halfpence, how many would you get for a shilling? (*b*) If a brick weighs a pound and half a brick, how much does it weigh? (*c*) If Moses was the son of Pharaoh's daughter, etc.; and (*d*) Uncles and brothers have I none, and so on. And since, after successive mornings with a sheet of foolscap and a stub of pencil, Philip's answers would almost invariably reappear as (*a*) 18; (*b*) 1½ lb.; (*c*) his sister; and (*d*) himself, Colonel Pim grew more and more impatient, and Nature had long ago given him a good start.

He had a way, too, when carpeting poor Philip, of flicking his shepherd-plaid trouser-leg with his handkerchief, which seemed useless to every one concerned. And at last, instead of transferring his nephew from Mr Browne to Christ Church, Oxford, or to Trinity College, Cambridge, or to some less delectable resort at an outlying university, he first (before setting out in pursuit of big game all around the world), consigned him to a tutor, who thanked his lucky stars the expedition would take the colonel a long time; and, on his return, he gave them both a prolonged vacation.

And *then* had fallen the bolt from the blue. On the morning of his twenty-first birthday, which had promised to be so cool, so calm, so bright, Philip received a letter from his uncle. He opened it with joy; he read it with consternation. It was in terms as curt as they looked illegible, and it was merely to tell him that what the colonel called a post (but which was, in fact,

a high stool) had been secured for his nephew, and that unless
Philip managed to keep his seat on it for twelve consecutive
months he would be cut off with a shilling.

Of these drear months about two and a half had somehow
managed to melt away, and now not only was the stool rapidly
following them into the limbo of the past, but at this very
moment the colonel was doubtless engaged, and with his usual
zest, in keeping his promise. What wonder, then, Philip was
not exactly a happy young man as he wandered this sunny
populous May morning aimlessly on his way. There was nothing
—apart from Everything around him—to make him so, except
only one minute stroke of luck that had befallen him before
breakfast.

When he had risen from his tumbled bed in his London
lodgings, the sight of his striped bank trousers and his black
bank coat and waistcoat had filled him with disgust. Opening
the grained cupboard which did duty for a wardrobe—and in
the indulgence of his tailor it was pretty full—he took down
from a peg the festive suit he was now wearing, but which
otherwise he had left unheeded since Easter. He found himself
faintly whistling as he buttoned it on; but his delight can be
imagined when, putting his finger and thumb into an upper
waistcoat pocket, he discovered—a sovereign. And an excellent
specimen of one, with St George in his mantle and the dragon
on the one side of it, and King Edward VII's head—cut off at
the neck as if he had sat to its designer in his bath—on the
other. This, with four others very much like it, had been
bestowed on Philip many months ago by his Uncle Charles—a
maternal uncle, who had since perished in Paris. As the rest
of Philip's pockets contained only 7½d. in all, this coin—how
forgotten, he simply could not conjecture—was treasure trove
indeed.

Now, poor Philip had never really cared for money. Perhaps
he had always associated it with herrings and half-bricks.
Perhaps he had never needed it quite enough. Since, moreover, immediately opposite his perch at the bank there hung a
framed antique picture of this commodity in process of being
shovelled out of receptacles closely resembling coal-scuttles into
great vulgar heaps upon a polished counter, and there weighed
in brass scales like so much lard or glucose, he had come to
like it less and less. On the other hand, he dearly enjoyed

spending it. As with Adam and the happy birds in the Garden of Eden—linnet and kestrel and wren—he enjoyed seeing it fly. In this he was the precise antithesis of his uncle.

Colonel Crompton Pim loved money. He exulted in it (not vocally, of course) *en masse,* as the Pharaohs exulted in pyramids. And he abhorred spending it. For this (and for many another) reason he had little affection for mere objects—apart, that is, from *such* objects as golf clubs, shooting boots, or hippopotamus-hoof inkstands, and he had not the smallest pleasure in buying anything for mere buying's sake.

His immense dormitory near Cheltenham, it is true, was full of furniture, but it was furniture, acquired in the 'sixties or thereabouts, for use and not for joy. Prodigious chairs with pigskin seats; tables of a solidity that defied time and of a wood that laughed at the worm; bedsteads of the Gog order; wardrobes resembling Assyrian sarcophagi; and ottomans which would seat with comfort and dignity a complete royal family. As for its 'ornaments,' they came chiefly from Benares.

And simply because poor Philip delighted in spending money and hated impedimenta such as these with the contempt a humming-bird feels for the corpse of a rhinoceros, he had never been able to take to his uncle—not even for the sake of what he owned. And it was impossible—as he fondly supposed—for any human being to take to him for any other reason. No, there was nothing in common between them, except a few branches of the family tree. And these the colonel might already have converted into firewood.

Now, as poor Philip meandered listlessly along the street, fingering his Uncle Charles's golden sovereign in his pocket, he came on one of those gigantic edifices wherein you can purchase anything in the world—from a white elephant to a performing flea, from a cargo of coco-nuts to a tin-tack. This was the 'store' at which his uncle 'dealt.' And by sheer force of habit, Philip mounted the welcoming flight of steps, crossed a large flat rubber mat, and went inside.

Having thus got safely in, he at once began to ponder how he was to get safely out—with any fraction, that is, of his golden sovereign still in his pocket. And he had realized in the recent small hours that with so little on earth now left to spend, except an indefinite amount of leisure, he must strive to spend that little with extreme deliberation.

So first, having breakfasted on a mere glance at the charred remnant of a kipper which his landlady had served up with his chicory, he entered a large gilded lift, or elevator, as the directors preferred to call it, *en route* to the restaurant. There he seated himself at a vacant table and asked the waitress to be so kind as to bring him a glass of milk and a bun. He nibbled, he sipped, and he watched the people—if people they really were, and not, as seemed more probable, automata intended to advertise the Ecclesiastical, the Sports, the Provincial, the Curio, the Export, and the Cast-Iron Departments.

With his first sip of milk he all but made up his mind to buy a little parting present for his uncle. It would be at least a gentle gesture. With his second he decided that the colonel would be even less pleased to receive a letter *and*, say, a velvet smoking-cap, or a pair of mother-of-pearl cuff-links, than just a letter. By the time he had finished his bun he had decided to buy a little something for himself. But try as he might he could think of nothing (for less than a guinea) that would be worthy of the shade of his beloved Uncle Charles. So having pushed seven-fifteenths of all he else possessed under his plate for his freckled waitress, with the remaining fourpence he settled his bill and went steadily downstairs. Nineteen minutes past ten—he would have a good look about him before he came to a decision.

Hunger, it has been said, sharpens the senses, but it is apt also to have an edgy effect upon the nerves. If, then, Philip's breakfast had been less exacting, or his lunch had made up for it, he might have spent the next few hours of this pleasant May morning as a young man should—in the open air. Or he might have visited the British Museum, the National Gallery, and Westminster Abbey. He might never, at any rate, in one brief morning of his mortal existence have all but died again and again of terror, abandon, shame, rapture, and incredulity. He might never—but all in good time.

He was at a loose end, and it is then that habits are apt to prevail. And of all his habits, Philip's favourite was that of ordering 'goods' on behalf of his uncle. The colonel in his fantastic handwriting would post him two weekly lists—one consisting of the 'wanted,' the other of complaints about the previous week's 'supplied.' Armed with these, Philip would set out for the building he was now actually in. The first list, though not a thing of beauty, was a joy as long as it lasted. The second, for he had always flatly refused to repeat his uncle's sulphurous comments to any underling, he reserved for his old enemy, the secretary of the establishment, Sir Leopold Bull. And though in these weekly interviews Sir Leopold might boil with rage and chagrin, he never boiled over. For the name of Pim was a name of power in the secretary's office. The name of Pim was that of a heavy shareholder; and what the colonel wanted he invariably in the long run got. A chest, say, of Ceylon tea, 'rich, fruity, bright infusion'; a shooting-stick (extra heavy, Brugglesdon tube pattern); a quart-size tantalus, for a wedding present, with a double spring sterling silver Brahmin lock; a hundredweight of sago; a stymie, perhaps, or a click—something of that sort.

These 'order days' had been the balm of Philip's late existence. His eyes fixed on his ledger and his fancy on, say, 'Saddlery,' or 'Sports,' he looked forward to his Wednesdays—thirsted for them. Indeed, his chief regret at the bank, apart from little difficulties with his 9's and 3's, had been that his uncle's stores were closed on Saturday afternoons. And on Sundays. His hobby had, therefore, frequently given him indigestion, since he could indulge it only between 1 and 2 p.m. It was a pity, of course, that Colonel Pim was a man of wants so few, and these of so narrow a range. Possibly the suns of India had burned the rest out of him. But for Philip, any kind of vicarious purchase had been better than none. And now these delights, too, were for ever over. His fountain had run dry. Sir Leopold had triumphed.

At this moment he found himself straying into the Portmanteau and Bag Department. There is nothing like leather, and here there was nothing *but* leather, and all of it made up into articles ranging in size from trunks that would hold the remains of a Daniel Lambert to card-cases that would hold practically nothing at all. And all of a sudden Philip fancied he would like to buy a cigarette-case. He would have preferred one of enamel or gold or morocco or tortoise-shell or lizard or shagreen; or even of silver or suède. But preferences are expensive. And as he sauntered on, his dreamy eye ranging the counters in search merely of a cigarette-case he could *buy*, his glance alighted on a 'gent's dressing-case.'

It was a pig-skin, and it lay, unlike the central figure in

Rembrandt's 'Lesson in Anatomy,' so that the whole of its interior was in full view, thus revealing a modest row of silver-topped bottles, similar receptacles for soap, tooth-brushes, hair-oil, and eau-de-Cologne; a shoe-horn, a boot-hook, an ivory paper-knife, and hair-brushes, 'all complete.' Philip mused on it for a moment or two, perplexed by a peculiar effervescence that was going on in his vitals. He then approached the counter and asked its price.

'The price, sir?' echoed the assistant, squinnying at the tiny oblong of pasteboard attached by a thread to the ring of the handle; 'the price of that article is seventeen, seventeen, six.'

He was a tubby little man with boot-button eyes, and his snort, Philip thought, was a trifle unctuous.

'Ah,' he said, putting a bold face on the matter, 'it looks a sound workaday bag. A little mediocre, perhaps. Have you anything—less ordinary?'

'Something more expensive, sir? Why, yes, indeed. This is only a stock line—the "Archdeacon" or "Country Solicitor" model. We have prices to suit all purses. Now if you were thinking of something which you might call resshersy, sir'—and Philip now was—'there's a dressing-case under the window over there was specially made to the order of Haitch Haitch the Maharaja of Jolhopolloluli. Unfortunately, sir, the gentleman deceased suddenly a week or two ago; climate, I understand. His funeral obliquies were in the newspaper, you may remember. The consequence being, his ladies not, as you might say, con-curring, the dressing-case in a manner of speaking is on our hands—and at a considerable reduction. Only six hundred and seventy-five guineas, sir; or rupees to match.'

'May I look at it?' said Philip. 'Colonel Crompton Pim.'

'By all means, sir,' cried the little man as if until that moment he had failed to notice that Philip was a long-lost son; 'Colonel Crompton Pim; of course. Here is the article, sir, a very hand-some case, and quite unique, one of the finest, in fact, I have ever had the privilege of handling since I was transferred to this department—from the Sports, sir.'

He pressed a tiny knob, the hinges yawned, and Philip's mouth began to water. It was in sober sooth a handsome dressing-case, and the shaft of sunlight that slanted in on it from the dusky window seemed pleased to be exploring it. It was a dressing-case of tooled red Levant morocco, with gold locks and clasps and a lining of vermilion watered silk, gilded with a chaste design of lotus flowers, peacocks, and houris, the 'fittings' being of gold and tortoise-shell, and studded with so many minute brilliants and seed pearls that its contents, even in that rather dingy sunbeam, appeared to be delicately on fire.

Philip's light blue eyes under their silken lashes continued to dwell on its charms in so spell-bound a silence that for a moment the assistant thought the young man was about to swoon.

'Thank you very much,' said Philip at last, turning away with infinite reluctance and with a movement as graceful as that of a fawn, or of a *première danseuse* about to rest; 'I will keep it in mind. You are sure the management can afford the reduction?'

Having made this rather airy comment, it seemed to Philip impolite, if not impossible, to ask the price of a 'job line' of mock goatskin cigarette-cases that were piled up in dreary disorder on a tray near at hand. So he passed out into the next department, which happened to be that devoted to goods described as 'fancy,' though, so far as he could see, not very aptly.

Still he glanced around him as he hurried on, his heart bleeding for the unfortunates, old and helpless, or young and defenceless, doomed some day to welcome these exacerbating barbarous jocosities as gifts. But at sight of an obscure, puffy, maroon object demonstratively labelled 'Pochette: Art Nouveau,' his very skin contracted, and he was all but about to inquire of a large veiled old lady with an ebony walking-stick who was manfully pushing her way through this *mélange*, possibly in search of a *prie-dieu*, how such dreadful phenomena were 'begot, how nourished,' and was himself preparing to join in the chorus, when a little beyond it his glance alighted on a minute writing-case, so fraily finished, so useless, so delicious to look at, handle, and smell, that even Titania herself might have paused to admire it. Philip eyed it with unconcealed gusto. His features had melted into the smile that so often used to visit them when as a little boy he had confided in his Uncle Charles that he preferred éclairs to doughnuts. Its price, he thought, was ridiculously moderate: only £67 10s.

'It's the *décor*, sir—Parisian, of course—that makes it a trifle costly,' the assistant was explaining. 'But it's practical as well as sheek and would add distinction to *any* young lady's boudoir, bedchamber, or lap. The ink, as you see, sir, cannot possibly leak from the bottle, if the case, that is, is held the right way up—so. The pencil, the "*Sans Merci*," as you observe, is of solid gold; and the pen, though we cannot guarantee the nib, is set with life-size turquoises. The flaps will hold at least six sheets of small size notepaper, and envelopes to—or not to—match. And *here* is a little something, a sort of calendar, sir, by which you can tell the day of the week of any day of the month in any year in any century from one A.D. to nine hundred and ninety-nine thousand, nine hundred and ninety-nine. It could then be renewed.'

'M'm, very ingenious,' Philip murmured, 'and even Leap Year, I see. Is it unique, and so on?'

'No doubt of it, sir. As a matter of fact a lady from Phila-delphia—the United States of America, sir—ordered fifty fac-sillimies, platinum mounts, of this very article—only yesterday afternoon; they get married a good deal over there, sir; wedding presents.'

'Quite, thank you, no,' said Philip, firmly but pleasantly. 'They say there is safety in numbers, but there seems to be precious little else. Have you anything less reproducible?'

'Reproducible, sir? Why, naturally, sir. You see this is only a counter article. While catering for the many, sir, we are bound to keep an eye upon the few. For that very reason, the management prefer to have the costlier specimens under cover.'

'Again, thank you,' said Philip hurriedly. 'What evils are done in thy name, O Philadelphia! I may return later.'

He emerged from the Fancy Goods Department, feeling at the same moment crestfallen and curiously elated. His mind, in fact, at this moment resembled a volcano the instant before its gloom is fated to burst into a blazing eruption. Though very hazily, he even recognized the danger he was in. So in hope to compose himself he sat down for a minute or two on a Madeira wicker chair intended perhaps by the management for this very purpose, and found himself gazing at a large black Chinese cat, in the glossiest of glazed earthenware, and as life-like as Oriental artifice could make it. It was seated in a corner under a high potted palm, and it wore a grin upon its features that may have come from Cheshire, but which showed no symptom whatever of vanishing away. At sight of it—for Philip was not only partial to cats but knew the virtues of the black variety—a secret fibre seemed to have snapped in his head. 'Good luck!' the creature smirked at him. And Philip smirked back. A flame of anguished defiance and desire had leapt up in his body. He would show his uncle what was what. He would learn him to cut nephews off with shillings. He would dare and do and die!

He rose, refreshed and renewed. It was as if he had tossed off a bumper of 'Veuve Clicquot' of 1066. He must himself have come over with the Conqueror. A shopwalker lurking near was interrupted in the middle of an enormous gape by the spectacle of this Apollonian young figure now entering his department—Pianofortes and American Organs. There was something in the leopard-like look of him, something so princely and predatory in his tread, that this Mr Jackson would have been almost ready to confess that he was moved. Frenchily dark and Frenchily sleek, he bowed himself almost double.

'Yes, sir?' he remarked out loud.

'I want, I think, a pianoforte,' said Philip. 'A Grand.'

'Thank you, sir; this way, please. Grand pianofortes, Mr Smithers.'

'I want a Grand piano,' repeated Philip to Mr Smithers, an assistant with a slight cast in his left eye and an ample gingerish moustache. But in spite of these little handicaps Philip liked him much better than Mr Jackson. A far-away glimpse of Mrs Smithers and of all the little Smitherses seated round their Sunday leg of mutton at Hackney or at Brondesbury had flashed into his mind.

'Grands, sir,' cried Mr Smithers, moving his moustache up and down with a curious rotary constriction of the lips; 'this way, please.'

The young man was conducted along serried ranks of Grands. They stood on their three legs, their jaws tight shut, as mute as troops on parade. Philip paced on and on, feeling very much like the late Duke of Cambridge reviewing a regiment of his Guards. He paused at length in front of a 'Style 8; 7 ft. 9 in., square-legged, black-wood, mahogany-trimmed Bismarck.'

'It *looks* spacious,' he smiled amiably. 'But the finish! And why overhung?'

'Overstrung, sir?' said Mr Smithers. 'That's merely a manner of speaking, sir, relating solely to its inside. But this, of course, is not what we specificate as a *grand* Grand. For tone and timber and resonance and pedal work and solidity and *wear*—there isn't a better on the market. I mean on the rest of the market. And if you were having in mind an everlasting instrument for the nursery or for a practice-room—and **we** supply the new padded partitioning—this would be precisely the instrument, sir, you were having in mind. The young are sometimes a little hard on pianofortes, sir. They mean well, but they are but children after all; and——'

'Now let—me—think,' Philip interposed. 'To be quite candid, I wasn't having anything of that sort in mind. My sentiments are England for the English; and Bismarck, you know, though in girth and so on a remarkable man, was in other respects, a little—well, miscellaneous. It is said that he mixed his champagne with stout—or was it cocoa? On the other hand, I have no wish to be insular, and I *may* order one of these constructions later—for a lady: the niece, as a matter of fact, of a governess of my uncle Colonel Crompton Pim's when he was young—as young at least as it was possible for him to be—who is, I believe, thinking of taking—of taking in—pupils. But we will see to that later. Have you anything that I could really look at?'

Mr Smithers's moustaches twirled like a weathercock. 'Why, yes, sir. Just now we are up to our eyes in pianos—flooded; and if I may venture to say so, sir, Bismarck was never no friend of *mine*. All this'—and he swept his thumb in the direction of the avenue of instruments that stretched behind them—'they may be Grands, but they 're most of them foreign, and if you want a little something as nice to listen to as it is natty to look at, and *not* a mere menadjery fit only for an 'awl, there is a little what they call a harpsichord over yonder, sir. It 's a bijou model, de Pompadour case, hand-painted throughout —cupids and scallops and what not, all English gut, wire, metal, and jacks, and I defy any dealer in London to approximate it, sir, in what you might call pure form. No noise and all music, sir, and that *mellow* you scarcely know where to look. A lady's instrument—a titled lady's. And only seven hundred and seventy-seven guineas, sir, all told.'

'Is it unique?' Philip inquired.

'Unique, sir? There 's not another like it in Europe.'

Philip smiled at Mr Smithers very kindly out of his blue eyes. 'But what about America?' he said.

The assistant curved what seemed an almost unnecessarily large hand round his lips. 'Between you and me, sir, if by America,' he murmured, 'you're meaning the United States, why, Messrs Montferas & de Beauguyou refuse to ship in that direction. It ruins their tone. In fact, sir, they are what's called *difficult*. They make for nobody and nowhere but as a favour; and that instrument over there was built for——!'

He whispered the sesame so low that water rustling on a pebbled beach would have conveyed to Philip tidings more intelligible. But by the look in Mr Smithers's eye Philip guessed that the lady in question moved in a lofty, though possibly a narrow, circle.

'Ah!' he said; 'then that settles it. A home away from home. Charity begins there. I shall want it to-morrow. I shall want them both to-morrow. I mean the pianos. And perhaps a more democratic instrument for the servants' hall. But I will leave that to you.'

Mr Smithers pretended not to goggle. 'Why, yes, sir, that can be easily arranged. In London, I *ho*—conjecture?'

'In London,' said Philip, 'Grosvenor Square.' For at that very instant, as if at the summons of a jinnee, there had wafted itself into his memory the image of a vacant and 'highly desirable residence,' which his casual eye had glanced upon only the afternoon before, and which had proclaimed itself 'to be let.'

'Grosvenor Square, sir; oh, yes, sir?' Mr Smithers was ejaculating, order-book in hand. 'I will arrange for their removal at once. The three of them—quite a nice little set, sir.'

'Pim, Crompton, Colonel,' chanted Philip. 'R-*O*-M; deferred account; *thank* you. 4-4-4, yes, four hundred and forty-four, Grosvenor Square. I am—that is, *we* are furnishing there.'

But this gentle emphasis on the 'we' was so courtly in effect that it sounded more like an afterthought than a piece of information. Nevertheless it misled Mr Smithers. Intense fellow-feeling beamed from under his slightly overhung forehead. 'And I am sure, sir, if I may make so bold, I wish you both every happiness. I am myself of a matrimonial turn. And regret it, sir? *Never!* I always say if every——'

'That's very kind indeed of you,' said Philip, averting his young cheek, which having flushed had now turned a little pale. 'And, if *I* may be so bold, I am perfectly certain Mrs Smithers is of the same way of thinking. Which is the best way to the

Best Man's Department, if I take in Portmanteaux and the Fancies on my way?'

Mr Smithers eyed him with the sublimest admiration. 'Straight through, sir, on the left beyond them Chappels. On the same floor, but right out on the further side of the building. As far as you can go.'

'That is exactly what I was beginning to wonder—precisely how far I can go. This little venture of mine is a rather novel experience, and at the moment I am uncertain of its issue. But tell me, why is it our enterprising American friends have not yet invented a *lateral* lift?'

'Now that's passing strange, too, sir; for I've often fancied it myself,' said Mr Smithers. 'But you see in a department like this there's not much time for quiet thought, sir, with so much what you might call hidden din about. As a matter of fact, when I was younger, sir—and that happens to us all—I did invent a harmonium key-stifler—rubber, and pith, and wool —*so*—and a small steel spring, quite neat and entirely unnotice-able. But the manufacturers wouldn't look at it; not they!'

'I don't believe,' said Philip, folding up his bill, 'they ever look at anything. Not closely, you know. But if ever I do buy a harmonium'—he put his head a little on one side and again smiled at Mr Smithers—'I shall insist on the stifler. I suppose,' he added reflectively, 'you haven't by any chance a nice pedigree Amati or Stradivarius in stock? I have a little weakness for fiddles.'

Mr Smithers, leaning heavily on the counter on both his thumbs, smiled, but at the same time almost imperceptibly shook his head.

'I fancied it was unlikely,' said Philip. 'What's that over there; in the glass case, I mean?'

'That, sir?' said Mr Smithers, twinkling up, 'in that glass case there? That's a harp, sir. And a lovely little piece *that* is. Child's size, sir. What they call minnychoore, and well over a century old, but still as sweet as a canary. It was made, so they say, for Mozart, the composer, sir, as you might be aware, in 1781, and up in the top corner is scratched the letters A.W. No doubt of it, sir—A.W. I've seen a picture of the mite myself playing like an angel in his nightcap, and not a day over seven; you'd hardly believe it, and his parents coming in at the door. Surprising. Then Schumann, *he* had it, sir—I mean the harp; and Schumann, though I don't know how he could dissuade himself to part with it, *he* passed it on to Brahms, another composer—and very much thought of even though a bit nearer *our* day. But you'll find it all neatly set out on the brass label at the foot. It's all there, sir. There's many a custo——'

'Indeed!' said Philip; 'Brahms, Schumann, Mozart, what scenes we are recalling! And here it rests at last. The knacker's yard. How very, very sad. Why, of course, Mr Smithers, we must have that sent on too—and packed very, very carefully. Is the glass case extra?'

Mr Smithers gulped. 'I am exceedingly sorry, sir,' he said, 'exceedingly sorry, but it's not for sale; I mean—*except* the case.'

'Not for sale,' retorted Philip impulsively. 'But what is the use, Mr Smithers, of a mercenary institution like this unless everything in it is for sale? You cannot mean for raw advertisement?'

Mr Smithers was covered with confusion. 'I am sure, sir,' he said, 'that the directors would do their utmost to consider your wishes. They would be very happy to do so. But if you will excuse my mentioning it, I should myself very much miss that harp. I have been in this department thirteen years now. . . . My little boy. . . . It is the only thing . . .'

It was Philip's turn to be all in confusion. 'Good gracious me, I quite understand,' he said; 'not another word, Mr Smithers. I wouldn't *think* of pressing the point. None the less I can assure you that even if it *had* been for sale I should always have welcomed you whenever you cared to come to Grosvenor Square and take another look at it. And, of course, your little boy, too—*all* your little boys.'

Mr Smithers appeared to be lost in gratitude. 'If only——' he began, a light that never was on sea or land in his eye—but words failed him.

At the other end of the 'Chappels' Philip again encountered the walker, Mr Jackson, still looking as much like a self-possessed bridegroom as it is possible for a high collar and a barber to achieve.

'I see,' said Philip, 'you exhibit specimens of the tuberphone (and, by the way, I would suggest *a* instead of "er")—the tubaphone, the clog-box, and the Bombaboo, iniquities at the same time negroid and old-fashioned, but though in a recent

visit to Budapest I found even the charming little linden-shaded
shops—along the Uffelgang, you know, not, of course, a fashion-
able part of the city—crammed with models of the "Haba-
Stein," a microtonic instrument with five keyboards and Hindu
effects, intended, of course, for the polytonal decompositions of
the "Nothing-but-Music" school—*most* interesting; I see *no*
trace of it here. I am not a neoteromaniac, but still, we must
keep abreast, we must keep abreast!'

He waved a not unfriendly glove over his head, smiled and
went on.

Mr Smithers had also watched the slim grey young figure
until it had turned the corner and was out of sight. He then
had a word with his 'floor chief.'

'Pim, eh, Crompton,' said Mr Jackson, squinting morosely
at his underling's open order-book. '"Setting up house"?
Then I suppose the old gent must have sent in his checks. Not
that I'm surprised this nephew of his hasn't bought his black
yet. Close-fisted, purple-nosed, peppery old——! There won't
be many to cry their eyes out over *his* arums and gardenias.'

Mr Smithers, being a family man, felt obliged to seem to
enjoy as much as possible his immediate chief's society.

'All I can say *is*,' he ventured, 'that young feller, and he's a
gentleman if ever there was one, is making it fly.'

He *was*. At this moment Philip was assuring Assistant No. 6
in the Portmanteau Department that unless the Maharaja of
Jolhopolloluli's dressing-case could be dispatched next day to
reach No. 444 Grosvenor Square by tea-time he need not trouble.
'A few other little things,' he explained, 'are being sent at the
same time.' No. 6 at once hastened to the house telephone and
asked for the secretary's office. The line was engaged.

But he need not have hesitated, for when a young man with
a Pim for an uncle and of so much suavity and resource makes
his wishes known, this world is amiability itself. Philip was
warming up. However bland in outward appearance, he was
by this time at a very enlivening temperature. He had tasted
blood, as the saying goes; and he was beginning to see the need
of setting a good example. Customers, like the coneys, are usually
a feeble folk. His little sortie was turning into a crusade.

By this time he had all but finished disporting himself in the
Furniture Department. 'Three large drawing-rooms, one of
them "extensive,"' had run his rather naked catalogue, 'a

ballroom, a dining-room, a breakfast-room, and a little pretty dumpy all-kinds-of-angles morning-room with a Cherubini ceiling and a Venetian chimneypiece, eighteenth century, in lapis lazuli and glass. Bedrooms, let me see, say, twenty-two—just to go on with (but not in), eleven of them for personal use, and the rest, staff. That, I think, will do for the present. We face east or west as the case may be; and nothing, please, of the "decorative," the quaint, or the latest thing out. Nothing shoddy, shapeless, or sham. I dislike the stuffy and the fussy and mere trimmings; and let the beds be *beds*. Moreover, I confess to being sadly disappointed in the old, the "antique,' furniture you have shown me. The choice is restricted, naïve and incongruous, and I have looked in vain for anything that could not be easily rivalled in the richer museums. However, let there be as many so-called antique pieces as possible, and those as antique as you can manage. Period, origin, design, harmony—please bear these in mind.'

The assistants, clustering round him, bowed.

'If I have time I will look through the department again on my way down. Eight hundred guineas for the cheaper of the Chippendale four-posters seems a little exorbitant; and three hundred and fifty for the William and Mary wall-glass—I fear it's been resilvered and patched. Still, I agree you can but do your best—I say you can all of you but do your best—and I must put up with that. What I *must* insist on, however, is that everything I have mentioned—everything—must be in its place to-morrow afternoon—carpets and so on will, of course, precede them—by four o'clock. And let there be no trace left of that indescribable odour of straw and wrappings—from Delhi, I should think—which accompanies removals. 444 Grosvenor Square. Pim—Crompton—Colonel: R-*O*-M. Thank you. To the left? *Thank* you.'

This 'floor chief' hastened on in front of his visitor as if he were a Gehazi in attendance on a Naaman, and the young man presently found himself in a scene overwhelmingly rich with the colours, if not the perfumes, of the Orient. Here a complete quarter of an hour slid blissfully by. Mere wooden furniture, even when adorned with gilt, lacquer, ivory, or alabaster, can be disposed of with moderate ease; and especially if the stock of the tolerable is quickly exhausted. But Persian, Chinese, if not Turkey, carpets are another matter.

Philip sat erect on a gimcrack gilded chair, his cane and hat in his left hand, his gloves in his right, while no less than three sturdy attendants in baize aprons at one and the same moment strewed their matchless offerings at his feet, and an infuriated and rapidly multiplying group of would-be customers in search of floorcloth, lino, and coco-nut matting stood fuming beyond. But first come first served is a good old maxim, and even apart from it Philip was unaware of their company. He lifted not so much as an eyebrow in their direction.

In the meantime, however, the cash balance in his uncle's bank, and much else besides, had long since as rapidly vanished as the vapour from a locomotive on a hot summer's day. From the Carpet Department, vexed that time allowed him only one of London's chief treasuries to ransack—such are the glories of Bokhara and Ispahan—he hastened down to the wine counters. Here, childishly confident in the cellarage of No. 444, Philip indulged a pretty palate *not* inherited from his uncle: claret, Burgundy, hock, sherry, cherry brandy, green Chartreuse, and similar delicate aids to good talk and reflection. He was ingenuous but enthusiastic. Port he ignored.

From 'Wines' he made his way through the galleries exhibiting curtains and 'hangings' (he shuddered), and china and glass—'most discouraging.' His spirits revived a little when yet another defunct and barbaric prince, this time from Abyssinia, supplied him in the Car Department with a vehicle whose only adequate use, to judge from the modesty of its dashboard, the simplicity of its engine and its price, would be a journey from this world into the next. Nevertheless His Highness had left it behind him.

Fleeting visits to counters bristling with ironmongery, turnery, kitchen utensils, and provisions—and from motives of principle he omitted all mention of mulligatawny paste, chutney, West India pickles, and similar fierce and barbarous comestibles, vanished out of memory like the patterns of a kaleidoscope. The rather noisy annexe reserved for live stock Philip left unvisited. After deserts of dead stock it sounded inviting, but Philip's was a dainty nose and he was sorry for orang-outangs.

So too with books. He had clear convictions of what a gentleman's library should be without, but decided that it would take more leisure than he could spare this morning to expound them. Even the sight of a Work of Reference, however, is an excellent sedative; he ordered the choicest of Who's-whos, dictionaries, atlases, encyclopaedias, bird, flower, and cookery books, with a copy of 'Bradshaw'—and retired.

As for pictures and statuary, one anguished glance into the dreadful chambers devoted to the fine arts had sent him scurrying on like a March hare. Nor, as he rather sadly realized, had he any cause to linger at the portals of the Monumental Masonry Department, and he now suddenly found himself in the midst of a coruscating blaze of the precious metals and the still more precious stones. He had strayed into 'Jewellery'— a feast for Aladdin. Gold in particular—goblets and bowls and tankards, plates, platters, and dishes of it; clocks, chronometers, watches—from massive turnips, memorial of the Georges, to midgets like a threepenny-piece in crystal and enamel, many of them buzzing like bees, and all of them intent on the kind of time which is *not* wild or always nectarous, but of which Philip had always supposed there was an inexhaustible supply. But not, alas, for all purposes. Indeed, these officious reminders of the actual hour had for the first time a little scared him.

In the peculiar atmosphere that hangs over any abundant array of sago, cooked meats, candles, biscuits, coffee, tea, ginger, and similar wares, he had been merely a young bachelor on the brink of an establishment. But at sight of this otiose display of gewgaws in the lamplit mansion in which he now found himself, his fancy had suddenly provided him with a bride. She was of a fairness incomparably fair. The first faint hint of this eventuality had almost unnerved him. He lost his head and—his heart being unconcerned—his taste also. In tones as languid as the breezes of Arabia he had at once ordered her rings, bracelets, necklaces, pendants, brooches, ear-rings, not to speak of bediamonded plumes and tiaras, that would daunt the dreams even of the complete bevy of musical comedy young ladies on the British stage—not to mention that of Buenos Aires. And then, oddly enough, he had come to himself, and paused.

At the very moment of opening his mouth in repetition of a solo with which he was now entirely familiar—'R-*O*-M,' and so on—he sat instead, gaping at the tall, calm, bald, venerable old gentleman on the other side of the counter. He had flushed.

'Have you,' he inquired almost timidly at last, his eyes fixed on a chastely printed list of cutlery and silver ware that lay on the glass case at his elbow, 'have you just one really simple, lovely, rare, precious, and, well, unique little trinket suitable for a lady? Young, you know? An *un*-birthday present?'

The old gentleman looked up, looked at, looked *in*, smiled fondly, reminiscently, and, selecting a minute key on a ring which he had drawn out of his pocket, opened a safe not half a dozen yards away. 'We have this,' he said.

'This,' at first, was a little fat morocco leather case. He pressed the spring. Its lid flew open. And for an instant Philip's eyesight failed him. But it was not so much the suppressed lustre of the jewels within that had dazed his imagination as the delicate marvel of their setting. They lay like lambent dewdrops on the petals of a flower. The old gentleman gazed too.

'The meaning of the word "simple,"' he suggested ruminatively, 'is one of many degrees. This, sir, is a Benvenuto Cellini piece.' He had almost whispered the last few syllables as if what in workmanship were past all rivalry was also beyond any mortal pocket; as if, in fact, he were telling secrets of the unattainable. The tone piqued Philip a little.

'It is charming,' he said. 'But have you nothing then of Jacques de la Tocqueville's, or of Rudolph von Himmeldommer's, nothing of—dear me, the name escapes me. The earlier Florentine, you will remember, no doubt referred to in *Sordello*, who designed the chryselephantine bowl for the Botticelli wedding-feast. But never mind. Nothing Greek? Nothing Etruscan —*poudre d'or*? Are you suggesting that the Winter Palace was thrice looted in vain?'

The old gentleman was accustomed to the airs and graces of fastidious clients and merely smiled. He had not been listening very intently. 'You will appreciate the difficulty, sir, of keeping anything but our more trifling pieces actually within reach of the nearest burglar with a stick of gun-cotton or an acetylene lamp. This'—he stirred the little leather case with his finger as lithely as a cat the relics of a mouse, and its contents seemed softly to sizzle in subdued flames of rose and amber and blue —'this,' he said, 'happens not to be our property. It is merely in our keeping. And though to an article of such a nature it is absurd to put a price, we have been asked to dispose of it; and by—well, a client for whom we have the profoundest respect.'

'I see'; Philip pondered coldly on the bauble, though his heart

was a whirlpool of desire and admiration.   He swallowed.   The
remote tiny piping of a bird that was neither nightingale nor
skylark, and yet might be either or both, had called to him as
if from the shores of some paradisal isle hidden in the mists of
the future.   He glanced up at the old gentleman, but his bald,
long, grey countenance was as impassive as ever.

'I'll take it,' Philip said, and for a while could say no more.
When speech was restored to him, he asked that it should be
delivered not 'with the other things,' and not to any butler or
major-domo or other crustacean that might appear in answer
to a knock at No. 444, but by special messenger into his own
personal private hands.

'Precisely, at half-past four, if you please.'   The old gentleman bowed.   As there was not enough room in the money
column of his order-book for the noughts, he had written in the
price in longhand, and was engaged in printing the figures 444
in the place reserved for the customer's address, when a
small but clearly actual little voice at Philip's elbow suddenly
shrilled up into his ear: 'Mr Philip Pim, sir?'   At echo of this
summons Philip stood stock-still and stiff, his heart in his ears.
'The sekkertary, sir,' the piping voice piped on, 'asks me to say
he'd be much obliged if you would be so kind as to step along
into his office on your way *hout*, sir.'

The tone of this invitation, though a little Cockney in effect,
was innocence and courtesy itself; yet at sound of it every drop
of blood in Philip's body—though he was by no means a bloated
creature—had instantly congealed.   This was the end, then.
His orgy was over.   His morning of mornings was done.   The
afflatus that had wafted him on from floor to floor had wisped
out of his mind like the smoke of a snuffed-out candle.   Yet
still the bright thought shook him: he had had a Run for his
money.   No—better than that: he had had a Run *gratis*.

He must collect his wits: they had gone wool-gathering.   At
last he managed to turn his head and look down at the small,
apple-cheeked, maroon-tunicked page-boy at his side—apple-
cheeked, alas, only because he had but that week entered the
sekkertary's service and his parents were of country stock.

'Tell Sir Leopold Bull'—Philip smiled at the infant—'that
I will endeavour to be with him in the course of the afternoon.
Thank you.   That,' he added for the ear of his friend on the
other side of the counter, 'that will be all.'

But Philip was reluctant to leave him. These four syllables, as he had heard himself uttering them, sounded on in his ear with the finality of a knell. He was extremely dubious of what would happen if he let go of the counter. His knees shook under him. A dizzy vacancy enveloped him in. With a faint wan smile at the old gentleman, who was too busily engaged in returning his treasures to the safe to notice it, he managed to edge away at last.

Every mortal thing around him, gilded ceiling to grandfather clock, was at this moment swaying and rotating, as will the ocean in the eyes of a sea-sick traveller gloating down upon it from an upper deck. He felt ill with foreboding.

But breeding tells. And courage is a mistress that has never been known to jilt a faithful heart. Philip was reminded of this as he suddenly caught sight of a sort of enormous purple beefeater, resembling in stature a Prussian dragoon, and in appearance a Javanese Jimjam. This figure stood on duty in the doorway, and appeared to be examining him as closely as if he were the heir to the English throne (or the most nefarious crook from Chicago). As Philip drew near he looked this monster full in his fish-like eye, since he was unable to do anything else. But try as he might he couldn't pass him in silence.

'Ask Sir Leopold Bull, please,' he said, 'to send an official to show me the way to his office. He will find me somewhere in the building.'

'I can take you there meself,' replied the giant hoarsely. He could indeed—bodily.

'Thank you,' replied Philip. 'I have no doubt of it. But I should be much obliged if you would at once deliver my message.'

He then groped his way to yet another wicker chair not many yards along a corridor festooned with knick-knacks from Japan and the Near East, and clearly intended for speedy disposal. He eyed them with immense distaste and sat down.

'Nothing whatever, thank you,' he murmured to a waitress who had approached him with a card containing a list of soft drinks. Never in his life had he so signally realized the joys of self-restraint. And though at the same moment he thrust finger and thumb into his waistcoat pocket in search of his Uncle Charles's last sovereign, it was with a view not to material but to moral support. Years before he had often tried the same device when as a small boy deadly afraid of the dark he had managed at last to thrust his fevered head up and out from under his bedclothes, and to emit a dreadful simulacrum of a croupy cough. He had never known it to fail of effect, and it was always nice to know his mother was *there*.

So, too, with his Uncle Charles's sovereign. It was nice to know it was there, though it was not the dark Philip was now afraid of but the light. Resting the ivory handle of his walking-stick on his lower lip, he began to think. What would his sentence be? A first offender, but not exactly a novice. Not, at any rate, he hoped, in taste and judgment. Months or years? Hard labour or penal servitude? So swift is the imagination that in a few seconds Philip found himself not only—his sentence served, the smiling governor bidden farewell—*out* and a free man again, but fuming with rage that he had not managed to retain a single specimen of his spoils. The Jobbli dressing-bag, for instance, or that tiny, that utterly and inimitably 'unique' little Sheraton Sheridan writing-desk.

He came back a little stronger from this expedition into the future. For reassurance, like hope, springs eternal in the human breast. His one regret was not so much that he had been found out (that might come later), but that he had been found out so soon. How much bolder, less humiliating, nobler, to have actually bearded that old curmudgeon of an uncle of his, swapp or bogey in hand, in his den!

That in any event he would have been 'found out' on the morrow, as soon, that is, as the first van arrived at No. 444, he had realized long ago. He certainly would not have been found 'in'! But even one brief night in May seems, in prospect, a long interval between being a Croesus and a felon in Pentonville.

He was recalled from these reflections by a young man whose sleek black hair was parted as neatly in front and in the middle as his morning coat was parted behind. A few paces distant, like a mass of gilded pudding-stone, stood the giant from the Jewellery Department. Were they in collusion? Philip could not decide.

'If you would step this way, sir, to the secretary's office,' said the young man, 'Sir Leopold Bull would be very much obliged.'

Philip mounted to his feet and, though he flatly refused to

step *that* way, followed him—to his doom. That, however, was not to be instantaneous, for on his arrival Sir Leopold Bull, rising from his roll-top desk with a brief but thrilling smile, first proffered a plump white hand to his visitor and then a chair. It seemed to be a needlessly polite preamble to the interview that was to follow. Philip ignored the hand but took the chair.

'Thank you,' he said. 'I do hope you will some day take my advice, Sir Leopold, to *sim*plify the arrangement of this building. It is a perfect labyrinth, and I always miss my way.' With a sigh he sank down into the cushions. He was tired.

'My uncle, Colonel Crompton Pim,' he continued, 'is unable to spare a moment to see you this morning. I regret to say he strongly disapproved of the Bombay ducks, or was it the Clam Chowder, you sent him on Friday. They were beneath contempt.'

Sir Leopold smiled once more, but even more placatingly. 'I had the privilege of seeing Colonel Crompton Pim only yesterday afternoon,' he replied. 'He then expressed his satisfaction, for the time being, at the golf balls—the new *Excelsior* brand—with one of which we had the pleasure of supplying him *gratis* a week or two ago. The Bombay ducks shall be withdrawn immediately. I must apologize for not seeking you out in person, Mr Pim, but what I have to say is somewhat of a private nature and——'

'Yes,' said Philip, realizing how thin was the end of the wedge which Sir Leopold was at this moment insinuating into the matter in hand. 'Yes, quite.' And he opened his innocent blue eyes as wide as he could, to prevent them from blinking. He kept them fixed, too, on the close-shaven face, its octopus-like mouth and prominent eyes, with ill-suppressed repulsion. To be a fly that had fallen a victim to such a spider as this!

'It would please me better,' he went on, 'if you would arrive as rapidly as possible at the matter you wish to discuss with me. I am free for five minutes, but I must beg you not to waste our time. And please tell your porter over there to go away. Such scenes are distasteful to me.'

The face of the porter, who seemed to have been created solely for his bulk, turned as crimson as a specimen of *sang-du-bœuf*. He appeared to be hurt. But wages are of more importance than feelings, and he withdrew.

H 940

'You have had a busy morning, Mr Pim,' said the secretary. 'No less than seven of my assistants who have had the privilege of waiting upon you have been monopolizing me for some time with telephone messages. I hope I am not being too intrusive if I venture to congratulate you, sir, on what I suppose to be Colonel Crompton Pim's approaching——'

'Candidly, Sir Leopold,' said Philip firmly, 'that *would* be venturing too far. Much too far. Let us say no more about it. What precise charge are you intending to bring against me?'

There was a pause while the world continued to rotate.

'For which article?' breathed Sir Leopold.

Philip gazed steadily at the full, bland, secretive countenance. It was as if once again he had heard that seraphic bird-like voice sounding in the remote blue sky above the storm-clouds that now hung so heavily over his beating heart.

'Oh, I mean for delivery,' he said. 'Mine was—was a large order.'

'But, my dear sir, we shouldn't dream of making *any* such charge. *Any* service to Colonel Pim. . . .' The faint sob in the voice would have done credit to Caruso.

Philip stooped to hide the cataract of relief that had swept over his face, then raised his head again. How could he be sure that this was anything more than play-acting—the torture of suspense? 'Ah, well,' he said, 'that is no matter now. I gather there was some other point you had in mind—in *view*, I should say.'

'Oh, only,' said Sir Leopold, 'to ask if Colonel Pim would be so kind as to subscribe as usual to our Fund for the Amelioration of the Conditions of the Offspring of Superannuated Shop Assistants. Mainly orphans, Mr Pim. We must all die, Mr Pim, and some of us have to die earlier in life than others. Still, our average here is little worse than that of any other large London establishment. In Petrograd—or was it Los Angeles?—I am given to understand, a shop assistant at two-and-thirty is a shop assistant with at least one foot in the grave. It is the little orphans, the fatherless ones, who from no apparent fault of their own, have to be left to the tender mercies of a busy world! It would grieve you, sir, which Heaven forbid, if I told you how many of these wee small things there are now on our hands. Chubby, joysome, rosebud little creatures, as happy as the day is long. Nevertheless it

is a little thoughtless to marry, Mr Pim, when it is only orphans
one can leave behind one.   On the other hand, there is a silver
lining to *every* cloud. Without these infants we should be
deprived of a good cause. An excellent cause. And it's causes
that keep us going.   Last year I think Colonel Pim very kindly
contributed half a guinea.'

'In cash?' Philip inquired sharply.

'We debited his account,' said Sir Leopold.

'Well, then,' said Philip, 'please understand that my uncle
regrets that little laxity. He has hardened. He now entirely
disapproves of orphans and of orphanages. The shop assistant,
he was saying to me only the other day, is a person who should
be grateful to Providence that he has *no* justification for dabbling
matrimony. The more celibate they are, in his opinion, the
better. But recollect, Sir Leopold, that until we arrive at the
higher and fewer salaried officials in your establishment, I feel
myself in no way bound to *share* my uncle's views. Your staff
is as courteous and considerate as it appears to be unappreciated.
A man's a man for a' that. And a' that. Let us talk of
brighter things.'

Sir Leopold did his utmost to conceal the wound to his
vanity. 'I am sorry to seem to be persistent,' he assured his
client, 'but Colonel Pim only yesterday was so kind as to say
he would *consider* my appeal. I take it, then, that he has changed
his mind?'

'My uncle,' retorted Philip tartly, 'has a mind that is the
better for being changed.' For an instant he saw the face
before him as it would appear in due course in the witness-box;
and his very soul revolted. That pitiless Machine called Society
might have its merits, but not *this* cog in its wheel! 'I myself
implored my uncle,' he added bitterly, 'to give the orphans the
cold shoulder. What in the chronic sirocco of his next world
would be the use to him of a mere half-guinea's worth of cooling
breezes? Scarcely a sop in the pan. Indeed, only a passion
for the conventional prevented him from asking for his previous
donations to be returned.'

Sir Leopold appeared to be engaged in rapidly bolting something—possibly his pride. It was at any rate no part of his
secretarial duties to detect insanity in the family of any solvent
shareholder.

'There is only one other little point,' he went on rather

hollowly. 'Colonel Pim asked me to send him a detailed account of his purchases during the last month. We met by happy chance as he was yesterday alighting from a taxicab at the entrance to his bank. After to-day's purchases that will perhaps take an hour or two. But it shall reach him to-morrow morning—without fail.'

Philip had risen. It is better to stand when one is at bay. While with a gentle absent smile he stood drawing on his gloves he was faced with the wildest effort of his life—to make sure of what lay in hiding behind these last remarks. Anything *might*.

'Oh, he did—did he?' he remarked very softly. 'I fancy'— and at last he lifted his gentle eyes to meet his adversary's— 'I *believe* there's an empty whisky jar that has not yet been credited to him. Perhaps that was on his mind.'

'Well, Mr Pim,' said Sir Leopold, 'turning' at last, 'if *that*'s his only jar it's soon adjusted.'

Philip took a deep breath. He playfully wagged a finger.

'Now *that*, Sir Leopold,' he said, 'was blank verse. I hope you don't intend to put my little purchases of this morning into *rhyme*! The effort, I assure you, would be wasted on my uncle.'

He wheeled lightly, and turned towards the door. Sir Leopold, his face now at liberty to resume its office of expressing his feelings, accompanied him. Indeed, he continued to accompany him to the very entrance of his gigantic abode. And there Philip almost fainted. A deluge, compared with which that of Noah and his family was nothing but an April shower, was descending on the street.

'A taxi!' roared Sir Leopold at a group of his satellites in the porch, caparisoned in shiny waterproofs, and armed with gigantic *parapluies*.

But though at least nineteen of these vehicles were instantly battling their way towards this goal, Philip with incredible agility had eluded their attention. Before Sir Leopold had had time even to arrange his face to smile a farewell, our young friend had gone leaping up the staircase behind him, and had without a moment's pause vanished into the Tropical Department. One fugitive glance at its pith and pucka contents, and at the dusky assistants in attendance, had only accelerated his retreat. In less than half a minute he found himself confronting a young woman seated in the midst of a stockade of umbrellas.

The coincidence was too extreme to be ignored. He would at least carry off *some* little souvenir of his morning's outing. What better value could he get for hard cash than an implement that would be at the same time a refuge from the elements—for other he would soon presently have none—and a really formidable weapon at hand for his next interview with Sir Leopold?

He had but just enough breath left to express himself. He pointed.

'I *want* one, please,' he cried at the young woman. 'Cash.'

'One, two, three, four, *five* guineas?' she murmured, looking as if she were less in need of her stock than of her lunch. 'Partridge, malacca, horn, ivory, rhinoceros, natural, *gold*? Union, gloria, glacé, taffeta, cotton, mixture, or *twill*?'

'Not a toy; an umbrella,' Philip expostulated. 'To keep off rain. A nephew returning to school—ten years' wear. Gingham, alpaca, calico, cast-iron—*anything*; so long as it is hefty, solid, endurable, awful, and *cheap*.'

'We have here what is *called* an umbrella,' replied the assistant a trifle coldly. 'The "Miss and Master Brand." Lignum-vitae stick, whalebone ribs, blunted ferrule, non-poisonous handle, guaranteed not to break, fray, fade, or scale. Nine and elevenpence complete.'

'Bill; in haste; cash; just as it is; thanks,' cried Philip, and seized the dreadful object. With a groan he laid his Uncle Charles's sovereign in the narrow brass trough of the pay-desk. The obese young person in the wooden box seemed about to lift it to her lips, glanced at him again, put it aside, smiled, and gave him his change.

'The way to the back exit, I think, is over there?' Philip murmured, waving his gloves due west.

The young person smiled again, and he withdrew. He withdrew down the back steps and into the deluge: there to face a watery world, the possessor of ten shillings and a penny (in his pocket), a wardrobe of old suits, about a hundred and fifty books, three of them unmerited prizes for good conduct, a juvenile collection of postage stamps, a hypothetical legacy of a shilling, and an uncle who, if he faced his liabilities as an English gentleman must, had to all intents and purposes over-drawn his bank account that afternoon, by, say roughly, a couple of hundred thousand pounds.

From *On the Edge*.

'A NEST OF SINGING-BIRDS'

HILBERT had cooled down at last. And now so sweetly chimed his heart, so transporting a sense of peace had stolen over his mind, that he had all but repented of his hasty vow—never, never to run for a train again. And particularly for a train not his own. After the din and fever of the arterial road, this tiny station—Bovey Fausset—of which he was the sole occupant, with its Noah's Ark trees, its nursery bridge, and tall toy signal-post, was like a scene out of some Hans Andersen fairy-story. How very odd that those dreadful Victorians, those slaves of the squat god, Pocket, should have indulged in anything so ridiculous and charming! The whole thing looked as if it were made of cardboard, and just for fun. If, now and then, between trains, he could sit on here, on this hard, hot, narrow bench in this westering September sunshine—mellow as a vintage hock—how simple it would become to stuff lines of verse with sad melodious thoughts; to rhyme *pass* with *alas !—anguish* with *languish*. This morning, unfortunately, he had hastened out of the house *minus* his fountain-pen.

So narrow was the single track of glinting steel that he could have jumped it with ease—a hop, a skip, and clean over. If he had been sure he was not alone he would have made the attempt. But 'deeds of reckless daring demand an audience of the fair'! All along the twin platforms—snapdragons, cottage roses, dahlias —yellow sunflowers of every tint and magnitude, from Van Gogh tea-trays downwards, stood opulently exposing their charms to a host of bees and flies and butterflies in the gentle breeze—a breeze so gentle indeed that it had taken exactly twenty minutes to cool Hilbert's fevered brow.

If he had refused to believe that a ramshackle train going the wrong way could possibly be his own, if he had merely mocked at the silly fallacy of 'saving' time, he would long ago have detected how heavenly, how earthly-sweet this faint wind was, as if it were laden with the spices of the Hesperides. The little old leather handbag now squatting on the seat beside him and packed almost exclusively with pretty little *bibelots*—how *could* it have come to weigh so heavy. His own Works, too!

They simply irradiated the air—the sunflowers; and continued to be the bliss of Hilbert's outward eye until suddenly he remembered that their very splendour proclaimed that autumn had come. Autumn! Bedizened creatures, how odd that they should wait so long to bloom. But then poor Hilbert seemed now unlikelier than ever to bloom at all. Never. And this in spite of the fact that his present little expedition, which for the moment had come to so hapless yet serene a pause, just hinted that in a more favourable sphere and loaded up with some other kind of merchandise, he might have proved himself to be a really rabid go-getter.

The little expedition had been solely his own idea, too. Hilbert, in fact, had long had leanings towards literature. He was already the author of the quite recently published little volume of fancies, *pensées*, conceits, now in his bag. And so precisely mid-way were its contents between a respectable prose and a defensible verse that the harsh critics of an earlier era might have avowed that they had issued from a vacuum with the merits of neither. Hilbert's very few reviewers—still following a passing fashion to 'say it with flowers'—had been far more indulgent.

One of them, after a jocular sally (in July) at 'spring poets,' had referred to 'these, as doubtless we may assume, dainty first-fruits'; and another, after (possibly with the help of the printer) citing the title of the book as *Parlourings* instead of *Parleyings with Pegasus*, had pleasantly remarked that Mr Hilbert Winslow 'wielded a dainty and pensive quill.' This had been a no less welcome tribute for being purely metaphorical, since the pen Hilbert had that morning left at home on his dressing-table, between a rather decayed ivory-backed hair brush and an empty bottle of brilliantine, was an exceedingly bloated 'Swan.'

How odd that critiques as affable as these should have failed to sell a single copy of *Parleyings*. Even poems by Ellis, Currer, and Acton Bell had wooed three into the fold; and editors, of course, *must* know what is good for their readers! But then—though economy rather than foresight had counselled it—how fortunate that Hilbert had ordered only a hundred copies in all. 'I suppose it's the gilt,' his mother had remarked on seeing the binders' account, 'I suppose it's the gilt, darling, that makes it so expensive, but I am sure it deserves every penny.' Thirty of these Hilbert had squandered on the press. Three had gone to relatives, and twenty-two to friends and well-wishers—a phrase, alas! that for the literary novice is by no means equivalent to go-getter. And the family bookseller had taken twenty. Not on approval, of course, but, as he carefully explained, for 'sale or return.'

Within ten days, Hilbert was astounded to hear, this enterprising tradesman had disposed of the complete batch. And Hilbert had naturally asked for some description of his local patrons. At this the bookseller had looked a trifle confused. He had retrieved at last—but very vaguely—a tall, dark gentleman in spectacles; and then—'a lady, yes, a lady, sir.'

It was at mention of the lady that Hilbert's heart had sunk. Telepathy, perhaps. But although next morning he had peeped into his mother's bedroom and afterwards covertly surveyed the bookcase in her little sitting-room, he had actually detected only one copy of his little masterpiece. This was lying with her Prayer Book on the barley-sugar-legged walnut *prie-dieu* at her bedside, and its fly-leaf was adorned with his signature. 'I always *told* my beloved one, darling, that some day you would be famous; although I must say books never entered my head. I fancied perhaps something useful. Your Uncle Charles, you know, once went down in a diving-bell.'

But even if, in the abundance of her maternal heart, Hilbert's mother *had* acquired those nineteen copies, a little discreet questioning soon showed that she could not possibly have read them all. 'Knowing my precious boy, as I do,' she had assured him, 'there 's no need to *study* the book. Why, darling, I might have made up every word of it myself—though I should *never* have thought of the title! Let me see, in *which* story of Charles Dickens is it that that poor old Mr Pegasus is drowned?'

It needed only Hilbert's mastery of arithmetic to calculate that he had thus been left with twenty-four copies in all—copies stranded, as he feared, high and dry. So having decided that since the mountain showed no symptom of coming to Mahomet, Mahomet had better make the first advances, at intervals of a few days he had sallied out with the little brown bag which now shared with him the autumnal sunshine of his painted bench, and had already managed to dispose of ten of them. One on the seat of a bus, two in the corner of a tram, four on the shelves

of an unsuspecting second-hand bookseller, one on the verger—
a widower—of St Swithin's, who left it by an oversight on the
lectern, one on the counter of an obscure haberdasher's shop,
and two (in late dusk) pushed through a dentist's letter-box.
Like the young Benjamin Disraeli, all in his finery and plush,
and facing a discordant House, Hilbert had muttered to himself:
'Some day they *shall* read me.' By which he meant the fastidious few. The degradation of becoming a best-seller had
never even in fancy so much as darkened his mind.

Thus it came about that he had this morning set out bound
for a quarry a little farther afield—a populous town that boasted
no fewer than three booksellers—a town, it seemed, pining for
sweetness and light. Nevertheless he had twice failed to sell a
copy of his *Parleyings*, in spite of offering a very liberal discount.
And the third bookseller was so barbarous in appearance that he
had not even made the attempt. So he had given it to the boy.

Indeed, when it came to a question of *acquiring* a stock-in-
trade rather than of disposing of one, booksellers as a species
appear to be singularly busy and absent-minded men. They
would palm off on you a complete encyclopaedia in chaste
morocco without turning a hair; whereas the very notion of
purchasing even one copy of a *bibelot* seemed to threaten in-
solvency. To get the slightest attention from Mr A—a man
with thick and powerful spectacles precariously perched on a
broken nose—Hilbert had been compelled to buy a second-hand
copy in purple leather of *Poems of Passion* by Ella Wheeler
Wilcox—even though in business transactions passion is anathema and, unlike Sappho, Mrs Wilcox had always left him cold.

With Mr B, on the other hand, a little fussy man with a somewhat ragged black moustache, the purchase of a shilling shocker
had sufficed, Hilbert having no further stomach left for a rival
wooer of the Muses. In spite of the profit thus to be derived,
neither Mr A nor Mr B had consented to accept his commission.
'If you will *leave* a copy with me, sir, I will look it over and let
you know,' had been their reply—and in almost identical terms.
And Hilbert had with difficulty resisted the temptation to don
a false beard, return to the shop and persuade *this* busy B to sell
him his particular copy before he had had time to be as good as
his word.

Outside B's rather musty little shop Hilbert's four-year-old
Austin Seven, as if in umbrage at her master's ill-fortune, had

decided that she needed a rest-cure, and the railway had proved to be his quickest way home. Nevertheless every ounce of Hilbert's moral fibre and better nature had revolted at the notion of his ignominiously returning home with his four unwanteds. But how dispose of them? After all, *Parleyings with Pegasus* was his firstborn. Mere paternal affection alone shunned the temptation of leaving his offspring under the seat. It was of course his infants, not his literary masterpieces, that Jean-Jacques Rousseau had abandoned. There are degrees of consciencelessness.

What then was the alternative? Tracts being obsolete, the only literature nowadays bestowed gratis is the circular. There are Philistines who resent even these. It is a sad fact, Hilbert mused, that human nature should suspect a taint in anything that is given away—unless it is accompanied by tea or tobacco. The cost of circulars, he supposed, worked out at about ten a penny; whereas every single 3s. 6d. copy of his *Parleyings* had cost his mother 10s. 11·375d. net. He had done the sum himself.

None the less, the frigidity of Messrs A and B had only fanned the flame of his enthusiasm. In spite of all such rebuffs Hilbert had made no attempt to unbridle his Pegasus. There was plenty of sugar where the Parleyings had come from; and some day— Some Day—he would find himself in the saddle cantering gaily off to Mt Helicon. Nothing could exceed his assurance of this. Ever since he had been a fat little boy with flaxen finger-curls he had had a passion—undiluted, ineradicable—for putting himself into words—the very best words in the very best order.

So had William Shakespeare. Why, at this very moment there was scarcely an object around him which was not pleading for its real right setting: *The flaunting sunflower at the platform's brink ; The spidery arch that spans the wayside track ; Sadly I sat while Autumn's furtive rust.* Whithersoever his eye roamed his vocabulary coyly responded. *Mots justes*, like midges, fairly danced in his mind. Hilbert had quite recently decided that his next volume should be in verse: a poetry book. This would, he knew, be shockingly out of fashion. Rhymes were gone; punctuation was gone; verse, free or otherwise, need not nowadays even trouble to scan. But then stops for Hilbert had always been a stumbling-block, and their absence does, of course, keep any kind of verse from reading like mere prose. While as for rhymes, even a Petrarchan sonnet per morning would be child's

play without them. He would defer his decision concerning
these little trifles, in the assurance that he could dispense with
them at a moment's notice.

He could, too, no less safely postpone any premature effort to
put his *political* views into verse, until at any rate he had discovered what these were. At present any such phrase as Propaganda for the Amelioration and Solidarization of the Proletariat
positively scared him. It sounded as if life were made of the
spongiest india-rubber. Were even the Muses nowadays no
better than *bourgeoisie*? He pined to be clear about such
things; but might none the less in a year or two fall back on
being obscure if, meanwhile, other means of self-communication
had failed him.

Then, too, there was what was called the Problem of Sex.
From infancy Hilbert had fought shy of problems. And this
one? Could he not when necessary take it in his poetic stride?
Freud, after all, was only a foreigner; and his obsession one concerning which, he fancied—a flush suffusing his cheek the while
—if only he consented to delve a little, he was himself less
ignorant than un-'knowing.' There were candid Manuals, of
course. The broken-nosed Mr A had laid in a pile of them.
And he had a friend. . . . Besides, he had often vaguely felt that
so far at least as his notion of poetry was concerned, Sex—with
the capital, that is—was very little better than a dubious cul-
de-sac. The further you went in the longer it took you to get
out. Anyway a *blind* alley—like one's appendix. Caecum,
wasn't it called, which, provided that it just functions in the
usual way—*what* hideous words they secreted!—mattered no
more than any other human requisite. One's brains, say.
What's more, he was pretty confident that until any crisis
came, as with one's poor vermiform appendix itself, there was
no need to have it out—no, not with anybody! There was no
need at any rate for indecent *haste*. Besides, as yet, he felt, he
couldn't think very badly about life—not as yet. It had not
at any rate proved itself to be a positive sink—of anything.
Why not, then, repose for a little while upon the future? The
murmurous, heavy-bosomed sunflowers languishing at him from
across the gleaming metals exhibited not the faintest hint of
haste.

By and large, in fact, Hilbert was conscious at this serene and
happy moment of no particular urge or vocation to become a

'modern' poet—even if he could manage the technique. And that, of course, brought him back to the question whether poetry —of any kind even—was really wanted. Had it of recent years become a mere luxury, a sort of literary cosmetic? It certainly sometimes seemed so. And yet, in spite of mercenary booksellers, tepid reviewers, an invidious aunt, and retired uncles whose staple topic of conversation at afternoon tea was the moral necessity for a young man to be self-supporting, Hilbert didn't believe it. There must be *many* Hilberts still carrying on the smouldering torch! He had lived, comparatively speaking, laborious days. He had seldom toyed with any Neaera's hair. His electric lamp could frequently be seen burning long after midnight. When engaged in polishing his *pensées* had he not frequently even forgotten to touch his morning's glass of milk?: 'I'm sure, Hilbert dear, it's very unwise to compose even poetry on an empty stomach.' Why then had he failed? And here—not twelve inches away—was Mrs Wilcox in limp leather pleading to answer his questions! Passionately pleading. But, passionately or otherwise, he refused to pay her the faintest attention.

Anyhow, his own answer was No—a thousand times, No! This England had *not* forsworn herself, and not even calling her Britain would make her. Nothing should ever shake his rooted conviction that every boy and every gal that's born into this world alive must in due season and if given the opportunity, take to rhymes—and maybe even to *vers libre*—as naturally as a duck to water—or rather, as kittens take to cream. He had himself. Why, for centuries past every Society Beauty, every prime minister even, must have been bred up on *Goosey Gander*; and was there a labour leader in the land who had not taken *Little Jack Horner* to heart before he was five? It must be these sterilized, fossilized old grown-ups who are the offenders. Like William pears, humanity is apt to go sleepy with age, and no doubt it is education that is to blame. All ruts. A diet of indigestible facts—husks. What wonder we were all so repulsively alike? Possibly if nobody had been educated, the demand for poetry, and incidentally for his *Parleyings*, might have . . .

Here Hilbert paused. But he was not going to betray his sense of truth by any appeal to his own vanity. He would stick to his point. As scores of lady authors, and many of them titled lady authors, were continually proclaiming in the newspapers, every adult who has fallen in love, or felt homesick, or smiled at an infant, or bowed to the new moon—and what human crustacean can have evaded the complete quartet?—has momentarily at the least *been* a poet, however much he might resent the charge if he were challenged. Had he not seen his own family butcher—his right hand nonchalantly clasping a black three-cornered knife, its point embedded in his block—gazing pensively on and on out of his shop at the sunset, just as if the ensanguined clouds dappling the blue were as much of his own make as was the necklet of sausages dangling behind him on its rack?

No: Hilbert had complete faith in his fellow-creatures—a remnant at any rate; and here and now he was going to prove it justified. Why, of course, one can't *'make'* poets, since *every* human being is thus by Nature ready-made! This inspiring thought had actually and instantly brought him to his feet, bag in hand, though the signal was still steadily against him. He took a pace or two and sat down again, but only because he fancied the porter who a moment before had peered out of a little den at the other end of the other platform had heard his footsteps. His blue eyes glistened, his cheek paled a little. So swiftly the imagination flies that Hilbert had already betted himself an even five shillings that he would prove his thesis *four times over* before he got home that evening.

What is more, he vowed that if he failed, say, twice—no, say, thrice out of the four, he would give up all hope of Pegasus altogether. He would buy a sixpenny padlock and lock the stable up. He would let grass grow between its cobbles and house-leeks on its tiles. And it wouldn't matter a bit if now and then silly sentiment should persuade him to sit and snuff the equine atmosphere, to watch the sparrows, and to overhear an occasional thud of hoof on brick, or rattle of manger rope. For since Pegasuses are immortal, not even the S.P.C.A. could inquire why you had immured one particular specimen out of the light of the morning and had not even supplied it with a bottle of old hay.

It was the simplest thing in the world, this project of Hilbert's. He had already dabbled in the experiment. It was merely, for one brief afternoon, to play Paul Pry to the world at large. Englishmen (he wasn't quite so certain about Englishwomen) are so unaccustomed to talking to strangers that when they do, they are far more inclined to ease their hearts of all their ills, to say out really what they not only mean but feel—to confide, to confess, to tell secrets. And once the heart itself begins to talk—you simply cannot help it—*poetry*, just its gold *dust*, is bound to follow. Your tongue takes to itself cadences, tunes, even metres which are positively lyrical! That is why money-lenders, stockbrokers, schoolmasters, bookmakers, and most officials are so prosaic—they live in their heads and abandon their feelings. Who ever heard of a tax-inspector or a gas collector making up rhymes? Why did cabinet ministers so seldom resort in their speeches to blank verse? Simply because their *hearts* were not in their work.

'Emotion remembered in tranquillity'—yes, at his very first chance Hilbert would get the beggars to talk—of their feelings, of their pasts—preferably of their hidden pasts. Then he would wait. And the very first syllable which even a neutral would agree so much as hinted that the speaker had even the slightest claim to be representative of the tiny island that had been responsible for the greatest, noblest, deepest, oddest, crankiest, imaginativest, essentialest poetry in the whole history of the world—the very moment those lips, bucolic or otherwise, audibly proved themselves to have been even touched with (even a fading cinder of) the divine fire, well, that would be a definite proof of Hilbert's thesis. And for immediate reward out would come one of the four copies of his *Parleyings* now reposing in his bag, and the first quarter, the first twenty-five per cent (as Messrs A and B would prefer to call it) of his good deed for the day would have been done.

It is true, of course, that poetry *needs* no reward. But does even the poet himself need a Neaera if he is already in blissful possession of an Amaryllis? And it was not until a full moment after this happy metaphor had occurred to him that Hilbert wondered if it had any bearing on his argument.

He might, of course, encounter only Scotchmen. And they, in spite of being the strident sponsors of Burns and other local bards, are so thrifty by nature that they appear in general to keep to statements like 'Ech,' or 'Ye dinna,' or 'Och, mon.' Whereas Irishmen delight in blarney, *and* have a poetry all their own. As for the Welsh, well, Hilbert had never really penetrated, so to speak, beneath the beards of the Druids. He would, then, have to be cautious.

But what a lark it would be! From first to last in his experiences of private publishing he had never dreamed of such a reward. What's more, there was charity in it. He was going to give—even to give himself—away!

Yet again that distant porter had peered out of his lair in his direction. No doubt he was looking for the 4.10. And rightly so, since at this moment it was 4.44; and perhaps he wanted his tea. So did Hilbert. But he had been so intent on other cravings that he had failed to notice it. This time, however, the porter had not gone in again; on the contrary, he was sallying out. Why, thought Hilbert, watching him, is a green-glassed lantern so magical an object in full daylight? Was it because, like poetry itself, it is of no immediate use? And why, in a dear medieval little wayside station like this, where heavy luggage must be scarce, had the porter bow legs?

He was crossing the line, lantern in hand, as blindly and deliberately as even Destiny paces on. And Hilbert, as childishly as ever, loved crossing the line. He envied him. And, yes—he was coming this way. How awful! Hilbert was so utterly isolated that he would be morally bound to speak to him, and that might entail a protracted conversation. He had yet again realized that he detested talking to strangers. Or, rather, he detested the thought of talking to strangers; particularly strangers engaged in really practical occupations— ploughmen, carpenters, hedgers and ditchers, grooms, plumbers. They always made him feel so absurdly ignorant and what is called supererogatory. Well, one thing, the porter's peculiar fiddle-face resembled a sexton's lantern, he was well over middle age, and looked rheumatic and taciturn.

'*What* a lovely afternoon!' exclaimed Hilbert. The porter slowly and cautiously surveyed his surroundings, high and low. He reminded Hilbert of a bivalve at taste of salt water gently chinkening open its shell.

'It is *that*, sir,' he replied at length. 'We usually get this kind of weather here.'

'Really!' said Hilbert. 'Really! Perhaps one doesn't notice it enough. Of course, as it's so very quiet—I mean when there are no trains about. . . .'

'Ay,' said the porter, his black eyes firmly fixed on the almost maidenly smile of the young man, 'ay, that's part of it.'

'Yes,' said Hilbert.

'Quiet!' repeated the porter. 'There was a gennelman here

not long ago who said that looking under that bridge was like a picture frame. And if you make allowances, sir, so it is. Sometimes it's just the same; and sometimes it's quite different.'

Hilbert stooped a little to peer through under the bridge—green-bright meadows, changing woods, the distant hill. But so dark, so vacantly pitched were the eyes of the porter as he surveyed it himself that Hilbert refrained even from nodding his head.

'Quiet!' repeated the porter. 'Look at them sparrows there. You can sometimes catch the tic-tac of their claws on the metals as they hop it over.'

Hilbert listened. 'No,' he said, 'I can't.'

The porter smiled—a slow, tranquil smile, like the shifting chequer of leaves on a tomb in a churchyard. 'You have only just come, sir,' he said. 'And perhaps it's *time* as does it. But what, now, they varmints pick *up* among them flints,' he continued, 'considering I've never seen nobody much *feeding* hereabouts, needs an eye I've never got. And I've watched 'em hours at a stretch till I've felt my own nose sharpening. I expex they know best. But when it comes to they pied wag-tails after the *flies*! Tic-tac? Not them. Lor' bless you, they are that dainty and easy in the air you'd think they'd gone to school to their own shadows.'

Hilbert eyed him. Hans Andersen, indeed: the horsy creature was talking like a book.

The immense bulbous hob-nailed boots were now less than half an inch from the edge of the platform. He appeared to be quite indifferent to an habitual danger. Indeed he turned and spat very carefully on to the track, then eyed his companion again. 'She won't keep you mooning much longer, sir,' he reassured him. 'You can hear her low-like humming on the metals like them evening bumbledores even when she's a good three miles still to come.'

He spat again, turned away, and his bow legs were steadily carrying him off. Hilbert had been listening, but only half heeding, he was so intent on the cavernous face. The next instant his mind had reverted to the 'picture frame,' and to the tic-tac, and the iron rumour of the 'she' he was awaiting. How intensely odd—incredible! Why, one of his favourite chapters in his *Parleyings* had been all about birds—and in a prose he had fondly hoped was not wholly out of keeping with them. He

had referred in it to William Davies's unforgettable robin—
'half-way up his legs in snow'—to Lesbia's sparrow, and Skelton's
too, but he had clean forgotten the wagtail—nimble Sallie Dish-
washer—and had never himself even noticed her shadow; no,
nor the tic-tac either. And if such little things as these were not
at least on the way to *poetry* he was a Double Dutchman and
deserved to write it in his native tongue. To think that Heaven
should have consented to reward him so swiftly! The spring
locks of his little bag flicked back with a spirited clap, his hand
dived in, he clasped a copy of his *Pegasus*, grass-green as Flora's
mantle, and hastened after the porter.

'*Would* you,' he cried, a little breathlessly, calling after him,
'accept this? A—a keepsake?'

The porter turned, opened his mouth, and looked at the book—
as if he were Robinson Crusoe contemplating a powder-puff that
had been washed up on to his beach. Then he dusted his large
right hand on his green corduroy trouser-leg, and held it out.

'Why, sir,' he said, 'that's an uncommon kind thought of
yours, and very welcome too, I'm sure. My daughter, now;
she's none too clever in her intellects, poor dear. She'll take
a deal of pleasure in it, even though she keeps only to the covers.
If there's one thing that keeps her smiling, sir, it's pretty
colours. Green in particular. And eyes like hers, watching out
quiet in the porch most fine mornings, don't seem to cotton much
to many words; though what she don't say, sir, would be a sight
better worth hearing than most.'

'No,' said Hilbert. 'Yes, I mean.' It was an awkward pause,
but the porter did not seem to be indulging either in sentiment
or irony. He continued to clasp the dainty little book between
grimy finger and thumb as gently as Cupid a daisy; but found
no more words to say. Conscious of looking a little hot, damp,
and diffident, Hilbert nodded, smiled, and returned to shut his
bag. One from four leaves only three, he announced to himself.
The sum reminded him of the Young Man with the Cream Tarts,
though he rejoiced that the wager he had made with himself did
not entail his having to *eat* his little books.

A peculiar faint drumming, as of a prodigious harp-string, had
begun furtively to resound. The porter was ding-donging an
old bell. 'She,' then, was probably not more than a mile away
now. Yes, here she came, puffing out delirious clots of wool and
advancing on the toy railway station as meditatively as a

gigantic snail. If Hilbert took a few lessons from the porter at Bovey Fausset he might at last succeed in detecting her at double the distance. 'Man's senses,' suddenly exclaimed a small dry voice from deep down beyond his sub - sub - consciousness, 'man's senses are his highway to the infinities.' Hilbert determined to make a note of that. Meanwhile he was hoisting himself into his chosen compartment.

When at last he had settled himself into his corner, and—his eye on the revolving scenery beyond the window—had paused long enough to make the survey a little more polite, he ventured to glance at his only companion. This old gentleman looked about seventy. He was frail but fibrous, and consisted of a series of narrow cylinders that were all but oblongs; a high, narrow head, a long, narrow body, and two right-angled legs in black trousers. His waistcoat was faintly speckled, and his little white cambric bow was like that of an old-fashioned waiter. He was reading a dumpy leather-bound book, and appeared to be as far away from the rocking clatter of his surroundings as a sleeping infant would be during a performance of *Götterdämmerung*.

Did Jesuit priests ever wear speckled waistcoats? Hilbert didn't know—indeed he knew very little about the society, though he had often coveted the privilege of meeting one of its members. They were always aware, he had somehow divined, of exactly what they were talking about. How motionlessly the old gentleman's eyelids hung over his shuttling eyes. The lean-knuckled, blue-veined hand clasping the book never stirred. 'Pious—no question,' Hilbert was whispering to himself, 'but a thoroughly good sort, I should guess. Austere, though. He looks,' he added a moment afterwards, 'as dry as an old biscuit.' It might be exceedingly questionable manners—but dared he venture?

Nothing venture, nothing win. And though the porter had been a purely gratuitous godsend, Hilbert couldn't expect an average of one disposed-of volume every quarter of an hour, even though less than sixty minutes would see him home again.

He leaned forward as winningly as might an uncommonly good-natured barmaid. 'I am so very sorry, sir, to interrupt you, but could you tell me if this is the *up* train?'

The old gentleman's good angel first gently composed her wings; he himself then lifted his eyelids, lowered his book, and glanced at the young man—out of small, bright, blue-grey eyes, as keen as a kestrel's. He watched him a moment, and a tiny wrinkle showed at the corner of one of them.

'*Up* ?' he repeated. 'Let me see. That's going north, isn't it? Yes, and the sun is descending on your side. Observe the shadows. I haven't any doubt in the world we are both of us on our way *up*! And that, I sometimes endeavour to remind myself, is the way I once hoped to be going. Alas! I can be perilously absent-minded.' He had smiled outright now, as if in private confabulation with his little jest. Still, there had been that in his 'up' and in the wintry twinkle that accompanied it, which had set Hilbert speculating. It was a kind of Sesame. He peered into the cavern thus revealed, and though he could see but a little way, evidently it was neatly kept. There was a vista. But had the old gentleman passed his test?

Now, poetry, he was thinking to himself, depends at least in part on condensing, without, possibly, any clear excuse for it, a wide metaphorical view out of some tiny morsel of quite commonplace fact. 'Bird thou never wert,' for example; and 'Of his bones are coral made.' That being so, the *up*, surely, was just on the mark. This decision, however, left the question whether its author—who was in every line and accent and feature as unquestionably a firm believer in the virtues of a sound prose as the 'Great Bear' himself—could possibly care to accept what poor Hilbert was tempted there and then to label, say, a hybrid medium—his *Parleyings*? For both their sakes Hilbert wished to be considerate. But his fingers had already strayed towards the catch of his little brown bag.

'Thank you very much,' he said. 'Very much indeed. It is always a—a relief to know, to be sure one is not in the wrong train—when travelling, I mean. But I am not a traveller in the other sense—not *commercially*, I mean, nor perhaps . . . It's only that—well, that a friend of mine has suggested . . .' His eye faltered and fell under the old gentleman's steady scrutiny. 'I was wondering, sir, if you would do me the kindness of accepting—*this* ?'

He snapped open his bag and withdrew the first copy that presented itself. 'It's—it's only *prose*, even if that, I'm afraid.'

'You are exceedingly kind, sir,' said the old gentleman, bestowing on Hilbert a formal but courteous nod of the head as he took the book between his lean old fingers. 'Thank you. I am not a great reader, indeed have little leisure for it, but when the opportunity comes I shall be most happy to peruse the book.'

At which, heedless of the blush which he was aware had mantled his brow, Hilbert managed to retrieve his fib. 'As a matter of fact,' he blurted, 'it was *not* exactly a friend. I—I mean—I, that is, am the author. It is'—he had sighed in spite of himself—'it is my first—er—effort.'

'Indeed!' said the old gentleman. 'That makes the gift doubly welcome. Until this moment we had never met, and now, in what remains of this life'—he tapped the book with his finger—'we shall never be parted.'

Goodness, Intelligence, and their younger sister, Courtesy—here, Hilbert decided, were the three Graces all at play in this one aged and quiet face; and, for Dorian porch to the temple within, those strait, keen lines between the eyes.

For some little time, as his new acquaintance had at once resumed his reading, Hilbert sat watching the passing country-side—sheaves heavy with harvest in the stubble fields, green-feathered 'roots' in others; whirring flights of autumn birds. Another year was emptying itself away. We plough the fields —and scatter.

'And now, in what remains of this life, we shall never be parted'—well, if that was not a wholly non-prosaic welcome to a greenhorn little book from the trembling hands of a novice less than a third of one's own age—well. . . . Nevertheless Hilbert felt the least bit uneasy. Not at the difficulty of deciding whether what is non-prosaic is *per se* poetical; but because he had not confided to the old gentleman *all* the facts of the case. But while he was pondering on how delicate a task that might have proved, his head nodded, chin on chest, and he fell asleep.

He awoke so sluggishly that he was aware of a voice declaiming on and on long before he had decided whether or not to open his eyes.

'What *I* say is, treat 'em rough and ready and they'll lick your boots. Pamper them, and they won't give you not so much as a Thank-you. But no; Aggie never was the one to take advice. Never. Not her. In at one ear and out at the other; though, if she hasn't had her lesson now—pretty heavy on the stomach and her whole life in ashes, as you might say—I'm not the one to rub the salt in. Straight up from the country, fare and all, that girl had come—somewhere from down Swindon way, so she *said*. And before she 'd been in the house a week, in came m' lady from the Pictures at getting on for one in the morning with her No. 2 in young men beside her as large as life, and she, I give you *my* word, dressed up to the knocker and as bold as brass in Aggie's blue hat and her best glassy kids. There —on her *feet*, mind you!'

'Go on!' murmured a second unseen speaker, apparently hampered with adenoids.

'I should just about say she did go on! And her husband sitting there with his pipe between his teeth as if butter wouldn't melt in his mouth. Not much. Swinging his legs and yawning his head off. And *him* reely and truly the founting head of all the trouble—brazen trollop. Not that I wouldn't allow it was chiefly Aggie's *fault*. As you make your bed in this world, so you must lay on it. Spoiled, that was what *that* girl was, like the one that had gone before her. Gas stove fresh from the works, Bristle's sweeper, pink-edged kitchen crockery and a spring mattress all complete—I never heard the likes of it. What things are coming to I *don't* know. What 's more, he defended her, put in *his* spoke, he did. "No more than a child; up from the country"—that kind of smooth-me-down. Child! Country!—ask *me*; a chit with rouge and lipstick all over her face, and that pasty-skinned you could have seen the smirk on her sly cat's features without a candle in the dark!'

'Go on! And that young feller and all!'

'Yes, and so they did, all three of 'em, hammer and tongs, though as for him he was nothing but a blind and soon made himself scarce. As for what Aggie thought of that Albert of hers, she kept that for upstairs and the door shut—not for *that* baggage to be listening in to. A bit of her mind Aggie gave him, too, though I will say she hasn't too much to spare. And when the pair of them come down next morning, lo and behold! nothing but what remained of the slut's meat breakfast on the kitchen table—meat, mind you—and the girl herself gone, lock, stock, and barrel, and Aggie's best set of real silk undies gone with her.'

'Silk! Real! Lor'! I never! Go *on*!'

'Nor didn't Aggie. Fare paid and faked-up references, until I expect she 's got to Buckingham Palace by now—or Holloway. And that angelic-looking in spite of her sauce, you might have been staring straight into the Garden of Eden every time she opened her mouth.'

'Go *on*!'

'Yes, and ask *me*, that's what kept *him* quiet. Give a man a face to look at, and the devil himself might just as well throw in his checks for all what he thinks is nothing but envy and slander. That ended it. He couldn't stand it any longer, and she went back to her mother, Aggie did, and to that poky upstairs dressmaking business all over again. But it's that pore little Amy *my* heart bleeds for. Pore mite, with her saucer eyes shivering there on the brink! Better her daddy safe in his grave, if I had my choice! It's my belief we're here because we are put; and you might as well be a cabbage as think you have got any say about it. I never did hold with it, and never shall.'

But this time the second unseen refrained from expressing any view at all. She hadn't even invited her friend to 'go on.'

Hilbert, having rapidly attempted to digest this second-hand miscellaneous slice of human experience, opened his eyes and peered out in the direction of the voice at what now occupied the further corner of the carriage, whence alas, his tranquil old Jesuit, while he himself was dreaming, had silently departed. Thus motionless, he explored yet another stranger.

She was a woman dressed up in what Hilbert supposed to be cretonne, and that of a bold and remarkable design, and she wore pink stockings. She had a long face and high knee bones, an eye like a suffering, if not long-suffering, and contemptuous hen, and a mouth that told an inexhaustible tale of inward woe and outward wailing. Beside her stood a tall gaping basket, woven of gaudy bast into a pattern that would intoxicate a Hottentot. Its maw gaped as omnivorously as a shark's.

Now Hilbert, above all things, wished to be fair—to himself, to his apple-green firstfruits, to humanity in general, and above all to the Muses. Possibly because the talk he had just heard had been poured into his ear while he sat between sleeping and waking, he could recall a good deal of it. And if style is the man himself, certainly *its* was a large part of this lady. Like a humble-bee in a garden, he hardly knew where to alight first. On Aggie's blue hat or the devil's checks? Or on the fat open-mouthed young blonde squatting squarely in front of her—concerning whom the merest fleeting glimpse had disclosed that she must have very few clothes on?

Hilbert was fraily human enough too to be bowled over even by the most casual of references to the Garden of Eden, and he narrowed his inward eye a little at recollection of the 'pore mite's' — little Amy's — 'brink.' He felt disquieted. His chapter on 'Images' had suddenly in memory fallen a little flat. His old Jesuit had packed a lifetime into a word of two letters, the word 'up.' Aggie's friend preferred abandon, and so was far nearer the cauliflower in effect than the cabbage. But *was* there any connection between cauliflowers and poetry?

What would Mrs Wilcox have said? Far too much, he was afraid. And already on nimble wing he had sped off to Matthew Arnold, to his 'criticism of life,' and was reassured.

In his precise pernickety fashion Hilbert had once been inquiring enough to look up this word 'criticism' in a formidable dictionary, and had then discovered that Matthew Arnold had by no means meant just *criticism*—niggling, gnawing, fretting, shredding, ravelling out, the activities of moth and rust—but discernment, insight. He had memorized the poet's very words: 'Criticism,' he was gently repeating to himself, while a simmering silence continued to prevail between the two amazons now watchfully aware that the grey-flannel-suited young man in the corner was awake—'Criticism is a disinterested endeavour to learn and propagate the best that is known and thought in the world.' But 'the best,' mused Hilbert, surely, of its *kind*?

He ventured on another peep at Aggie's friend. And their glances met: a glance on the one side like a venomous dart from the blow-pipe of a man of Borneo, out of an eye bead-like, reddish, hot, and fiery, which had instantly transfixed as if with a needle his own round orb of a pale and pensive blue. It was Hilbert's that faltered; but not before he had decided that of her kind she had lavished on him a draught not only black, but piping hot and strong.

The heat, the violence, the conviction, the expansiveness of her remarks! That hugger-mugger stage, the domestic drama, the ferocity. *Should* he try poems, after all? 'Go on!' indeed. He would willingly have paid the full price for a middle stall in the front row of Covent Garden if only she would consent to go on in the same strain—until the end of his journey. And surely, wouldn't sweet William, Swan of Avon, have simply revelled in her fumes? 'Stay put!' She! Never. But heavens alive!—the train was slowing up. The lady had swivelled round her henlike head straight at him, and had clutched at the handles of her basket as if in sheer defiance of the Universe. In another moment she would be gone—for ever. But meanwhile she was at it again.

'What I say is, trewth's trewth; and I don't care what eavesdroppers perking their ears up in corners unbeknown and shamming doggo may have heard me. A woman may work her fingers to the bone for a man and him not so much as a Thank-you. But Aggie—*she* go back—never! Though she's no more of what I should call female *charm* than a tallow candle.'

She had risen; the train had stopped. There was no time now even for a word of congratulation, let alone a convincing decision. Aggie's friend's pink, loose-mouthed young companion had already squeezed lingeringly past his knees and was alighting. The bast bag yawned like Limbo a few inches under his nose. With a triumphant, contrite, glancing gaze up into the woman's constricted visage, and with lightning rapidity, Hilbert opened *his* little bag, extracted yet one more copy of the *Parleyings*—his third—and slipped it in. Could enterprise go further?

Well, there may well have been a streak of the troubadour in his hereditary make-up; it accounted, perhaps, for the fact that his 'purple patches' were occasionally of a purple a little loud. As the wheels of his carriage began more rapidly to revolve again, he stood up at the window, smiled charmingly at both parties, and—raised his hat.

Decisions are always reviving. Refreshed after his nap, alert and alone, he returned to his corner. And there, amid the rattle of glass and wood and metal—the long-shadowed September sunshine beyond his window, rusty gold on sheaf and stack and thatch and pensive beechwood—he burst out laughing. Never for a moment had he dreamed that the mere circulation of his *Parleyings* could require such critical skill. He was three up, one to play, and (he glanced at his watch) there was still thirty minutes to go. Why, he could probably have disposed of the complete edition on a five-shilling fare in two days' railway travelling. Much would depend on what happened to his 'fourth.' At which, as if he had positively beckoned it with his finger, the name-board of the station he had but a

moment before left behind him, flashed back into his consciousness. His own was three behind it! He had overslept.

By nature impulsive, Hilbert at once seized his bag, tugged
at the brim of his hat, and prepared to alight; and then, seeing
that the train was bumping along at not much less than twenty
miles an hour, he sat down again. When he did get out—a few
minutes afterwards—the only human being in sight (after he
had explained his sad case to the ticket collector) was a curate
—a strapping young man, with lips like a cherry, and the assured
air of a juvenile archdeacon. How odd; two of a cloth, if not
of a kidney, in less than an hour! Still, if the Church went on
like this all would be well.

The cherry effect—Hilbert felt assured, as he stalked his latest
prey up the wooden steps and over the bridge—was only skin
deep. The young man walked with decision, and so held his
head as if he were dead certain it was brimmed with brains of
an inestimable value. But yet it was a head that looked a little
unpromising—for Hilbert's purposes. A trace of the Byronic,
perhaps, but none of the Wordsworthian. Its mere shape and
carriage suggested that it was seldom closely connected with its
companion piece, the heart. Its owner might no doubt be bound
for a New Jerusalem, but what little Hilbert detected of it hadn't
the least resemblance to Blake's.

Hilbert began to fear it might be as easy to extract plums
from plain duff as what he wanted from this athletic young
ecclesiastic. Still, *dum spiro spero*, though he must waste not
a moment.

The curate had seated himself, and from a side-pocket had
extracted a copy of a bluish-covered magazine. Hilbert passed
him by, paused, wheeled, coughed.

'I 'm so sorry; but I have been taken on,' he said, 'by mistake.
I went to sleep, in fact. This *is* the platform for Dunmow
Downs, isn't it?'

The young man in holy orders looked up. 'Absolutely,' he
said. 'I am expecting—er—a friend by the next one in, and
my own station is the one before it. Bad luck.'

'Not at all,' said Hilbert, continuing to smile because he was
listening so hard. 'It 's this drowsy autumn weather.'

'Yes,' said the young stranger, whose jacket and trousers and
nattily tailored 'vest' were *all* of pepper and salt, and who, from

dog-collar to black brogue shoes, was as neat as a new altar vase, 'it *is* a bit close. Thunder, perhaps. I always wake *myself* by knocking my skull on the window frame once for each station I have to go. It's infallible. But then, when *I* go to sleep I always intend to; and I never dream.'

'Gracious Heavens!' groaned Hilbert inwardly. He surveyed the choice shaven face with ill-concealed consternation. He must try another tack. 'One misses so much, too,' he went on seductively, 'even if one does. Dream, I mean. That lovely bit of landscape, you remember, with the pewits and the old mill, between here and Bewley Marshes. And *especially*'—he stooped forward a little—'especially when it is getting towards evening, and the sun is low.' The very cadence of the words was an anodyne and a spell.

At this the young man eyed Hilbert steadily, and eyed him whole. Then he slowly refolded his magazine, replaced it in his pocket, and said: 'Yes. I suppose nice scenery *is* a pleasant adjunct to railway travelling—but I haven't much time for it myself.'

'No,' breathed Hilbert, and nodded. 'Yes,' he added, 'a great adjunct. And now the swallows will soon be flown.'

'Odd beggars, aren't they?' remarked the curate. 'All that irrational journey just to come back! Purely mechanistic, you know; it's merely the light that does it; not even the weather. Only the other day I happened to pick up a scientific periodical, or rather a quasi-scientific periodical—*The Aviarian,* you know —and some old Lincolnshire windbag was saying . . .'

The ensuing soliloquy, which ranged from natural or quasi-natural history to—in Hilbert's modest opinion—completely unnatural socialism, lasted exactly five and a half minutes. And the moment his new acquaintance had warmed up, he needed no stoking.

Quite the reverse, for when in desperation Hilbert had managed to interejaculate: 'But I do sometimes feel, you know, that being absolutely broke and *not* on the dole merely because one is not a sweep or a stoker or a bricklayer, and being so vilely harassed and harried that one becomes half daft and physically *sick* with——'

'Speaking for myself,' shouted the curate, 'there is absolutely *no* silly trouble or ailment of body or mind—or heart, *ha, ha,* either—that cannot be cured by a cold bath.'

'Yes; and even life itself,' Hilbert had faintly murmured. To which, with an inhalation that seemed to have exhausted the air for yards around them, his companion had retaliated with: '*Life*, you say! Why, as for *life* . . .' and on he went.

It was soon as much as Hilbert could do to refrain from listening. If the sea—sad prospect—consisted solely of sand, then this electric young cleric—at least on his favourite topics —talked like a spring tide.

But it is not, Hilbert was dolefully reflecting, from sand of this nature that Poesy's buds of Sharon raise their gentle heads. He had had too much luck at the word 'Go!'; and now wind and weather were failing him. His little bag was three copies lighter, but by yet another not quite light enough; and how much heavier was his heart!

Four minutes before his self-allotted time was up a train rolled into the station. And yet—such are the oddities of human destiny—until its guard's van with screeching brakes jangled into view, Hilbert hadn't the faintest notion that it was bringing with it the strangest and blessedest fraction of his future life on earth. Its last but one grained-box compartment proved to contain the 'er—a friend' to whom it seemed, cen- turies ago, the curate had airily referred. And at one glance at its only occupant he was lost. Everything in the world, in Time and in Eternity, if not perhaps forgiven, was utterly forgotten.

She was standing at the open window, looking out, but not as if she had ever entirely desisted from looking *in*—an oval face with highish cheek-bones, and eyes and mouth from which a remote smile was now vanishing as softly and secretly as a bird enters and vanishes into its nest. A moment of dazzling vertigo had swept over Hilbert's being. That mystery of age- long severance and incredible reunion and recognition! Where . . . when . . . had they met before? Only Heaven could have told him, and he had no need to know. In a flash of acute foreboding he had instantly scanned the eight ungloved fingers that clasped the window sash. That once almost meaningless 'er—a *friend*' had suddenly echoed in his heart like a knell. But no; every one of the eight was ringless—every single one. He turned his head away, as if momentarily exhausted yet unspeakably revived.

'Ah, there you are, Sis!' the curate had now breezily

announced, 'and *only* twelve and a half minutes late! . . . *What* was that about Karl Marx I was saying just now before I was interrupted . . . ?' His voice, like that of a Bull of Bashan haranguing his subservient heifers, had come booming again over his shoulder towards Hilbert—and Hilbert, as meekly as a dove, had followed him in.

Seated opposite brother and sister, almost forgetting to breathe, and in a panic of spirit that was past all mundane concerns, he forgot who he was, where he was, what: his bet, Messrs A and B, his Jesuit, Aggie, and even his little bag and the Muses. His one and only wish in this strange world was that the peculiarly disguised young Good Samaritan in the opposite corner should continue his discourse—his dessication and disposal of Syndicalism, the National Recovery Act, Major Douglas, dictatorships, Nazism, Aryanism, and every other *ism* —just *ad infinitum*. When he stopped, the train would have stopped and—well, she would be gone. Meanwhile, to that vibrant, lusty 'Oxford' voice, an occasional faint 'Yes,' or a much fainter 'No,' was proving no more of an obstruction than a pebble is to a cataract.

What *she* was thinking of, or rather, not *thinking* of, Hilbert hadn't the faintest notion. And yet, such is the inflammability of the imagination, but one single glance into this fair serious face had sufficed him for the vernal stirrings of a latter-day *Paradiso* (and that in *terza rima*) to which even the long and hairy ear of Fleet Street would be compelled to incline. But now, alas! as he had forlornly foreseen, since the train had stopped, the voice had stopped, and so had his own semi-conscious 'cerebration.'

'Well, Miss Mute, and what do *you* say?' The young curate had bawled his second mocking challenge at his Griselda-like sister as if it were a bone to a dog. And she, as if to be serious was a refuge for everything worth having in a world so noisy and exclamatory and absurd, turned not to her brother, but to Hilbert. She sat there, quite still, for a full moment, one hand resting lightly on either side of her lap, and then, smiled. A volley of the quasi-archest and hollowest ecclesiastical laughter followed.

'Oh, *she*!—she never says anything!' the young man had assured his fellow-traveller, and—with a breezy 'Good day to you!'—he was gone.

Left alone for the fourth time since, hot and panting, he had galloped up into Bovey Fausset station, Hilbert drew his brown bag a little closer. It contained at this moment, apart from his Wilcox and his other shocker, that one forlorn copy of his *Parleyings*. And this now would never, never, never leave his possession. He might perhaps get another copy exquisitely bound in green tooled lambskin, its margins edged with a tiny design of doves and daisies, just in the remote hope that destiny would give him one more chance. But that copy would have nothing whatever to do with his bet, which by a niggardly twenty-five per cent had now, it seemed, been irretrievably lost.

For now not only was his time up, but, since he had to be honest with himself, if only for his old Jesuit's sake, the *terms* and conditions of his wager had been poetry '*audibly* proved.' And she—she had said nothing, not a word. And of course, strictly speaking, Thomas Gray's 'mute . . . Milton' was a contradiction in terms. Hilbert could quite easily have explained all this to her—if only she had been there to explain it to! Meanwhile he had realized also that there is a goddess whose name is Silence, and that it is in her light and loveliness that the buds of Sharon break into bloom.

'You see,' he was patiently explaining to himself, as he pulled the bell in the old eighteenth-century porch of his mother's house, for he had forgotten his latchkey, 'you see what is *called* poetry is merely a trying to put into words what can, of course, never, never be really *said*.'

A tiny barking like the remote jangling of Chinese temple bells had greeted him from afar; and a voice no less silvery had thereupon expostulated: 'Silence, Pym! You naughty, foolish Pym, don't you know who *that* is! And now go and tell the poet that he is exactly forty minutes late for tea, bad boy!' But Hilbert was too deep in thought to have heeded this familiar greeting. He had gently closed the door. 'Never,' he added *sotto voce*, as he hung up his hat. '*Never*, I am afraid.'

From *The Wind Blows Over*.

SAMBO AND THE SNOW MOUNTAINS

SAMBO'S *great*-grandfather had been a king in his own country, though it was only a small country. Sambo's *grand*father was brought to the White Man's Land by a missionary, whose name was Grimble, the Rev. Silas Makepeace Grimble. He had been born in Aberdeen. Sambo's *father*, after being Mr Grimble's eldest son's valet *and* coachman, set up in business as a barber. But though he merrily did his best, he couldn't get enough customers, either for hair-cutting, singeing, shampooing, or shaving. He would sometimes sit for hours in his empty shop beside the basin, staring out into the sunny street. So at last he was compelled to pull down the blind, put up the shutters, and take down his pole; and he soon afterwards died; and was laid to rest beside his beloved Dinah.

That leaves Sambo. Sambo was *Dr* Grimble's page-boy— Dr Grimble being the Rev. Silas's great-nephew. The doctor lived in a tall brown house made of wood. It had three Lombardy poplar trees in front of it and honeysuckle grew over the porch. Sambo had many duties. With his twenty-one little silver buttons in front of his tunic, and a little peak behind over his tight trousers, he used to open the door to his master's patients and show them into his waiting-room. It was a small but cheerful room with mosquito-screens at the windows, black and white oilcloth on the floor, a picture over the fireplace, and a lovely fall of coloured horsehair piled up in the grate beneath, all through the summer. This cascade hid the ugly bars of the grate. So in summer there was no need for Sambo to blacklead them.

Sambo also helped his master to mix his medicines. When the doctor had put the drugs into the bottle, Sambo added the water; when the doctor had rolled out his pills, Sambo put them into the pill-boxes. By means of a large stick of red sealing-wax and a little blue gas-jet, he used to seal down the paper after he had wrapped up the bottles and boxes. He enjoyed the sealing-wax part of his work far better than the bottle-washing—in a small square leaden sink under a tiny brass tap.

All this was in the early afternoon. When the bottles had been neatly wrapped and numbered, Sambo used to put them into his basket and carry them off to his master's patients. Sometimes he had to walk one mile, sometimes three, sometimes even five—and right into the country. The time so taken depended on how many candy shops, other boys, performing animals, street musicians, dog-fights, and other pleasures or dangers he encountered on his way to and fro. So long as he was home again at his master's house by six, all was well. In the evening he waited on the doctor while he ate his supper, and this the doctor did very quickly. Sambo brought him his grog about nine, and then went to bed.

On the whole, Sambo was happy, though until he became *un*-happy he had not noticed it much. Though he scampered with beating heart at sound of his master's call, he admired the reddish hair that stood in a little wall above his forehead, his gold spectacles, and handsome watchchain. He had enough to eat, time to be lazy in, and a truckle bed with a flock pillow in a little box-room under the roof. There was only one thing against him. He was black. He was as black as all his ancestors. He was as black as a bale of velvet, as a cellar with no windows in it, as a chimney full of soot.

He might not himself have much noticed this if the pale-faced boys of the town were not always reminding him of it—particularly a pug-nosed little rascal called William who was page to a dentist of the odd name of Tooth: Mr Tooth. This William, whenever he met Sambo—partly because he was jealous of his buttons (which were silver), and even of his two-lidded basket (which was covered with mottled American cloth), but mostly because he knew no better—would yell at sight of him: 'Yah! Blackamoor! Yah! tar-face! Yah! you little grinning bandy-legged monkey-jibbed lump of ebony! Off the streets with you! Streets is for white men!'

At this Sambo, pretending not to have heard him, would at once cross the road. White or black or coffee-coloured, it was beneath him, he told himself, to be seen fighting with a dentist's boy. But he knew in his heart he was afraid of William, and he crossed the road. Still, it was chiefly his black skin that was now in Sambo's mind. And *now* it troubled him not only because of his enemies, the street boys, but for his own private sake also. After all, he knew that the rest of him, what was inside, was little different even from his master's. And even his skin was not his fault. Yet the more intently he pored over his young face in his bedroom scrap of looking-glass, the blacker he seemed to get.

This could not have been so in his own country. There, to be black was bliss. His great-grandfather, as he knew, had been a king in that country and it was white boys who would be laughable there. Indeed, when first the Rev. Silas Grimble appeared in Poojooboo, the black women and children laughed so much among themselves at his tall hat, pale face, and silvery whiskers—supposing that his clothes were as much a part of him as its spots are part of a leopard—that at last they became quite friendly with him. They liked him because he looked so amusing. But not even they—not even the piccaninnies—laughed at him to his face. That was not their manners. If, then, William the dentist's boy had taken ship to Poojooboo to find Sambo on the throne, the boys in the streets under the bread-fruit trees would have yelled their *Yahs* at *him*—but not out loud.

Sambo knew enough of all this, mused on it when he was alone, to make him feel not only unhappy but homesick. It was not, then, that he pined merely to be a white boy. There were white boys he knew by sight he wouldn't have pined to be for anything in the wide world. No, he only saddened more and more at having to stay black. He wanted to be *all* white and yet himself. This sorrowfulness came over him in curious ways.

On getting up in the morning, for example, he would remember again—if there had been any light to see him by—how black he must have looked between his sheets. Or again, after blowing out his candle on going to bed—and Dr Grimble gave him only an inch at a time so that he should not under-sleep himself—he would realize that without his nightshirt he could not be seen in the dark. There was nothing sad or dreadful in either of these facts—not really; but they stayed in Sambo's mind. They haunted him as a spectre might a copse.

Perhaps if Sambo had not been so slow in his mind he might soon have learned to be less vain. But he had never been told that to grieve over what one is not may be as vain as to simper at what one is. He had been told very little. So night and morning, Sambo stared at himself in the scrap of looking-glass he treasured. Round, glossy, solemn, his young face stared back at him; and alas, as black as jet!

But though Sambo was slow by nature, though his master always told him things twice over to make sure, though on his rounds he always walked much farther than he needed to walk because he made mistakes in arranging the houses he had to walk to, Sambo was persevering, even stubborn. What he began he finished. If mere trying could have blanched him, he would soon have become as fair in aspect as an albino. He took the greatest pains.

First he prayed to be made white, and almost sobbed in his bed, watching in vain for the angel he had hoped might come down through the starry night at once in answer. Then he gave up the kitchen black bread that by rights was his, and lived on the white scraps of French rolls left over from his master's table. The doctor's livery was a dark green, with yellow edging. But Sambo was allowed to wear a white drill waiting-jacket in the mornings—after eleven o'clock. This he himself washed and ironed three times a week and wore in private whenever his master was out, particularly on the days when the doctor went to see his Aunt Clara and spent the night at her house. Often in fear Sambo slept with his head under his bedclothes lest the night itself darkened even the dark. But all such efforts were in vain.

At last one morning—but by no means for the first time— he heard the doctor mention scarlet fever, and that very afternoon he himself carried round a large bottle of medicine to the patient who was suffering from this sad malady. This gentleman lived in a square house covered with vines and creepers, and Sambo could see the shutters drawn close across the windows behind which he lay in bed—bright red, as Sambo supposed, from head to foot.

This reminded him of another patient of the doctor's—a lady who was from Mexico and whose fever had been yellow; and of a little girl with auburn curls who had been at death's door with yellow jaundice, and whose small brother was afterwards brought to the doctor suffering from pink eye. His master too had once had for cook a negro mammy who at full moon was always oppressed with what she called 'de blue debbles.' And what but the doctor's medicines had cured them all? Surely, pondered Sambo, if physic could take away scarlet, yellow, blue, and pink, it could wash out black?

Sambo cast his eye towards his master's shelves of bottles and jars and could scarcely wait in patience until he was alone again. He had often been warned not to meddle with them. But then, what a happy surprise it would be for the doctor if one morning Sambo appeared in his bedroom to pull up his blinds as white as himself. He might double his wages.

So one by one Sambo tried every kind of medicine on the shelves in turn, except the poisons which were kept locked up in a small cupboard. Of each he took no more than the least sip and only one sip at a time. If, after removing the glass stopper, the medicine had a very pungent or nauseous smell, he took even less. As with the bottles, full of essences and tinctures, so with the powders and the pastes and the pills. Of every powder he took no more than half a saltspoonful; enough to cover the tip of his little finger of every paste; and half a pill of every kind and size.

Most of these medicines made no difference at all—but then, being little more than a child, Sambo did not at first venture to taste more than one of them at a time. Others made him giddy, or hot, or breathless, or limp, or excited, or silly, or talkative, or thirsty, or hungry—or just the reverse; and one or two of them made him sick. After these his face looked a little green, but even then it was only a black-green and soon passed away. In spite of all this pain and trouble, Sambo remained precisely as black as ever, then, if not a little blacker.

It was odd perhaps that the doctor never noticed either that any of his medicines were dwindling, or that Sambo sometimes looked peculiar. But then he was not an observant man, and he was short-sighted. Besides, though Sambo did not know it, it would have made no difference to his master if he were grey or brown, striped, dappled, or piebald. So long, that is, as he did his work well. On the other hand, the doctor was quick enough to notice when Sambo made a mistake—let his little leaden tank run over, delivered a medicine at the wrong house, packed the wrong pills in the right box or vice versa. And then Sambo noticed *him*. But Sambo always made it a rule to take very little indeed from any jar or pot that was less than half full.

When Sambo had tasted every kind of physic in his master's dispensing-room—sweet, sour, salt, bitter, dry, oily, thick or thin, including even one or two little remedies that were kept for the doctor's best patients' pet or lap-dogs, stuff to make the eyes bright, or the hair grow, or the teeth clean, or the nails lustrous, and nothing was of any avail, he became sadder than ever. Still, he did not despair; and this was a blessing, for if he had, his poor heart might have become almost as black as his face. Instead of despairing, he began to read the doctor's books. But since of the words on every page he had to look into a dictionary to find the meanings of at least twenty up to one hundred, and then forgot them, he did not get on very fast or far.

And then one day—he had just brought in the doctor's grog on his salver—Sambo dared to ask him a question.

'If you please, Massa Doc'r,' he said, 's'posin' you 'm wanted to be ebber so black like poor Sambo what fijjick would Massa take?'

Unfortunately the doctor was a little deaf as well as short-sighted, and all he said was: 'No, no; that will be all to-night.'

On hearing this, Sambo rejoiced. He thought his master meant that this very evening, after he himself was gone to bed, he would try to turn himself black: '*That*—the taking of the physic—will be all to-*night*!' It seems almost impossible, but Sambo did. And he waited up until he fell asleep about three in the morning kneeling at the doctor's keyhole in the hope of seeing it happen.

He asked his master only one more question, and this was the last question he had ever need to ask. He had thought it over and over for three whole days before. It was a much bolder and braver thing to do even than to call back at the dentist's boy: 'Yah! Chalk-face! Yah! Mammy's milkysop! Off of de streets wid you! Streets am for gentlemen!'

At nine o'clock as usual the following evening he went into the doctor's room with the silver grog-tray in his hand—but nothing on it. It so chanced the doctor was asleep in his chair with his mouth open. So Sambo had to clank with his salver on the table to wake him up. That made the doctor vexed.

Then he noticed the tray was empty, and he said: 'What's that for?'

And Sambo said: 'Dere isn't no rum left, Massa Doc'r'—for rum was the doctor's fancy.

'Where is it gone?' said the doctor.

'*Me* had it, Massa Doc'r,' said Sambo.

'You!' shouted the doctor. 'What for?'

'Oh, Massa,' said Sambo, falling on his knees, 'to make pore Sambo lose his black. To wash him grey, Massa Doc'r, then white like the little lambs, like Massa Doc'r himsel'. Oh, sir, begorra, I wash and wash and wash, and scrub and scrub and scrub, and rum only polish Sambo's nose and smart his eyes.

> A pill, a pill, is all he ask,
> Dat take away his ink-black mask,
> And make him quicker at his task.'

Sambo had spent exactly eight hours and a half in making up and learning this piteous rhyme. He thought his master could not but understand that if he had taken so much trouble he *must* be in earnest. He thought that the instant his master knew the rum had made no difference to Sambo's black he would tell him what would. Instead, the doctor, who, disappointed of his grog, was now very angry, lifted Sambo up in one hand, boxed each of his ears in turn with the other, opened the door, and dropped him on to the mat outside it. And so poor Sambo had failed again.

Still, the doctor was not an unkind-hearted man, and next morning he had forgotten all about the rum. In fear that he might remember, however, Sambo had been wise enough to smear a little blacking on the polish which so much rubbing had made on the tip of his broad nose. But there had been no real need to do this. The doctor had quite forgotten, and the same day a whole keg of the best Jamaica rum went down into his cellar.

So the days and even weeks went by. Sambo did not dare to dream even of asking his master any more questions. Instead with a faint heart he tried mixing together one or two and even three of the different drugs and powders, and, thumb and finger clutching his nose, he swallowed these. On his annual half-holiday he even went so far as to swallow a pill which he had mixed with sal volatile and paregoric and then dried into a larger pill with some of the doctor's medical soap and a pinch of senna. It was a very big pill and he nearly choked in the effort, as he sat in the doctor's garden under a blossoming pear tree. But though a sort of dusky pallor crept over his cheek, it was at least twenty tints away from being as white as the myriad flowers over his head; and by the evening, when he was better, Sambo was wholly his natural black again.

Last of all, his rolling eye glanced along the row of locked-up medicines called Poisons in the doctor's cabinet. *Could* some of them be poisons simply because they would turn a white man into a blackamoor, he wondered? And was the doctor afraid of taking one himself by mistake? *Could* they? But Sambo dared not tamper with the lock.

And still he pined. Lying awake sometimes between his white sheets, the full moon silvering his fuzzy head and gleaming in his treacle-black eyes, he would gaze at her till they ached in his head. Up there, he thought, perhaps. . . . But before he could follow this fancy far, he was usually fast asleep.

One afternoon, out on his rounds, he met the dentist's boy again. His heart all but choking him, he set down his basket on the 'sidewalk,' put his fingers into his ears to keep out the hated *Yahs*, and waited until William had come up with him. Then, trembling all over, he asked the pug-nosed urchin in a shrill quavering voice what was the matter with being black.

'What's the matter?' squeaked the urchin, mimicking him: 'why, dat,' slapping him on one cheek, 'and *dat*!' slapping him on the other. And with redoubled *Yahs* off he went.

So Sambo grew sadder and sadder. Yet by this time he was sure that he knew almost as much about doctoring and physicking, pilling and draughting as his master. And he had all but worn out the dictionary. One of his jobs every day—after whiting the three steps on to the street, polishing up the knocker and the bell-handle, sweeping out the waiting-room, and making the doctor's coffee, was to arrange his master's letters (that had been brought by the postman) on a tray. These he carried in, after thumping at the doctor's bedroom door, with his coffee.

And there came one morning a letter addressed to his master in a most beautiful handwriting. Sambo had never seen such spidery letters, such exquisite curves. Besides this, a most delicious perfume and odour eddied up from the speckless paper to his nose. He lifted the envelope and sniffed and sniffed again. What valerian is to a cat, so was the scent of this envelope to Sambo. He longed to have it for his own.

It seems indeed that Sambo's Satan must have been by at this moment, though he himself could not imagine how Satan could spare the time to tempt so small a darkey. Sambo's night-dark oily eyes glanced around him. He *saw* no one near. And instead of taking up the letter at once to his master, he undid three of his round silver buttons and pushed it in under his tunic. There it remained throughout the morning—the unhappiest he ever had. When he came in the afternoon to a high wall under some bushy linden trees, he sat down beside his basket in the sunshine and shadow, opened the letter, and set to spelling it out.

First came the address from which it had been written: *White Slopes, The Snow Mountains*. And this, after half an hour's patient endeavour, was what Sambo read:

'The last Miss Bleech presents her compliments to Dr Grimble, and wishes to say that she is a very old woman now and ill in bed. She would be much obliged if the doctor would bring physic and come and see her as soon as he can.'

In ten minutes Sambo had spelled it through again. He could not understand why this letter began not with 'Dear,' as all the few other letters he had ever seen began, but in this strange fashion: *The last Miss Bleech*. Yet perhaps it was her very name that made him in his small mind's eye *see* this old lady; as plainly as if she lay in her bed before him under the linden trees! Her face wore the kindest of smiles. But it was her address still more that fascinated him. It was like the stare of a snake at a canary. That sudden sweep of frosty whiteness—it shone in on his sorrowful spirit with a radiance he could hardly bear. If only he had wings! Here, the streets were often dark with rain and wind, the doctor's house was at best a gloomy abode, and the white faces of every one he saw seldom met him with any but the blackest of looks. There was neither help nor hope anywhere to bring the change he pined for. If only his master would send *him* on this journey, tell him what to do, and what physic and juleps and lotions to take with him in his stead!

Sambo knew well this was impossible. He should have driven the very thought of it out of his head. But even under the green lime trees the Satan he feared must have been there beside him. He pushed back the letter under his tunic, hooked his basket over his arm, and finished his afternoon's round. He had made up his mind. He would say nothing about the letter. He would pack up the physics himself. When he got to where the letter said, he would tell this old lady, the last Miss Bleech, that the doctor had sent him. And there, surely, would be the end of all his troubles. This sinful plan had grown up within him as quick as Jonah's gourd. He went home on fire with it; and waited only until the next time the doctor went off to visit his Aunt Clara to carry it out.

Poor Sambo. His master had told him little about his oughts; and though he knew that borrowing money without leave was wrong, he did not know that it was almost as wicked as *stealing*. He had been kept 'in the dark.' But he did know that it might be a very long way to the Snow Mountains, that he would have to travel there in a train, and that to travel in a train you must go to the railway station and buy a ticket. In the middle of that night, then—and the doctor had gone off with his little black bag about three in the afternoon—Sambo crept downstairs, opened his master's drawer, and took out from it in greenbacks and silver dollars about half of the money he found in the little tin box inside it. For a moment he stood listening, his bulging eyes ashine in the candle-light, his pale-palmed hands trembling. But no sound at all came out of the empty night. If in his dreams his master *was* watching him, he had not uttered a word.

The money safe in his pocket, he stole up to a room where the doctor's old mother used to sleep when she was alive. He had sometimes peeped in here before, in dread of her ghost, and once in curiosity and in the bright light of day, he had peeped too into the wardrobe that stood facing the empty bed. His lighted candle in his hand, his black feet bare, his small ivory-white teeth chattering, he crept soundlessly and more darkly than a shadow into this chamber. He opened the great wardrobe door. From every hook there hung limp and lifeless the old clothes of the doctor's old mother—gowns and shawls and mantles; puce and violet, mauve and purple; and on a hook all to itself a little satin bodice, lovelier than any and of a faded vermilion, which must have been worn by her when she was young. Sambo gasped for delight at sight of all these colours, these silks and satins. He gently put out his finger as if to touch them. For Sambo's master, even though he had a quick temper, had been very fond of his mother, and so could not bear to part with her clothes.

Else, Sambo perhaps would never have reached the Snow Mountains. For among them there hung a cloak made only of ermine. This had been a present from the doctor to his mother on her seventieth birthday, and must have cost a mint of money. For love of her son and for pride in it she always wore it after that when she went out at night to hear music or to sup with her friends, though this was seldom.

Sambo carefully placed his candlestick on the dressing-table in front of the large dark looking-glass, and standing on a chair took down the cloak from its hook. He not only took it down, he put it on. Then he got up on to a stool, and by the flickering beam of his candle surveyed himself in the glass. Out of its quiet depths showed his round black fuzzy head, his dark liquid eyes, gleaming teeth, small black hands—and from chin to heel flowed down this silken, silvery, soft white fur—except for the little black tufts on it.

Sambo had never seen so marvellous a thing before. He could hardly even sigh for wonder. This it was then to be the great-grandson of a king! There was but one small trouble in his mind—the tufts. And lo and behold, on the dressing-table there lay a pair of the old lady's embroidery scissors, of silver and mother-of-pearl, and with tapering steel points. Sambo sat down on the floor, and heedless of how the cold night hours glided away, snipped out with the scissors every single tuft of black he found in the cloak. He gathered them up, opened a bandbox, put them in, huddled up the cloak into a bundle, took his candle and went back to his master's room.

There, for his candle was now guttering out, he lit the gas and turned it low. From the shelves above his head, since he could not borrow from all, he took down the third and seventh bottles of the powders from every shelf—his small heart being dark with superstitions—and he put a little of each of their contents into some pill-boxes. He took only powders because he was afraid on a long journey that bottles might break. Now Dr Grimble served up his pills in boxes of different colours, according to what ailment the pills were for. So Sambo had ten boxes in all, two of which were of the same colour, as there were five shelves. These ten boxes he put into his basket. In other boxes he put some of his favourite pills, and he could not resist one bottle of Nicey-Nicey, as the doctor called it. It was this nicey-nicey that he mixed with his medicines to make them go down sweeter. Sambo also put into his basket one or two little shiny knives, some long scissors, a slim wooden pipe with a cup at the end of it for listening to hearts with, and a pair of dark-glassed tortoiseshell spectacles: and that was all.

When he had finished packing his basket the grey of dawn was showing through the cracks of the window shutters. His cheek almost as grey itself, though he did not know it, he stole downstairs. His basket on one side of him, and a bundle—containing his money, both his nightshirts, and two old bandana handkerchiefs—on the other, he sat down to breakfast. It was still early morning when, having eaten the doctor's breakfast as well as his own, Sambo let himself out of the house, crept past the whispering poplar trees, and ran off.

It was a bad thing to do, but perhaps if the dentist's boy had told Sambo what was the matter with being black, he might never have gone at all. But go he did; and all that day until evening fell, he hid in one of the mangers in the stables of an old empty house that he had often noticed on his rounds—its rambling garden deep with grass and busy with birds. Part of the time he nodded off to sleep, but most of it he sat with clammy hands and open mouth listening in dread of the baying of the bloodhounds sniffing him out; of Satan; but far more, of never reaching the Snow Mountains. Only once he ventured from his hiding-place to see if any of last year's apples were still mouldering in the grass. He found none, and had to go hungry.

In the dusk, his basket and ermine cloak over his arm, he skulked off to the railway station and asked for a ticket to the nearest station to the Snow Mountains.

'Who wants it?' said the man.

'Massa, sir,' said Sambo.

'If he wants a ticket for the Snow Mountains, why doesn't he say so?' said the man.

'Me no know,' said Sambo, and the man gave him a ticket. Sambo dared ask nobody any other questions, but spied about until he saw a tall wooden pole surmounted with a finger-board. On this was scrawled in charcoal: 'To the Snow Mountains.' It pointed to a train—standing empty in the murky gloom of a siding—and an ancient, faded, blistered, ramshackle train it looked.

There was not a human soul to be seen here, or even sign of any, not even of the engine-driver. And when Sambo at last sidled up to inquire of a huddled shape sitting in the dark in

how many hours' time the train would be starting, no tongue
answered, and he found he had been whispering to a huge sack
of bran! So without more ado he climbed up into one of the
carriages—and very dark and musty it was inside—lay down
on the hard wooden seat, covered himself with his ermine cloak,
and in less than no time fell asleep.

He awoke in a dreadful nightmare, not knowing where he
was, and supposing there had been an earthquake. When he
scrambled to his knees and looked out of the window, he found
that the train was jerking and jolting along over a very narrow
track in the light of the moon, and on either side the track was
nothing but the wide glare and glitter and whiteness of ice and
snow. The scene stretched on into the distance, a waste of
frozen snow. It was a strange thing that any train could have
gone rambling off so quick into the north like this. But then
Sambo had been fast asleep, nor knew how long. And but one
glance at the glory of the snow did him more good than if he
had swallowed the whole of his master's medicines, including
the poisons.

The train went on, clanking and clattering—Sambo could
even hear the tinkle of the broken ice, and still the moon shone
down, and now it began to snow again, but very sparsely.
Sambo hung as far as he could out of the narrow window to
peep into the carriages ahead of and behind him. Both it
seemed were empty. Now and again he saw a house, but it
was always only a little house and far away. And once the
track made so sharp a curve that he could see even the twinkle
of the fire in the engine-cabin and what looked like a black man
crouching there, though he couldn't be sure. And as they were
scuttling along as fast as ever, and Sambo was soon drowsy
again with watching the snow, he lay down on his hard seat in
the warmth of the cloak and once more fell asleep.

When he awoke, the train was at a standstill. Sambo heard
a bell ringing, and looked out of the window. It was bright
full morning. And there he saw a low narrow platform, crusted
thick with snow, and an open shed. Above the shed were the
words: 'The Snow Mountains. *Change!*' He had only time
enough to take out his basket and his bundle and his cloak
before there came a long mournful hoot from the engine, and
in a moment the train was gone.

And still there was no one to be seen. So Sambo, who was

cold, put on his cloak, and, with his basket under it on one arm,
and his bundle in his hand, he came to the wicket gate of the
station. An old man with a beard was standing there, a
lighted lantern in his hand, though the sun had risen. This old
man asked Sambo for his ticket. And Sambo, having given him
the ticket, asked the old man where the last Miss Bleech lived,
'*White* Slopes am de name,' he said.

'You go along and along there,' mumbled the old man,
pointing to a winding narrow road beyond the station, 'until
you begin to go up and up. Then up and up you go and follow
the trees.'

Sambo thanked him and went on his way. In spite of his
long and heavy sleep in the train, his leg bones ached and he
was very weary. His basket grew heavier, his cloak hotter,
the path steeper. The sun shone down on the whiteness and
dazzled his eyes. The pine trees by the wayside had hours
ago gone far beyond his counting. He could not even guess
how many miles he had tramped scrunching on through the
snow when of a sudden he came round a bluff in the hills and
saw with joy indeed what he felt sure must be White Slopes.
For *there* was the strangest house in all the world. Peaked and
sloping, wide and narrow, and clotted with snow, its shining
roofs stood high above its walls and windows. It was not a
house but a great Mansion. Up, up, into the solitary mountains
Sambo had climbed, following the pine trees that marked his
narrow path, and here at last was where he longed to be. What
should he do next?

Before he started he had thought he would tell the old lady
that his master had sent him. 'Massa Doc'r ill in bed, he say:
he sent Sambo.' These would be the words he would use.
Then he would mix a little of the powder from each of his
coloured boxes in turn with some of the nicey-nicey and a little
water, and would give her one teaspoonful of each of them every
day. He knew his physics now by heart; and though they had
done him no good, not at any rate the kind of good he longed
for, they had done him no harm.

As long as the medicines lasted, he felt sure the old lady
would let him stay with her. When she was better again,
perhaps she might ask him to be her house-boy. How happy
that would be! For if only, poor Sambo felt certain, he could
remain long enough in this white shining mansion among the

mountains, and in these radiant wastes of snow, surely, surely, his black would slowly vanish away. Had not his master's window curtains, even in sunlight incomparably less fair and bright than this, turned from blue to faded grey?

The faintest of breezes came sighing through the air, so faint that it scarcely stirred the glittering crystals at Sambo's feet. He shivered. And his thoughts grew darker. Supposing the old lady, when he appeared before her great bed, did not believe that his master had sent him? Supposing she asked him questions, discovered that he had stolen his medicines; that he was a little black cheat? What then?

He eyed again the strange house, rising in solitude under the blue sky among the slopes of the mountains. He fancied that in the distance he saw living shapes, moving on the terraces beneath it, though he could not detect what they were. What then? he asked himself again, and began to be afraid. And though even Sambo himself could not have believed that Satan would ever venture into a place so full of light and peace as this, an even wickeder thought had stolen into his mind. Why should he not pretend that he himself was his master, that *he* was the doctor? There had been not a word in the letter to say that the last Miss Bleech knew his master. Not one word. That was perhaps why she hadn't begun her letter with the word 'dear.' Perhaps, then, if he himself gave her only half the doses he had intended to give her, she would get better only half as quickly. Then he might stay on and on and on—and never go back. No, never.

As he sat there in his ermine in the snow with this thought in his mind, there suddenly sprang into view beneath him a wild white buck rabbit, with eyes like burning coals. At least Sambo thought it was a rabbit, though it was much bigger than any he had ever seen before. Stiff as a post in the snow, and for the best part of a minute, it glared at Sambo—not fiercely but because its eyes were so full of light. Then, as if assured he meant it no harm, it made a little noise that was almost like laughter, and scuffled its hind legs rapidly in the snow. Other creatures like it answered. And soon the whole expanse beneath Sambo—and there was a dark lake of ice encircled with frosted trees at its foot—was alive with rabbits—hundreds and hundreds of rabbits, large and small. They paid no heed to Sambo, no more than if he had been as spotlessly white as they were themselves. Perhaps, thought he, they had not noticed his hands or his face. But the old lady would. When she saw he was black, she would not only not believe he was a doctor, but might tremble with scorn and hatred. What then?

He was so tired and hungry he could think no more. So, his basket on his arm, he set off again, and presently came to the back parts of the house. Apart from the faint-coloured shadows cast by the sunlight on its roofs and walls, it was white all over. Here there were many little outhouses like beehives capped with snow, and they seemed to have been all of them freshly whitened. Peeping about Sambo saw in a corner under the house a large tub or butt, put there as if to catch the rain. He stole over and, lifting himself by his hands to its edge, peeped in. The butt was half full of a thick white liquid, like whitewash. He hauled himself up, and stooping over, broke the thin sheet of ice that wrinkled its surface, and dipped in his finger. It came out white as milk. If the tip of a finger, why not his whole body? Surely here was the end of all his troubles!

He hesitated no more. He stripped off his ermine cloak, his silver-buttoned tunic, his black trousers, his shirt, his shoes, everything he had on. And there and then, naked and shuddering with the cold, he climbed up over the edge of the butt, let himself down, and three times over dipped himself head to foot in the creamy ice-cold water—face, hands, woolly hair and all. Once safely out, he ran about until he was caked dry. Then he put on his clothes again. No one, it seemed, had heard his splashing; no one had seen him. But as he was snapping-to the silver clasp of the cloak at his throat, having put on his master's goggles from out of his basket, he heard a little noise. Out of its dark shining eyes a gentle deer stood watching him in the snow. It was hornless and as white as he himself; nor did it start back or hasten away when he came near. He put out his white crudded hand and stroked its gentle head. And because of the friendliness of the deer, he was afraid no more. Cloaked and peering, he went round to the front of the house, and mounting the steps, knocked solemnly on the great door.

It was opened by the butler. At least Sambo guessed him to be the butler, for he had seen many butlers. But he had never seen one so old or so odd to look at. Over a long starched waistcoat his spotless swallow-tailed coat almost brushed the floor. His nose was even broader and flatter than Sambo's, his lips as thick and his hair as woolly, and, except for his face, he was almost as white. He looked sorrowful, too, and full of care. And though Sambo's lips were stiff, partly with the whitewash and partly because he was telling a lie, Sambo told him not who he was but who he was *not*. He then asked him how his mistress did, and if she were well enough to see the doctor.

'Ah, massa, massa,' replied the old butler, lifting his hands in grief; 'worser and worser!' And without another word he led Sambo up the wide white staircase and along a corridor whose windows looked out upon the mountains; and then he tapped at a door.

When Sambo saw the last Miss Bleech in her great bed, her high, narrow, silvery head reclining on the pillows, her far-away blue eyes fixed on the window in front of her, he knew that she was not long for this world. And he wept inside to think it. It seemed she must be at least ninety-eight, if not even ninety-nine. Her voice was so small and low he could scarcely hear what she said to him. But when the butler told her who this visitor was, she smiled at Sambo. She was rejoiced to see him, even though she could see him but dimly. Not too dimly, however, to realize that this was not only the whitest of doctors that had ever come to do her good, but the whitest of human beings. All her other doctors, though she had needed few since her childhood, had been dressed up in solemn long black coats to match their hats and trousers; and of all things in the world she liked black least. Or rather, she loved white best; though Sambo did not know this then.

But first, she thought only of *his* comfort. She bade the butler show him to his room. It had been specially prepared against the coming of the visitor whom she had been pining so much to see, and it was next her own. She told Sambo, as he stood there—small, staring, and motionless at the foot of her bed—that she knew how cold and wearisome a journey his had been. Nor did the old lady so much as sigh when she said she would not be troubling him for long. Her one hope was that he would stay with her as many days as he could spare.

Sambo, who had often mimicked his master's speech and manners behind his back, imitated them, as well as he could, now. He told the old lady that he thought she was looking a little better, and that he would do his best to make her quite well again. So long as there is breath in the body, he said, there is hope. 'Care, fijjick, sleep,' he said, lifting a finger. But he kept his dark spectacles turned away from the light of the window as he spoke, in terror lest she should look close into his whitewashed face and know him for a cheat.

When Sambo was alone in the lofty room that had been made ready, when he looked round him at the tall bed canopied with white velvet, the sofa, the carpet—deep and thick as moss, but white too itself as snow—he sat down on a stool and burst out crying. He was young, he was alone, he was weary; but it was his villainy that weighed heaviest. Still, he cried only for a few moments, and at once hastened over to the great glass on the dressing-table to see if his tears had left their traces on his cheek. No; he had dipped deep in the whitewash, and stains there were none. Indeed, at first glimpse of himself—that sheeted face, small hoary hands, a dwarf in ermine—terror seized him. It was as if he had met his own ghost. And then he sighed. He was whiter even than his master! He eased the buckle at his throat, turned his head, and looked out of the window.

Beneath him the mountain fell away in snowy terraces towards the valley far below. Trees and bushes heaped in snow and glistening in the sun of evening met his wondering gaze. The sweet yet sorrowful cry of winter curlews wafting their way through the windless air came to his ear. And beneath them strayed strange creatures he had neither seen before nor knew the name of. Some were antlered, some were small and nimble, and all of so pale a colouring that they could scarcely be seen against the snow. And though, so vast was the view from his window, they were scattered far apart, they seemed to be at peace with one another. Not a voice yelled *Yah*, no cry of wrath or pain pierced the air. It was as if, gazing out over these snow mountains and valleys, smooth and radiant beneath the blue, Sambo had been transported into the place called *Nowhere*. And for a while he forgot that he was black.

Day after day he tended the old lady, putting so infinitesimal a pinch of his master's powders into her physic-bottles and so much nicey-nicey that she enjoyed taking her medicine, and would even sip instead of merely swallowing. Sambo would sit for hours in silence at her bedside, touching her hand now and again with his rough-washed fingers, not in order to tell if she were feverish but merely to comfort her, and to prove that he was there. And the longer he stayed with her the more she came to find ease and comfort in his company, and the sadder Sambo grew: first, to think that she was now too old ever to be young again; and next, that he was deceiving her. But try as he might, and though he often lay long hours awake brooding on this, he could not find words to tell the old lady, whom he now loved dearly, what a dreadful net of falsehood he was in.

Once when the black was beginning to dim his whitewash he had to steal down to the outhouses for another coat. And though this time the sudden shock of cold from his tub brought on a hacking cough, fortunately, packed up in his basket, he had brought with him a powder good for coughs, and as his patient did not need it, he took it himself.

When his cough was better, he would sometimes sing to her, in his shrill falsetto, songs of his own people that he had heard as a child. Among her favourites, and his, was the lament beginning, 'Weep no more, my lady!' And as he sang it, the black rolling eyes of the child would meet the faded blue of his friend's, and it was as if by the mere grace of the music they shared an unsearchable secret.

> Weep no more, my lady,
>   O, weep no more to-day!
> We will sing one song for the old Kentucky home,
>   For the old Kentucky home, far away. . . .

And then, for better cheer, Sambo would warble up, 'Shine, shine, Moon!' or, 'So Early in the Morning'; though at the words:

> When I was young, I used to wait,
> On Massa's table lay the plate,
> Pass the bottle when him dry,
> Brush away the blue-tail fly. . . .

his memory ran back in a flash to his master, and his voice shook.

At length, one afternoon, after a long silence, as he sat on his customary stool by the great bed, he asked the old lady if she minded things *looking* what they are *not*. And he turned his face full into the light as he said it.

'Why, but no, my dear kind doctor,' she replied to him. 'It is not what things *look* like that matters *most*; but what they are.' When she was young, she went on—almost, as if without knowing it, she were reading his thoughts—once, when she was young, she had loved colours—every faintest colour and hue and tint visible in the rainbow; though some of them of course were her favourites. But all colours, her father had explained to her, even when she was a little girl with short pigtails dangling round her head, lie hidden in *white*. 'White,' her father had told her, 'is not a colour at all; it is *all* colours.' She had never forgotten that. And the longer she lived, she told Sambo, the more she had come to delight in white: snow-drops, anemones, the convolvulus; dew before the sun rises; hoar frost; foam of falling water; the sea's spray. So at last she had come to live in these mountains where there was snow nearly all the year round, and all living creatures shared in its splendour.

'Listen, doctor, is it not the voices of birds I hear? Look out, now, at their wings of light!'

Sambo lifted his heavy head and looked out of the window. But the birds must have been in the old lady's mind. There were none in the heavens.

He asked her then if she had ever travelled in the Black Man's Land, in the country of the Darkeys. Was it not a dreadful thing, he entreated her, to be born like that? Black?

'Why, no, dear doctor,' she assured him eagerly. 'Never to me. That again is what my father used to tell me. White gives back all colours; black welcomes them in. What is the centre of every seeing human eye, he would say; *black*. Besides all things on earth have an out and an in. Even an apple hangs there on its twig for the sake of its seeds. A black man whose mind is free from darkness and his heart from cruelty is in truth whiter than *any* one whose soul is in the shades.' And she smiled to herself after listening to this little sermon to one so learned as a doctor; but she had seen that Sambo was in some trouble of mind.

'Ay,' said Sambo in a lamentable voice. 'And de blackest ob all dings, lady, *dat* is a lie!' And he hastened out of the room.

It was curious perhaps that one so young as he, and with so little royal blood left in him by now, should have wept as he did at the thought of a lie. But weep he did.

That night, after he had given the old lady her physic—and it was all but all of it nicey-nicey, for most of his powders were gone—when he had seen that she was in comfort, and had lit her wax candle in the silver candlestick beside her bed, he bade her good night, and locked himself into his room.

A shallow tin white bath lay underneath his bed. He dragged it out in front of his dressing-table and emptied the cold water out of his jug into it. There was no more than an inch or two of water in the shallow bath, and he was three coats thick with whitewash. So that it took him a long time to sponge and rub and scrape himself black again, or as nearly black as he could manage. When he had finished and was dry, he lay down on the sofa to rest awhile, for he wished to rise at daybreak. Then he would tell the old lady all he was, his one fear being that it might make her worse. But it was impossible the next morning to make the last Miss Bleech worse, for when Sambo, having unlocked his door, went in at daybreak, she was dead.

He stood at the foot of the bed, gazing out of his blackness at the placid face upon the pillow, at the birdlike hands on the counterpane. And he nodded his woolly head, in his grief, as if to say, Too late! At last he stole nearer and ventured to put out his ink-black fingers and touch her ice-cold hand.

'*Sambo* am here, lady,' he whispered.

But there was no look in his friend's fixed eyes to show that she had heard. And as in his misery he stood there, he saw beside the candlestick a slip of paper, folded in two. 'My last wishes' was written on it and beside it was a long envelope, sealed down. Sambo took the slip of paper to the window, and though the handwriting was very spidery and shaky he had learned it long since under the linden trees, and in a few minutes he had read the message within.

'Dear friend, and far more than Doctor,' it said, 'after your kindness and goodness to me, beyond any physic, I wish to leave you all I have. You will see that my butler and the others shall never want. Take care of the animals, and never put on anything but white for me. And may heaven bless you. *Emily Bleech.*'

Sambo read this over and over; then put it back where he had found it. His grief and love were almost greater than he could bear, but there was only one thing he could *do*. Having emptied his bath-water out of the window, he hastened downstairs. Not a soul was stirring. It was as if the strangers of night had but a moment before left the round beehive outhouses to their daily solitude. Three times Sambo dipped himself from crown to sole in the great tub; and came out like chalk. He was doing what his friend wished him to do.

After a few days had gone by, and Sambo's heart was less troubled, he did one or two things that he wished for himself. When he ran off from his master he had no thought of money except what would take him to the Mountains. It was only time he pined for in which to grow white. And now time stretched out before him like the sands of the desert, the face of the sea. And he thought again of what was past. He made up a parcel of money—containing twice as much as he had borrowed from his master; one single Stars-and-Stripes bank-note with a great many noughts on it to pay for the ermine cloak; and a hundred dollars over for the missing medicine. This parcel he dispatched secretly to the doctor, with *From Sambo* written inside the paper, but no address. At the same time he sent fifty dollars to the most famous candy shop in the doctor's town, telling them to deliver to Mr Tooth-the-Dentist's boy a large jar of maple sugar, a keg of dates, a cake of a black dainty made of molasses called brandy-bread, and a blue-and-white pot of the finest Chinese ginger.

After all, Sambo thought, he might never have come to the Snow Mountains if it had not been for this caterwauling young vagabond, and he would know by this that Sambo was 'off the streets!' As for the butler and the other servants, they could never even have hoped for a kinder master. 'Of all de massas he was best.'

And yet, in the years that followed, as he lived on at peace in his mansion in the Snow Mountains, gazing out of his window —a thing he never wearied of—a strange craving at times would creep into Sambo's mind. And the fear would take him that Satan was nearing again. At this he would steal to his looking-glass, and confront, on and on, that speckless face of chalk from eyes as motionless and dark as basalt.

'O but for a moment,' a voice would cry out on him as if from the very recesses of his being, 'O but for a moment, to be black again!' And always, to silence the voice, Sambo would pick a few snow-flowers and go down and lay them on his old friend's grave. There he would stay for a few moments, alone in the valley, looking up at the tranquil hills; and then, slowly and solemnly shaking his whitewashed head, would return again—comforted.

From *The Lord Fish*.

A REVENANT

It was an evening in November; too early in the year, that is, for winter coughs to have set in. And coughs to the lecturer are like reefs to the mariner. They may wreck his frail craft. So extreme indeed was the quietude in the Wigston Memorial Hall in which Professor Monk was speaking that if he had remained mute for but a moment, even the voice of the gentle rain that was steadily descending out of the night beyond upon its corrugated roof would have become audible. Indeed his only interruption, and it had occurred but once every quarter of an hour, had been a sudden, peculiar, brief, strident roar. On his way to the hall he had noticed—incarnadining the louring heavens—what appeared to be the reflected light from the furnaces of a foundry. Possibly it was discharging its draff, its slag, its cinders. In any case, a *punctual* interruption of this kind is a little dramatic; a pregnant pause, and it is over. Nor did it affect him personally.

The professor had read somewhere that on occasion a certain eminent mathematician will sink in the midst of one of his lectures into a profound reverie, which may continue for ten minutes together. Meanwhile his students can pursue at leisure *their* daydreams. But students are students, not the general public. He himself, while avoiding dramatic pauses, could at once read out loud and inwardly cogitate, and he much preferred a sober and academic delivery. He never allowed his voice to sink to a mutter or rise into a shout; he neither stormed nor cajoled, nor indulged even in the most modest of gestures. A nod, a raised finger, a lifted eyebrow—how effective at their apt moments these may be! He flatly rejected, that is, the theatrical arts of the alien—to let his *body* speak, to be stagy, oratorical.

He even regarded the bottle of water that stood on his reading-desk as a symbol rather than as a beverage. A symbol not, of course, hinting at any connection with sacred Helicon, but of the fact that his lectures were neither intoxicating nor were intended to be intoxicating. How many times, he wondered, had he repeated his present experience? Scores, at least. He had become at last a *confirmed* lecturer.

And yet, to judge by his feelings at this moment, he might almost have been a novice—a chrisom child. This was odd. The particular lecture he was engaged on—its subject the writings of Edgar Allan Poe—was one of his own favourites. He had delivered it at least half a dozen times, and always with a modest satisfaction. No more than just that. It owed, of course, a great deal to its theme; one that possessed an almost repulsive attraction for the queerest of readers. *Any*thing about Edgar Allan Poe was edged with the romantic, tinged with the macabre—that strange career, its peculiar fruits.

Nevertheless, and not for the first time, as the professor stood alone up there on the platform, full in the glare of an arc-lamp suspended almost immediately over his head, he had become sharply aware not only that he was, with one single exception, the only human being present who was not sitting down, but also that he was the only human being present who was making a noise. The realization, in this intensity at any rate, was new to him; and it made him a little uneasy. Not that he had much patience with members of his own calling who pretend they dislike lecturing. That must be affectation. He enjoyed it. But he would enjoy it even more, he sometimes mused, if he could carry off with him a clear and definite notion as to the *effect* of what he had been saying.

Any impression of this kind might, of course, prove sadly disillusioning, but it would at least be positive. As a professional man, that is, Professor Monk lived in a faint mist. It was not that he pined for encouragement. Certainly not. His appeal was to the intelligence rather than to the emotions. He aimed at nothing in the nature of what in his subject's native land is known as the 'heart-to-hearter.' He had views, and tried to express them; it would therefore be helpful to discover if they were shared or rejected. Such evidence was very scanty. Again and again when, his lecture safely over, the customary rattle of applause had followed its last word, he had sat speculating precisely how much of it was due to good manners and how much to a natural sense of relief. A sigh is so much less audible than the clapping of hands. *Any* physical reaction after one has been sitting cramped and mute for a solid hour is of course as instinctive as sneezing is after snuff. But English audiences are oddly inscrutable.

For this reason he had more than once been tempted to insert in his paper a sentence or two that he himself felt confident was shocking, or even to leave out all the negatives on any particular page, all the *nots*—just to see the effect. But even English audiences are less easy to shock than once they were. Besides . . . well—not to-night. His only desire at the moment was to get finished, to have done. An unfamiliar longing had swept over him to go away, and never come back. Oh, for the wings of a dove, he was sighing with the Psalmist. And he knew why.

It was not the hall itself that was to blame. Lecture halls are much alike. Sunday-schoolish in atmosphere, they usually resemble railway waiting-rooms in their general effect. The fierce light beating into his spectacled eyes and on to his high conical brow was a slight embarrassment—it dazzled if it did not daze. He was accustomed to that too, however. After all, lecturers must be seen, even if they are not heard. He wished again what he had often wished before—that so-called house decorators, when engaged on places of public assembly, would choose for their paint other tints than a dingy duck green edged with a chocolate brown. Why, again, should the chairs selected suggest an orphanage? Were they assumed to be the only certain means of keeping listeners awake?

Still, this was all in the usual way of things. There was no walk in life without its vexations. As for his chairman, all that he could see of *him* at the moment was a puckered ecclesiastical boot. Simply, however, because he was motionless, he was not necessarily either inattentive or asleep. And what if he was? He himself had a genuine sympathy for chairmen. They were usually far too busy men, and tired. He had shared their trials and temptations. Nor had he the faintest hint of a complaint to make against his audience. He would have preferred, naturally, the farthest few rows of chairs to look a little less vacant; but this was a compliment to the occupants of the rest. All those who had come had stayed, and—though owing to his glasses he was unable to see them very distinctly—those who had stayed had been markedly attentive. He remembered a facetious friend once gravely asserting that it is impossible to thin a lecture down too much, and that, if it is to be appreciated to the full, at least one attempt at the jocular is essential every quarter of an hour. Make them laugh; it clears the air. That, however, was not his own method. He had neither thinned nor temporized, nor tried to amuse. Moreover, everybody was listening; no one had laughed; the theory was absurd. Then what was wrong?

Immediately in front of him and at the end of the room a circular white-faced clock hung midway above the two low, rounded arches which led out of the hall. Its hands now pointed to fourteen minutes to nine. The end then was in sight. And so, lowering his head a little, and pausing an instant, he ventured to take a second long, steady look at what he was now perfectly well aware had been the cause of his disquietude—a solitary figure who was standing (almost like a statue in its niche) within the left of these two doorways.

This person had been the only late-comer. At one moment the alcove was vacant, at the next *there* its occupant was. He must have sallied in out of the night as furtively as a shadow. The lecturer much preferred late-comers to early-goers. The former merely suggested the impracticable—that he should begin again; the latter that it was high time to stop. There was no doubt, however, that this particular listener had been a little on his nerves. Once having vaguely descried him, he had been unable to forget his presence there. Why stand? And why stand alone? He should himself have had the audacity to beckon him in. A warm word of welcome would have been by far the most politic method of—well, he might almost say, of accepting his challenge.

Unfortunately, any such word was now too late. Motionless in the dim light—his dark voluminous cloak around him, and hat in hand—there the stranger stood, leaning indolently the while, one foot crossed over the other, against the hollow of the arch. The attitude suggested a pose, but, pose or not, he had not altered it. The glare of the arc-lamp in the professor's eyes, his very uneasiness indeed, prevented him from clearly distinguishing the distant features. But the turn and inclination of the head, the perfect composure, the attitude, vaguely arrogant, of a profound attentiveness—everything suggested that this particular individual was either wholly engrossed in his own thoughts, *or* in what he was listening to. The latter should have been a consoling reflection. But, alas! one may be engrossed in destruction—as was Nero when Rome was burning, as is always the Father of Lies, and the angel of Candour. Well, what of that? Like the professor himself, he had come, he would go; and that would be the end of the matter.

It was none the less a little odd that of all those present none seemed to have become aware of this conspicuous interloper. Yet he was obviously a stranger in these parts. What chance could have summoned him in? Not necessarily the woeful November weather. For as the professor all alone had come walking along on his way to his lecture through the drizzling lamplit streets, he had passed by not only a flaming picture palace, radiant with seductive posters, but the vestibule of a dingy dejected little theatre—which appeared a good deal more inviting, none the less, than the spear-headed railings and dank brick wall of the cobbled alley which led into the Memorial Hall.

There were, then, rival attractions in the town. If so, why had this theatrical-looking personage not taken advantage of them? Or was he himself one of a company of touring play-actors idling his time away until the call boy claimed him for the second act? Had he ventured out of his green room for a breath of air, or for a draught even more exhilarating? Why again is it that extremely actual things in appearance may at times so closely resemble the imagery of sleep? But what folly were all such speculations. Nevertheless, Professor Monk had continued to indulge in them, and with an amazing rapidity, while he continued to read his paper. To satisfy them was quite another matter.

His voice—and he enjoyed this scrupulous resonant use of it —his voice rang on and on, sounding even louder than usual in his own ear by reason perhaps of this attack of what might be called psychic indigestion. Nor was he aware of any suddenly revealed reason to be distrustful, let alone ashamed, of his paper. When looking it over he had taken the opportunity of re-reading some of the stories, most of the poems, and an essay or two. He had consulted here and there one of the more recent Lives. Its actual composition had taken him a good deal more than a week; and it was at least systematically arranged. In four parts, that is: (*a*) the Environment; (*b*) the Man; (*c*) the Tales and Poems; (*d*) the Aftermath. Even if he had been able to extemporize he would have preferred to keep to the written word. It was a safeguard against exaggeration and mere sentiment.

As, tall, dark, steel-spectacled, and a little stiff, he stood up there decanting his views and judgments, it ensured that he said only what he meant to say, and that he meant only what he said. He disliked lectures that meander. He preferred facts to atmo-

sphere, statements to hints, assumptions, 'I venture's,' and
dubious implications. He detested theorizing, fireworks, and
high spirits. The temperamental critic is a snare. And though
poetry may, and perhaps unfortunately, *must* appeal to the
emotions and the heart, the expounding of it is the business of
the head. Besides, a paper simply and clearly arranged is far
easier to report. He hoped that his audience would go away
with something definite in their minds to remember, though he
was not so sanguine as to suppose that they would remember
much. 'Hammer, hammer, hammer,' he would laugh to himself, 'on the hard high road!'

Until this hour indeed it was highly probable that many of
them had never read, even if they had ever heard of, much more
of Poe's writings than *The Pit and the Pendulum*, and possibly
The Bells. Others may have accepted him merely as the melo-
dramatist of *The Maelstrom*, or *The Cask of Amontillado*, the
sentimentalist of *Annabel Lee*, the cynic of *The Masque of the
Red Death*, and the fantast of *The Fall of the House of Usher*.
A few of the more knowledgeable might have stigmatized him
not only as a gross sensationalist, of little character and no
morals—and an American at that—but something of a poseur
and a charlatan. This was a view, he confessed, that had been
shared by no less distinguished a compatriot of Poe's than the
great novelist, Henry James; who had dismissed his work as a
poet in three contemptuous words—'very superficial verse.'
Yes, and thrillers are thrillers and shockers shockers, whether
they are old or new. He himself could not agree with so sweeping a verdict, but he would not disguise the facts.

It would be only too easy indeed, he had declared, to treat the
subject of Poe in what might be called a pleasing, persuasive, and
popular fashion. He had tried to avoid that, to be frank and
just without becoming censorious. He had admitted that to
look for lessons, instruction, spiritual insight, and what in his
own country is called uplift, in the career and writings of the
author of *The Premature Burial*, *The Black Cat*, or such poems
as *The Conqueror Worm* and *Ulalume*, was like looking for prim-
roses and violets fresh with dew in a funeral wreath of artificially
dyed *immortelles*. And though he would agree—and here he had
cast a deprecatory glance at his chairman—that it was a lecturer's
office to expound rather than to indict, he could not avoid a
dutiful word or two on the ethics of his subject. He had

expressed his agreement with Longfellow that life is both real and earnest, that books are more than merely a drug, an anodyne, a solace, a way of escape. Poets, too, have their specific value, and, unlike Plato, he would certainly not dismiss them from his Ideal Republic. 'Not bag and baggage!' None the less poetry is in the nature of honey. It is not a *diet*. He himself was of opinion that a delight in beauty cannot be considered a substitute for the desire for knowledge, an excuse for any laxity of moral fibre, or for the absence of any serious convictions. And he had no wish to be partisan. However that might be, poets themselves, though they secrete this enticing honey, have not always proved themselves the best of bees. Their characters and their conduct, alas! are seldom as impeccable as their syntax.

A man's style, whether in prose or verse, in some degree, of course, reveals that man himself. And Poe on the whole wrote well. But we must be careful. A style that may be good from a merely literary point of view is not necessarily the work of a good man, nor is a bad style necessarily the work of a rascal. Otherwise, how few men of science—philosophers even—would escape damnation! Though again, what a man writes may reflect himself, as in a sort of looking-glass, it does not necessarily reflect the complete self. By no means, surely, is the whole of Burns in his love lyrics. Was even *Paradise Lost* all Milton? If so, the less Milton he. Byron, Baudelaire, Horace, Herrick, had they nothing of heart, mind, and soul but what was imaged in their writings? What then of Poe?

The professor had confessed impatience with the iridescent *veil* theory of poetry. Did the worn-out slogan Art for Art's sake, if examined closely, mean anything more profound than pudding for pudding's sake, or plumbing for plumbing's sake? Nor is a poem as a poem the better or worse for having been written at an age when most young people prefer the excitements of cricket or basket-ball; are, in fact, in Matthew Arnold's words, young barbarians at play. Genius may sometimes manifest itself in precocity; none the less, such a poem as Poe's *To Helen*, which he professed to have written at fourteen, must take its place with the rest of his work. It must stand or fall on its poetic merit.

Nor again, the lecturer had insisted, is any piece of literature the richer or more valuable for having been composed in an attic, in wretched circumstances. Not for a moment had he conceded that between poetry and poverty there is only the difference of the letter V—'The viol, the violet, and the vine'— that sort of thing. Men of imagination may be naturally sensitive, delicately poised, easily dejected—it is the price they pay for so precious an inheritance. But is it too extreme a price? Even Robert Louis Stevenson—an artist to his finger-tips—had not excused the man of genius the obligation of meeting his butcher's bill. Indeed he had said harsher things than that. Chaucer proved himself a man of affairs; Shakespeare made a handsome fortune and retired in his later forties to his birthplace; Robert Browning in the prime of life was occasionally mistaken for a prosperous banker; Westminster Abbey was at this moment positively surfeited with poetic remains. And that is hardly the Valhalla of the disreputable.

But even as a child Poe had been perverse and self-willed. And certainly in the brief months he spent at Jefferson's beautiful and serene University of Virginia, and in his even briefer career as a cadet in the lovely natural surroundings of West Point— though every allowance of course should be made for the young and the gifted—he had without question shown himself arrogant, fitful, quarrelsome, unstable. Had he been the reverse of all this, which of its better qualities would be missing from his work?

There was, of course, the other side of the account to consider —Mangan, De Quincey, Coleridge. One could hardly, alas! think of their writings dissociated from certain weaknesses not merely of constitution but of moral fibre. Mangan had died in poverty in deplorable circumstances in the same year as Poe himself, 1849; and this too was the death-year of Beddoes, while Emily Brontë had died only the year before—a strange eventuality, since there was much in common between them all—ill health, adverse fortune, extremes of mood and imagination. But Branwell's habits rather than her own were Emily Brontë's scourge, and the tragic and morbid end to Beddoes's career seemed to be proof of 'a sadly unstable mind.'

On the other hand, virtue, the lecturer was bound to confess, is not the prerogative either of the Stock Exchange or even of the Church; and our public-houses, our workhouses, and other abodes of the unfortunate and the unwise are thronged with human beings incapable even of scribbling a limerick or of rhyming *dove* with *grove*. In other words, it is by no means only the rarely gifted that are responsible for all the failures in life.

Poe's two years as private soldier, corporal, and sergeant in the American Army, though it had been an experience forced on him, had proved him capable of endurance, discipline, and responsibility. He had been sober and diligent, and had won the respect of his officers. No man of genius need be the worse off for *that*! In after years he had remembered the experience with sufficient tolerance at least to make its surroundings the scene of one of the best, one of the most original, and, even better, one of the least bizarre of his short stories: *The Gold Bug*. *The Gold Beetle*, as we should say. And though the writing of verse and even of poetry is seldom fated to be much more than its own reward, fiction may well be.

One of Poe's earliest stories, indeed, had won him a substantial prize; and it was only editorial discretion that had prevented him from carrying off a prize for the best poem also. 'Your *Raven*,' wrote Elizabeth Barrett from her sick couch in Wimpole Street, 'has produced a sensation. . . . Our great poet, Mr Robert Browning, was struck much by its rhythm.' There was little indeed to suggest that Poe had any extreme aversion to becoming a popular writer. Again and again success—and 'I mean,' the professor had emphasized, with a tap of his finger on the desk, 'I mean *material* success'—had been within his grasp. Yet his feeble fingers had refused to clutch at it.

None the less, the professor had refused to ally himself with those who maintain that to be popular is a proof of mediocrity. There were great books whose appeal is universal. Poe's triumphs, however, had been brief and very few. It could hardly be otherwise with a writer so egregious and idiosyncratic.

In spite of a personal charm and fascination almost hypnotic in effect, even at times on those of his own sex, Poe utterly refused to tolerate any opinions or convictions contrary to his own. He was obstinate and contumelious, scornful of the workaday graces that so sweeten human intercourse, and—to change the metaphor—*oil* the wheels of life. In his youth he had been treated harshly perhaps, had been denied what no doubt he regarded, but quite erroneously, as his rightful inheritance—his foster-father's fortune, for example; but he had failed to profit by so drastic a lesson. It could scarcely be said that it was the mere hardships of destiny that had prevented him from rivalling in general esteem even Longfellow himself, who, whatever his failings, seems to have been consistently true to his principles, was accepted as the laureate of his own people, and was a man of as many simple and homely qualities of head and heart as he was nobly leonine in appearance. And *he*, again, had made a fortune!

To compare, moreover, Poe's work with Emerson's was like comparing a neglected graveyard, dense with yew and cypress under the fitful lightings and showings of the moon, with a seemly, proportionate, if unadorned country parsonage, in the serene sunshine of a transatlantic morning in May. Man for man, Poe had not the virtues of Emerson, and Emerson had neither the exotic gifts nor the failings of Poe. Let us acknowledge it then. If in literature there is such a thing as the diseased, and even the sordid, why not attempt to exemplify, even though it was exceedingly difficult to define them? The professor had, rather tentatively, made the attempt.

On the technical side of Poe's work, he had himself always realized that his appreciation had been less full and less penetrating than it might have been. Here his lecture had skipped a little. But had it been otherwise how many of his listeners—those rows of silent faces—would have continued to listen? There were children among them. One little girl had a slumbering infant in her arms! Temper then the wind to the shorn lamb. Craftsmanship, artistry, he had announced however, is vital alike in prose and verse; but you cannot really separate words from what they say. And the highest art is the concealment of art; and, beyond that, the concealment of the concealment. Could this be said of Poe's technique? Is not rather one of the chief defects of his poems their flawless mastery of method? Poe, it seems, had never *lisped* in numbers, but (quite apart from his own account of the composition of *The Raven*), we know how laboriously many of his later numbers came.

Still, if writing is an art, so also in its modest way is the compiling of a lecture. The professor had dealt briefly with what he described as Poe's mere tricks as a versifier, his verbal repetitions, his childish delight in the jingling of rhymes, and in emphatic metres. He had referred to his theory and practice of lyrical brevity—and there is no such thing as a *poem* that cannot be read and enjoyed in the course of half an hour. There was, he agreed, a measure of truth in this, but surely it is a

question for the reader to decide—the reader, say, of the Iliad,
the Divine Comedy, the Prelude. For his part, there could not
be too much of a good thing. He had agreed also that the
primary impulse of poetry is the sharing of pleasure rather than
the teaching of lessons. But there are various kinds of pleasure,
they are of differing values; and poems whose chief appeal is to
the senses—whether they are in the nature of a stimulant or a
narcotic—should for that very reason be examined in the light
of reason.

He had, however, left that examination to his listeners, and
instead had specified where and when and to what end certain
of the poems had been written—*The Bells*, for example, which
from being a few lines enshrining an idyllic and rapturous
moment in the company of the charming but minor poetess,
Mrs Whitman, had gradually been expanded by the poet into
the rather heady masterpiece of its kind now only too familiar.
It had been not only easier but more practical to do this than
to attempt a close analysis.

Apropos of Mrs Whitman, he had broken off to refer to the
poet's rather numerous infatuations and attachments, or one
might almost say *de*tachments—those fleeting and even fugitive
Egerias—from the lovely and doomed Mrs Stannard, the original
of his Helen and the idolatry of his boyhood, to the ladies to
whom each in turn in his later years he had proposed—and indeed
almost insisted on—marriage: after the death, that is, of his
young wife Virginia. Like many other poets, Poe had loved at
times unwisely and by no means always too well. He had sipped
deep of the cup of feminine adulation—whatever its sediment
might be. Scandal in consequence had not spared him, nor even
slander, but for the most part it had left him unscathed.

The professor had referred in this connection to the poet's
childlike, ethereal, camellia-pale Virginia, 'the tragic bride of but
fourteen summers,' whose brief life, with all the recurrent horrors
shared by them both and incident to her fatal disease, had been
but a protracted journey to an early grave. And that said, how
could he but also refer to Poe's humiliating dependence on his
more than motherly mother-in-law, Mrs Clemm? Muddie, as
he called her, to whom he wrote letters as naturally affectionate
and commonplace as most of his correspondence tended to be
high-flown.

There were indeed episodes in Poe's life which it would be

futile to pass over, and impossible to condone—dismal lapses, even apart from those due to physical disability and the ravages of drugs. Truth imposes on us the obligation to record what only sympathy and indeed humility can help us to understand. None the less, he had tactfully, regretfully refrained from bestowing that scrutiny on 'the dark side of the poet's career' which one is apt to fix on a drop of ditch-water seen through a microscope. Not that Poe himself had spared others. As a critic alike of humanity and of literature, his bias was on the side of severity; he despised a fool, ridiculed failure, had no mercy on his enemies, and little patience with aims and ideals contrary to his own. Whatever the value of his writings might be, in Poe's eyes 'an inferior poem was little short of a crime.' An arrogant assurance of his own powers was alike his weakness and his strength.

Unlike Poe himself, however, the professor had endeavoured to be moderate. As briefly as possible, he had told of the poet's last few sombre and disastrous days at Baltimore, that final ignominy when he had been found in a high fever, half naked, and scarcely sane, in the clutches of political miscreants who had confined him merely in order that he should serve their purpose at the voting booth. He had spoken of the horror and solitude of his death in the public hospital, that last forlorn cry of: 'Is there any help? . . . Lord help my poor soul!' He had lamented that all this had occurred within a few hours of the first occasion in the poet's life when, restored to the Elmira whom in his early days he had loved and been cheated of, promise for the future had never seemed for him so fair, so full of hope, and rich with opportunity.

And as he said the words, a sudden overwhelming billow of mistrust had swept over the lecturer's soul. It was as if a complete flock of geese were disporting themselves on his grave Why, in Heaven's name, instead of perhaps a glimpse of Goya's serene yet appalling picture, 'The Pest House,' had Rembrandt's curiously detached study, 'An Anatomical Lesson,' flickered at this moment across his mind? And this when his paper was on the point of completion—fourteen minutes to nine?

Solely, it seemed, by reason of the presence of this one silent stranger yonder, who, as he himself raised his eyes from his desk to peer at him over his spectacles, had answered him look for look, scrutiny for scrutiny, a moment before. The lecturer had made no statement he was ashamed of; nothing false, nothing even dubious. And yet his words seemed to have lost their savour. But however that might be, he reminded himself that one cannot by mere wish to do so blot out the past. The mind itself must be its own sexton beetle. One cannot unsay the said, even in a lecture. The very attempt would be ludicrous. He was being fanciful. He was falling a victim to what he cordially despised—the artistic temperament! So late in life! He had come to lecture, yet to judge from this sudden disquietude, he was being 'larned.' Well, he must hasten on. Life, like a lecture, is a succession of moments. Don't pay too extreme an attention to any one or two; wait for the end of the hour.

'I think perhaps,' he was declaring at this moment, 'the most salient, the most impressive feature of Poe's writings, as with Dean Swift's, though the two men had little else in common, is his own personal presence in them. Even in his most exotic fantasies, some of them beautiful in the sense that the phosphorescence of decay, the brambles and briars of the ruinous, the stony calm of the dead may be said to be beautiful; some so sinister and macabre in their half-demented horror that if we ourselves encountered them even in dream we should awake screaming upon our beds—even here the sense of his peculiar personality is so vivid and immediate that, as we read, it is almost as if the poet himself stood in the flesh before us—in his customary suit of solemn black, the wide marmoreal brow, the corrosive tongue, the saturnine moodiness.

'Flaubert's ideal of the impersonal in fiction indeed was utterly beyond Poe. His presence pervades such a tale as *The Pit and the Pendulum, The Cask of Amontillado,* or *The Tell-tale Heart* no less densely than it pervades his *William Wilson,* his *Masque of the Red Death,* his *Ligeia,* and *The Haunted Palace.* This may in part be due to the fact that his was a mind at once acutely analytical and richly imaginative. This is a rare but by no means unique combination of what only appear to be contradictory faculties. Incapable of compromise, Poe had remained preposterously self-sufficient, self-immolating, and aloof; and, in spite of occasional gleams of sunshine, a moody, melancholy, and embittered man. He was thus alike the master and the victim of his destiny. If not a positive enemy of society, there is little to suggest that—apart from literature—he was ever much concerned with the social problems, causes, principles, and ideals of his own time and place. With some justification perhaps—as events have proved—he distrusted democracy, detested the mob, and he warned his fellow-countrymen of the sordid dangers incident to an ignorant republic. These views none the less were those of an egotist rather than an aristocrat. By birth he was of little account—the son of a mere travelling actor.

'Nor, though he had, it is true, been brought up in the traditions of a gentleman of the Southern States and abhorred all New Englanders, was he by any means a giant among pygmies. Longfellow, Emerson, Washington Irving, Bryant, Whittier, Thoreau, Oliver Wendell Holmes were in varying degrees his contemporaries; and, first cousin to him, in mind if not in blood, Nathaniel Hawthorne. Since, too, *The Gold Bug*, like *The Murders in the Rue Morgue*, is one of the earliest tales of its genre in English, and *Treasure Island* is one of its remoter offspring, one might add Fenimore Cooper. He had lived, that is, in one of the Golden Ages of English literature—not that of our own day, the Brass.

'As for J. R. Lowell, an admirable critic of the widest range, in his knowledge alike of books, men, and affairs, though he was responsible for the caustic summary of Poe's work as three-fifths genius and two-fifths fudge, he was one of his closest and loyalest friends.

'I am not,' announced at last the professor, wearily, and never before had he been so tired of the sound of his own voice, 'I am not a mathematician, and cannot check Professor Lowell's vulgar fractions. But even if allowance be made for the fact that here in England even the parochial are inclined to sneer at the provincialism of all things American, it must be remembered that for years Poe was anathema, a man accursed among his own people. And it is certainly not in this country that since his death his work has been neglected. It had *not* been a beneficent influence'—the professor had once more assured his audience; and that not merely because 'it is easier to imitate fudge than works of genius. What a man does, however, must not mislead us in our judgment of what he *is*. Poe was a round peg in a square hole. The wise and the prudent in this world make the best they can of these conditions. Not so this ill-fated, saturnine, sinister poet. Whatever our debt to him may be, *he* flatly refused to follow their example.'

During the pause that completed this sentence—perhaps a

tenth part of a second—some imp in the professor's mind engaged in a violent argument with him as to which kind of peg and in what kind of hole he was himself just now; and then reminded him that pegs and holes may be of many shapes other than merely square or round—ovals, hexagons, oblongs, polygons. But he knew this imp of old, and dismissed him.

And now his lecture, which for the first time in his placid career had been little short of a martyrdom, was all but over. Though his air and manner conveyed no symptom of what was in his mind, hotly debating, ill at ease, dejected, not a little indignant, he had come to his peroration. Yet once again he lowered his head for a final fleeting glimpse of the stranger in the doorway, and ejaculated the few sentences that remained.

The last syllable had been uttered. His task was done. He had shut his mouth. For an instant he stood in silence facing his listeners—an intellectual St Sebastian—no less mute and more defenceless than an innocent in the dock. At the next he had turned stiffly, had gravely inclined his head in the direction of his chairman, and had sat down. He crossed his legs, he closed his eyes, he folded his arms. Though the electric vibrations of the hideous arc-lamp over his head continued to quiver beneath his skull, though a vile disquietude still fretted his soul, he had come back safely into his shell again. A moment before he had been a public spectacle; now he was private again; his own man and all but at liberty. Even better, he had ceased to criticize himself.

He was listening instead to his chairman, a smallish man in a clerical collar, and, in spite of that clerical collar, attired in a suit of a cloth much nearer grey than black. He had a square head, square shoulders, square hands, and a plain, good-natured, eager, and amusing face. Those hands were now in rapid motion in a mutual embrace one of the other; and, with enviable ease and fluency, he was assuring his audience how much they had all been instructed and entertained. He was rapidly confessing, too, that he had himself come to the meeting that evening knowing very little of Mr Edgar Poe's works. The name was familiar—but some of us hadn't much time for fiction. So far as he himself was concerned, life *was* real and earnest. He had, it is true, taken a hasty glance at a page or two of what appeared to be a very clever and harmless tale entitled *The Purloined*

Letter, and believed he could recite then and there the first few lines of *Annabel Lee*, *not* by the way to be confused with an old wholesome favourite of his, *Nancy Lee*. Their lecturer, however, had not, he fancied, mentioned this particular piece, and had passed over this story, though he had referred to others that were concerned with an even graver crime than that of pilfering, nay—let us give the dog the name he deserves—*stealing* a letter. He meant, brutal murder. There were far too many murders in the fiction of our own day. On the other hand, an orang-outang, whatever its extremes of conduct may be, has not been given a conscience. He is not *morally* responsible. Man, whether his descendant or not, *is*.

Tales of crime were, alas! very prevalent in these days, much too prevalent, he feared. Quite respectable and well-educated people not only read but wrote them. They were yet another symptom of the unrest of the age. The professor had, of course, referred to America—the United States. Was it to be credited that in that great English-speaking country the harmless if slightly colloquial expression, 'Taking a man for a ride,' actually signified consigning a fellow-soul into eternity? On the other hand Mr Edgar Poe, he gathered, could not be held responsible for the present sad state of Chicago. He understood he was a Virginian, a Southerner, and though one of the tales mentioned by the professor bore what he feared was the only too appropriate title, *MS. Found in a Bottle*, the poet, it seemed, had lived not only prior to the Civil War, but long before the days of Prohibition. That, however, was only a blessing in disguise. For in view of what the lecturer had said of Mr Poe's sad and afflicting end, they must remember that those responsible for the Volstead Act had *meant* well. There were tragedies in every life, skeletons in every cupboard. And the lecturer's subject was no exception. As for his marriage with a wife then only fourteen years of age, though no doubt it is true that Juliet in the play was also of equally tender years, she was emphatically not Romeo's first cousin. He himself could not approve of this arrangement. We mustn't run headlong into wedlock.

Then, again, he heartily agreed with the lecturer that the piece *To Helen* was a remarkable feat for a lad in his early teens —*most* remarkable. But he deplored any suggestion that *all* lads of fourteen should be encouraged to be equally precocious. There were dangers. Even, too, though a man may be his own worst enemy, he may yet attain renown as a writer. Poe himself had. Nevertheless he implored them one and all to remember that it is better by far for ever to hold one's peace than to write, however attractively, what it may some day be too late to recall. That solemn thought, he gathered, was their lecturer's urgent lesson to them this evening.

Before, he concluded, before inviting that stronghold of their society, Miss Alibone, to propose a vote of thanks to Professor Monk, he would like to announce that at their next meeting their old friend Mr Alfred Okes, so busy in so many fields, was to talk to them on the subject of conchology—the science of sea-shells, from the whelk to the conch—the latter being famous in mythology, though it was frequently mispronounced. And on *that* occasion there would be lantern slides.

'I ask you, sir'—he suddenly rounded on the professor with the most tactful and endearing of smiles—'I ask you, sir, to accept our heartiest, our most cordial thanks for your most entertaining, informative, and, I will add, even edifying discourse. We have been well fed.'

The professor unsealed his tired eyes, looked up, smiled a little wanly, and hastily pocketed his paper. In a few minutes, the hall already nearly empty, he had followed his chairman down the five well-worn, red-druggeted steps into the ante-chamber. There he was welcomed by a row of empty wooden chairs, a solid grained table, a copper-plate engraving in a large black frame over the chimney-piece of a gentleman in side-whiskers, whose name, owing to the foxed condition of the print, he had been unable to decipher, and the ashes of a fire in the grate. It had been feebly alight when he arrived. It was now dead out. Why did this seemingly harmless chamber at this moment resemble the scene of a nightmare? He could not tell. His chairman seemed to be finding nothing amiss with it. He was adjusting his grey woollen muffler, he had bidden him a hearty good night, he had turned away, adding jovially over his shoulder, as he hurried forth: 'Ah, Professor Monk, here's a little friend to see you—eager no doubt to drink at the fountain-head. Come in, my dear'—and was gone.

The little friend, however, who was now beaming at the professor from under a dark felt, medallioned school-hat and from behind gold spectacles straddling a small, blunt, resolute nose, was in fact anxious only to secure his autograph and still more

anxious to discover if he could possibly be related to Miss *Mima*
Monk, the famous film star. 'It 's the same name, you see,' she
said, 'that 's why.'

Alas! the professor was compelled to confess, he had no relatives in the neighbourhood of Los Angeles. He opened the little
green and gold birthday book, and turned a little wearily to
November 8, to read: 'Words are the only things that last for
ever.—*William Hazlitt.*' The child watched him as he made the
dot after his sedate signature a little more emphatic.

'We 've learned some of Mr Poe's poems in class,' she was
assuring him breathlessly. '*I* think it 's *lovely*. Our teacher
says *The Bells* is meant to sound like real bells—it 's all imitation.'

'Yes, indeed,' the professor replied, 'it is called onomatopoeia.'

'Omonatopoe-oe-oeia,' she trebled after him like a wren, and
with yet another coy and beaming smile had taken her book
and departed.

Her footsteps, it seemed, had suddenly quickened into a
scamper, then she too was gone. The professor sighed, and rose
from his chair. And then, suddenly transfixed, with one arm
actually half-way through the sleeve of his antiquated mackin-
tosh, he turned, realizing that what he had vaguely foreseen and
apprehended had come to pass.

The gentleman in the black cloak until this moment unperceived in the shadow at the turn of the door had advanced into
the room, and was now confronting him from the other end of
the varnished table. The glass-shaded electric lamp that hung
between them shed a lustre almost as of alabaster on his pallid
face and wide prominent forehead—a pallor intensified by the
darkness of his long hair, the marked eyebrows, the small
moustache. He was a man seemingly aged about forty, rather
under the middle height, and spare, but he carried himself with
an air of elegance, a trace even of the foppish. His black beaver
hat clasped between his delicate hands, he remained silent and
motionless, his chin, the least vigorous of his finely cut features,
lowered upon his black satin stock, his dark luminous grey eyes
fixed on the professor's face. There was a peculiar abstraction,
even vacancy in their depths—a slightly catlike appearance, as
if they were not wholly in focus; and this, in spite of the intense
regard in them—a regard which brought to the professor's mind
a phrase he had read somewhere—'they seemed to shed darkness in that place.' And though they expressed no hostility,

and Professor Monk had the advantage in stature, he was finding it difficult to meet them. They were strangely *occupied* eyes. Besides, the hall outside was now not only silent but empty; and it was atrociously cold.

The imp within his mind had begun chattering again. 'He stoppeth one of three,' was echoing in the professor's consciousness. Why *The Ancient Mariner*? The cold, perhaps. Meanwhile, he realized that he must break *this* ice. His silence was becoming discourteous. He glanced again at his visitor, and was again sharply reminded that he bore a striking resemblance . . . To what? To whom? There had been no pause in which to collect his thoughts. The professor met many strangers; how could he be expected with all the good will in the world to recall always either themselves or their names? Names are at best but labels.

'*Er*—good evening——' he began—but a low, insistent voice had broken in on him.

'Where *is* this place?' it was inquiring.

'This place? *Where?*' exclaimed the professor. 'Wigston, you mean?'

'Wigston—ah, yes. And England?'

The professor continued to listen, the prey now of another kind of discomfort. There are degrees of eccentricity—and he was alone.

'*That* was my impression,' the other was saying. 'And these people'—he raised his hat in a peculiarly graceful gesture towards the doorway—'these people were not completely ignorant of the subject of your address?'

'Indeed, no'; a deprecating smile had crept into the professor's face; 'though we mustn't of course expect——.' But he was not allowed to complete his sentence.

'And you yourself must have been deeply interested in your theme to venture on compounding a complete lecture upon it. Fifty-three minutes in all!'

'Indeed, yes,' interjected the professor warmly.

'I see.' The stranger paused. 'I observed that the date on the notice-board facing the street is 2nd November, and the year 1932. You will realize that I have myself come some little distance. There are—difficulties. But it was rather the name than the date which attracted me. Edgar Allan Poe's, I mean, and your own, too, of course. I fear I cannot compliment you upon its appearance.'

'My name! . . . Oh, yes, the street?' said the professor.

'Rain so sooty-dark upon a scene so dismal, the niggardly glare, the stench, and what might be described as the realism of it all! You yourself perhaps are unfamiliar with Virginia—Richmond, Charlottesville, the South. You are from Oxford, perhaps? Has that ancient seat of learning also endured of late the ravages of change?'

The slim erect figure had bowed slightly—with a deprecating politeness. The professor shook his head. 'No, not Oxford; London,' he said.

'Ah, yes, London. I am from . . .' But at this moment, unfortunately, the neighbouring foundry had once more metallically ejected its slag, and the word was lost. 'So Edgar Allan Poe'—his visitor pronounced the syllables as if they were in the nature of a sarcasm or even a jest—'so Edgar Allan Poe is remembered even in this benighted town?'

'Remembered!' cried the professor. 'Why, yes, indeed. My whole intention was to suggest for what reason he should be remembered. The acoustics of the hall, perhaps——'

'But, indeed,' the stranger was assuring him, 'I heard perfectly. I was engrossed. Engrossed. A host of remote memories, echoes, speculations returned into my mind. But I have ventured to intrude on you, not to pay compliments which you might find wearisome, but in the hope that you will allow me—even at this late day and hour—to ask you one or two questions.'

The professor's dark eyebrows expressed a faint surprise. 'As a matter of fact——' he began.

'Oh, yes,' the visitor hastened to add, 'I was aware that your chairman had invited questions—with a disarming cordiality indeed. But though, professor, you had remarkably attentive listeners, you will agree perhaps that they were rather passively receptive than actively critical. That was my *impression*. There is an old saying: Every time a sheep bleats it loses a mouthful. Well, yours at least never bleated. Apart from that, however, there are questions it may be more courteous to ask in private. Such as mine. May I continue?'

'By all means.' The professor's eye ranged furtively over the intensely unoccupied row of hard-wood chairs. 'Won't you sit down?'

'Thank you,' said the stranger; 'when I disagree I prefer to stand. I have come, as you see, unarmed, except in respect of the tongue. We are on equal terms, then, though you might perhaps agree that in matters of the mind one solitary question may be almost mortal in effect. First, then, am I justified in deducing from what you have said that one word would summarize your own personal attitude towards the man of letters you have lately been dissecting: the word "scorn"? You were at pains, I admit, to disguise it, to salve in one sentence the wound given by another. But the tone, the flavour, the accent —I could not be mistaken. And is not scorn, professor, a dubious incitement for the critic, the expounder, the appreciator of any artist and his work? Moreover, it is one thing to despise a fellow-creature, another to malign him.'

'Malign!' cried the professor. 'My sole aim and intention was to tell the truth.'

'Ay, and so you dragged the well. And *I* am now enjoying the flavour of its dregs. You had ninety-eight listeners this evening. I myself counted them. You gave me plenty of time—between your ideas, I mean. That was fortunate. Your *poet*, let me inform you, once read his *Eureka*—an essay in the imaginative synthesis of philosophical and scientific thought which you evaded so skilfully by the mere mention of it—he read, I say, his *Eureka*—his mistress jewel—on a stormy night in a bitterly cold hall in Richmond before an audience of only sixty souls in all. It occupied two hours and a half. You and your hungry little flock, then, had not only the easier ordeal, but also a less difficult subject-matter. Apart from the title of your paper, you divided it into four parts: The Environment; the Man; the Tales and Poems; the Aftermath. Am I right? Superficially, that is a simple and lucid arrangement. Did you keep to it? Hardly. Again and again, like the moth to the candle—or shall we say, to the star!—you returned to the poet's private life, to his unhappy childhood, aureoled, in your own pinchbeck phrase, "with the chameleonic hues of romance." To the follies and misfortunes of his youth, to his failures, his poverty, his bereavements, his afflictions of body and mind, and what you supposed to be his soul—to his miserable death. Well, we live and die, and must leave posterity to do its best—and its worst—with us. But was it necessary to regale your docile and ignorant audience with allusions to the poet's young mother, the forsaken, penniless actress, and to *her* vile, tragic death in a filthy tenement when he himself was a child? I grant you his Helen. She even reminded your quick wits of Troy. But what of his simple-minded and afflicted sister Eulalie? What of exhuming into the light of night the very remains of his ever-youthful and long-suffering Virginia —to pry and peer into *their* sacred secrets? You used the word morbid. Whose was the morbid, yes, and the sordid, when you declared that those poor relics had actually lain concealed awhile under the bed of one of her husband's besotted biographers? The ashes of Annabel Lee, forsooth! And selfless and faithful old Mrs Clemm, *her* mother, *his* more-than-mother, with her basket of broken meats collected from door to door to save her loved ones from starvation. And the poet's cloak, that in those icy winters in New York had to serve by day as a protection for his own wretched back, and by night as a coverlet for his dying Virginia's bed. You used the term, tragedy, professor; why did you turn it into a melodrama? Is there to be no humanity, on decent reticence concerning the life of a man who is dead, mainly because he was a writer? Is *every* poet at the hands of *any* showman doomed to suffer again and again the pangs of a Monsieur Waldemar? I ask you—I put the question.'

'Let me repeat,' said the professor frigidly, 'you have mis-judged my intention. You imply that a man's circumstances in life have no relation to his actions, to his principles, to his ideals. I deny it. Knowledge aids understanding. How else explain, excuse, condone?'

'Condone! It was, then, with the same compassionate aim that, having condensed a lifetime of forty years—not an ex-orbitant allowance—into a sensational and appetizing quarter of an hour, you dealt with the *man*? It was perhaps your passion for moderation that persuaded you only to hint at such words as mountebank, ingrate, wastrel, fortune-hunter, seducer, debauchee, dipsomaniac. Hints serve better. But words, professor, have the strange power of revealing not merely what a man consciously intends to say, but what, perhaps unknown to himself, he means and feels. And the simplest of your listeners can have been in little doubt of that. I confess to perplexity. Have the poets themselves ever claimed to be saints? Have the most exemplary of them ever professed to be anything but sinners? Name me one poet, one imaginative writer even, of any account, whom you yourself suspect of believing that his failings as a man in any sense or degree *aided* his genius. They may profess it—but not within themselves! Oh, yes, I agree that a man's writings indelibly reflect him and all of him that matters most. And since your poet's are all that is left of him in this world, and they alone are of lasting value, should we not look for him there? Did you attempt to depict, to describe, to illuminate that reflection? No: for that would have needed insight, the power to divine, to re-create. *You* are a stern and ardent moralist, professor. But since when has the platform become a pulpit? It needs, too, little courage to attack and stigmatize the dead.'

The stranger's wandering gaze had returned slowly to the professor's face. 'Provided, of course, you are confident that dead he will remain. None the less it seems to me a rather paltry amusement—carrion stuff.'

'I say again,' cried Professor Monk hotly, 'truth was my aim. I resent this attack. It is beside the point.'

'For my part,' said the other, 'I resent nothing. I am here merely to "drink from the fountain-head." But even if we admit that from his childhood up, as a human being, gentleman, and Christian, your poet fell far short even of the happy mean, is there no other standard by which to judge him? The decalogue he shared with every man, and, like most men, and many professors, he would long since have been forgotten if he had not proved himself—I will not venture to say worthy of remembrance, but—defiant of oblivion. What he *might* have done even in spite of his miseries and weaknesses, his tortured nerves and treacherous body—*that* no man can declare. But in respect, professor, to what he actually *did*—as an artist, a man of letters, a poet? Does that suggest that he ever consented to sell the smallest fraction of his soul for bread, or wine, or—brief anodyne against a world which he himself had no hand in creating—even drugs? Did he condescend to write down to his readers; or, worse, up? Did he betray his intelligence; prostitute his mind; parade his heart? Did he even attempt to improve the *shining* hour? You would agree that the writer in his solitude must obey scruples, hold fast to an aesthetic probity, serve with a forlorn devotion in a cause which the generality of men know nothing of. But *his* laws are unwritten laws. Not that I suggest that your victim even in this was blameless—far from it. But you yourself seem never to have been aware of such an ordeal. You made pretty play with the artistic temperament—with your morbid, and your moody, and your melancholy, and your misanthrope—but of the artist's *conscience* not one word.'

'Even if your allegations were not grossly exaggerated,' said the professor, 'surely there is little novelty in such a notion, and I had to consider my listeners.'

'Had the poets,' said the other, 'put their faith solely in novelty and considered only their listeners, there would have been no *Paradise Lost*, no *Hamlet*, and a few of the Greek tragedies. Surely only an artist's *best* is worth his trouble? And that being so—Heaven help him—can he, *need* he care who shares it? Let me repeat, I am not defending Mr Poe, God forbid; he is gone long since, as your genial friend the minister on the platform would put it, to his account. It could be only then in the strangeness of some sepulchral dream that he could or would return to a world he little liked, and was little liked by. But all this apart—these dingy relics, I mean, the unsavoury events of his life and the invaluable lessons to be derived from them: what conceivable concern had they with the very subject of your paper?'

The slate-grey eyes peered out dark with anger from behind the glass of their spectacles. 'Subject?'

'It has escaped your memory, it seems. Read your own handbills then. "The *Writings* of Edgar Allan Poe."'

'That is a quibble.'

'It is essential. Your better nature gave you the title of your paper. Your worse followed the easier, the more appetizing, the more popular, the charnel-house treatment of your theme.'

A pallor almost as extreme as that of his visitor had spread over Professor Monk's features. A hatred of this stranger, a hatred not the less bitter for being now innocent of contempt, was stirring in his mind. His glance fell from the fixed eyes to the thin satirical lips and thence to the delicate hands, but he realized that this petty effort to appear indifferent had woefully failed him. 'I consider,' he managed to say, in a low, hardly articulate voice, 'I consider this is an outrage and an insult.'

'That may well be so,' responded his visitor, with a hardly perceptible shrug of his cloaked shoulder. 'And I believe if your poet were here—I mean, professor, in the flesh—that he too would not hesitate to agree with you. But let us be honest

for a moment. Apart from other writers—Thomas Lovell
Beddoes and a Miss Brontë—you mentioned James Clarence
Mangan, hinting that possibly Poe himself definitely stole,
cheated him of his technique. Did you produce one single
syllable in proof of this? And if you had, when, may I ask
you, were poets forbidden to gild the silver they borrow? You
said that Poe shared with these writers something of their
dreams, their visions, their frail hopes and aspirations. How
far did you inform us regarding the meaning, the source, the
value and reality, quite apart from the fascination of those
dreams? Poe's complete mortal existence was a conflict with
his woe of spirit, his absorption in death and the grave, his
horror of the solitude of the soul, of the nightmares that ascended
on him like vultures from out of the pit of hell when he lay on
his hospital death bed. What do *you* know of these? What
will your listeners find of comfort, of reassurance in your academic mouthings and nothings when *they* come to face their
terrors of the mind, *that* unshatterable solitude?

'My only speculation is not concerning which of the authors
you mentioned you know least about, but what conceivable
satisfaction you found in reading their books. And believe me,
my dear professor, your groping remarks on poetic technique
were nothing short of fatuous. Not only can you never have
written a line of verse yourself, unless perhaps as an inky schoolboy you thumped out a molossus or a spondee or two on your
desk, but you can never even have read with any insight the
poet's essay on the subject. Indeed, what is your definition of
poetry? Did you refer to his? It is deplorable enough that
you have confused the imagination, that sovereign power, that
divine energy, with a mere faculty. Reason, yes. But is not
man's feeblest taper, like the sun itself in heaven, a *dual*
splendour—of heat *and* light? Are you aware that you made
no use of the word intellect, or divination, or afflatus, ay, and
worse, even music? Did not Poe himself maintain that "in
enforcing a truth, we must be simple, precise, terse. We must
be cool, calm, unimpassioned. In a word, we must be in that
mood which, as nearly as possible, is the exact converse of the
poetical?" That, you may claim, was a mood you endeavoured
to share. But did *he* never share it? Was opium or Hippo-
crene his aid in that? How then can you justify your commen-
dation of that vain piping wiseacre Emerson, who in his own

practice suggested that poetry is skim-milk philosophy and
flowery optimism cut up into metre, and dismissed all else as
jingle? Or your half-hearted rejection of Mr Henry James's
shallow gibe, "very superficial verse." Is beauty the less
admirable because it is skin deep? I know little of Mr James,
but assume from what you yourself said of him that one might
as justly dismiss his fiction as sillily super-subtle psychology.
Was *he* a devotee of the Muses—of Music? *Music*, let me quote
again, "music when combined with a pleasurable idea, is poetry;
music without the idea is simply music; the idea, without the
music, is prose, from its very definiteness."'

'Who said that?'

'Ah! Is it sense or nonsense?'

'I had an hour,' muttered the professor tartly, 'not all night.'

'And what virtual service,' continued his visitor more genially,
'is there in comparing poems different in aim, in kind, and in
quality? Has not even the ass its own niche in the universe?
Is not every work of art—yes, even your own lecture—something
single, unique; and are these precious comparisons anything
better than mere mental exercises? Heaven forbid, and heaven
forbids much, that I should legislate in such matters. My mere
question is, how can *you*? Believe me, while what you told us
of creative insight—invention as you called it—might set any
sensitive human heart aching with despair, your remarks on
the art of writing were nothing short of a treason to the mind.
They were based on inadequate knowledge, and all but innocent
of common sense. Have you ever read that Poe never *laughed*?
Perhaps not. And you had no reason to notice that one at least
of your listeners refrained even from smiling, though on my soul
I can imagine no moment in which he would be more bitterly
tempted to indulge in the cachinnation of fools than in this.

'"Questions"—questions! I awaited in vain the faintest
intimation that our poet was perhaps the first of his kind to
foresee the triumphs and the tyranny of modern science; that
he was no mere groping novice in astronomy, physics, and the
science of the mind. Creature of darkness his imagination may
have been: but was there no light in his *mind*? If you could
meet him face to face, professor, at this moment, here, now—
I ask you, I entreat you to confide in me, would you deny him
the light of his Reason? Would you? You might even try to
forgive his extravagances, his miseries; you might even agree that

even four-score years of purgation could hardly serve to annul the habits of a lifetime; and that yet in spite of his discordant nature, his self-isolation, he was happier in the solitary company of his own miserable soul than . . . But I must refrain from being wearisome. I will burden you with but one more quotation:

"We have still a thirst unquenchable. . . . It belongs to the immortality of man. . . . It is no mere appreciation of the beauty before us, but a wild effort to reach the beauty above . . . to attain a portion of that loveliness whose very elements perhaps appertain to eternity alone. . . ."

'Those tears, then, that respond to poetry and music are not from "excess of pleasure, but through a certain petulant, impatient sorrow at our inability to grasp *now*, wholly, here on earth, at once and for ever, those divine and rapturous joys of which, *through* the poem, or *through* the music, we attain to but brief and indeterminate glimpses." These words, professor, though you are evidently unaware of it, were Edgar Allan Poe's. And I—I myself have as yet found no reason to retract the conviction of their truth.'

Professor Monk's apprehension that his visitor, if not positively insane, was far from 'normal,' had become a certainty. Their eyes, or rather the sentinels that look out of them, had met again. Who goes *there*? they had cried one on the other. And again it was the professor's that had returned no countersign. But dislike—a transitory hatred even—of his censor had fallen away into a sort of incredulity. That he should have consented to such a catechism. That a mere lecture should have led to this! He had been hardly troubling indeed to follow the meaning of the last remarks he had heard. His sole resource was to mutter that though he was grateful for his visitor's suggestions, it was clear that they would never see eye to eye in these matters, that the hour was growing late, and that he must be gone. He even managed to grimace a slant but not unkindly smile. 'We live in two worlds,' he said, 'you and I, and I fear we shall never agree. None the less, and though you prefer to doubt it, I share your interest and delight in poetry, and, within strict limits, your admiration of Poe.' He cast a forlorn glance towards his hat perched in solitude upon a chair. 'We shall at least, I hope,' he added, 'part friends.'

'So be it,' replied his visitor, drawing his cloak more closely around him, raising slowly his heavy head.

'The cock he hadna crawed but once,
  And clapped his wings at a',
Whan the youngest to the eldest said,
  Brother we must awa'. . . .

I also must be gone. We have met by chance. Let us not
make it a fatality. By just such a chance indeed as that in
your dreams to-night you may find yourself in regions such as
our poet described, and may not, I fear, find much comfort in
them. So, too, this evening, I found myself—well, here: in a
region, that is, which it is your own excellent fortune to occupy
and which is yet of little comfort to me. Is there not a shade of
the Satanic in these streets? But what are waking and dreaming, my dear sir? Mere states of consciousness; as too in a
sense is this, your world of what you call the actual, and the
one that may await you. Opinions, views, passing tastes,
passing prejudices—they are like funguses, a growth of the
night. But the moon of the imagination, however fickle in her
phases, is still constant in her borrowed light, and sheds her
beams on them one and all, the just and the unjust. We may
meet again.'

The dark, saturnine head had trembled a little, the weak yet
stubborn mouth had stirred into a faint smile as the stranger
thrust out an ungloved hand from beneath his cloak over the
varnished wood of the table. Professor Monk hesitated, but
only for a moment. Critic though he might be, and so not by
impulse a man of action, he was neither timid nor unforgiving.
His fingers met an instant the outstretched hand, and instantly
withdrew, not because he had regretted the friendly action, but
because of the piercing cold that had run through his veins at
this brief contact. A sigh shook him from head to foot. A
slight vertigo overcame him. He raised his hand to his eyes.
For an instant it seemed as though even his sense of reality had
cheated him—had foundered.

And when he looked out into the world again his visitor had
left him. At last he was indeed alone. He stayed a moment,
still dazed, and staring at nothing. Then he glanced at his mute
typescript on the table, and then furtively into the grate. He
paused, musing. His fingers fumbled in his waistcoat pocket,
but encountered only a penknife. It was in part with a penknife, and when seated in his winter house before a burning fire,

that King Jehoiakim had destroyed the Prophet Jeremiah's manuscript. But though, unlike the angel's little book in Revelations, the professor's paper was no longer sweet on his tongue, and there were a few dead coals at hand, he had no matches. His evening had wearied him, but this vile altercation seemed to have sapped his very life. Had he changed his views concerning the genius of Poe as a writer?—not by one iota. As a man? He had always, he realized, disliked and distrusted him; now he hated him. But this was immaterial. An absurd conviction of his own futility had shaken and shocked him. Life itself is a thing of moments, the last being its momentary apex. And *now* he felt as dead and empty as some sad carcass suspended eviscerated from a butcher's hook. By a piece of mere legerdemain in this cold and hideous room his view of himself and even of his future had completely changed. The pattern in the kaleidoscope—was that then nothing but a trick? A few dull fallen fragments of glass now, and no pattern at all? Being a man of habit and purpose and precision, Professor Monk was well aware that a drug, however potent, and whatever its origin, wears out at length its own effects. So with this evening's enterprise; he might, he *would*, soon be his own man again. But meanwhile . . . well, he would await the morrow, when perhaps his second thoughts would be less impetuous—and he himself less hideously cold.

He stooped awkwardly for his hat, and as he did so caught a glimpse of the little wizened, warty, bent-up old caretaker peering in at the doorway. 'Ah, there you are, sir,' he was assuring him, with the utmost friendliness. 'I was beginning to think you had passed out without my seeing you. They do sometimes. No hurry, sir.' Professor Monk hesitated; then paused; while yet again the adjacent foundry discarded its slag.

'Which way did that—er—gentleman go?' he inquired.

'Gentleman, sir? I've set eyes on no gentleman. Except for one of them saucy young schoolgirls from St Ann's half an hour ago, I see them all come along out together like rain out of a gutter-pipe. And the Reverend Mortimer hard at heel after them. It's fine now, sir, and starry, but the wind's rising. I have been talking with a friend.'

'Ah, yes. Thank you!' replied the professor. But it was well under his breath that he repeated, 'Ah, yes.'

From *The Wind Blows Over*.

LICHEN

Ther cam a privee theef, men clepeth Deeth,
That in this contree al the peple sleeth,
And with his spere he smoot his herte a-two,
And wente his wey with-outen wordes mo . . .

EXCEPT for one domed and mountainous cloud of snow and amber, the sky was blue as a child's eyes, blue as the tiny chasing butterflies which looped the air above our shimmering platform —bluer far, in fact, than my new silk sunshade. I just sat and basted my travel-wearied bones in the sunshine; and thanked heaven for so delicious a place to be alive in.

It was, I agree, like catching sight of it in hungry glimpses through a rather dingy window. There had been frequent interruptions. First had come a goods train. It had shunted this way, it shunted that. Its buffers crashed; its brakes squealed; its sheep baa-ed, and its miserable, dribbling cattle, with their gleaming horns, stared blindly out at us under their long eyelashes in a stagnant dumb despair.

When that had gone groaning on its way, a 'local'—a kind of nursery train—puff-puffed in on the other side. And then we enjoyed a Strauss-like interlude of milk-cans and a vociferous Sunday school excursion—the scholars (merely tiny tots, many of them) engaged even on this weekday in chaunting at intervals the profoundest question Man can address to the Universe: 'Are we downhearted? No!'

These having at last wandered off into a dark-mouthed tunnel, the noonday express with a wildly soaring crescendo of lamentation came sweeping in sheer magnificence of onset round its curve, roared through the little green empty station—its windows a long broken faceless glint of sunlit glass—and that too vanished. Vanished!

A swirl of dust and an unutterable stillness followed after it. The skin of a banana on the platform was the only proof that it had come and gone. Its shattering clamour had left for contrast an almost helpless sense of peace. 'Yes, yes!' we all seemed to be whispering—from the Cedar of Lebanon to the little hyssop in the wall—'here we all are; and still, thank heaven, safe. *Safe.*'

The snapdragons and sweet-williams burned on in their narrow flint-bordered bed. The hollow of beautiful verdure but a stone's throw beyond the further green bank, with its square bell-tower and its old burial stones, softly rang again with faint trillings. I turned instinctively to the old gentleman who was sharing the hard, 'grained,' sunny bench with me, in sure and certain hope of his saying Amen to my relief. It was a rather heedless impulsiveness, perhaps; but I could not help myself—I just turned.

But no. He tapped the handle of his umbrella with gloved fingers. 'As you will, ma'am,' he said pettishly. 'But *my* hopes are in the past.'

'I was merely thinking,' I began, 'the contrast, you know; and now—how peaceful it all is.'

He interrupted me with a stiff little bow. 'Precisely. But the thought was sentimental, ma'am. You would deafen us all to make us hear. You tolerate what you should attack—the follies, vexations, the evils which that pestilent monster represents; haste, restlessness, an impious money-grubbing. I hate the noise; I hate the trespass; the stench; the futility. Fifty years ago there wasn't a sound for leagues about us but the wind and the birds. Few came; none went. It was an earthly Paradise. And over there, as you see, lay its entry elsewhither. Fifty years ago you could have cradled an infant on that old tombstone yonder—Zadakiel Puncheon's—and it would have slept the sun down. Now, poor creature, his ashes are jarred and desecrated a dozen times a day—by mechanisms like *that*!'

He flicked a gaudy bandana handkerchief in the direction the departing dragon had taken—a dragon already leagues out of sight and hearing.

'But how enchanting a name!' I murmured placatingly. 'Zadakiel Puncheon! It might have come out of Dickens, don't you think—a godfather of Martin Chuzzlewit's? Or, better still, Nathaniel Hawthorne.'

He eyed me suspiciously over his steel spectacles. 'Well, Dickens, maybe. But Hawthorne: I admit him reluctantly; a writer, with such a text to his hand that——. And how many,

pray, of his fellow-countrymen ever read him; and how many of
them pay heed to him?'

'But surely,' I interposed hastily, 'think of St Francis, of
Madame Guyon, of—of all the mystics! Or even of the cities
where, you know, Lot . . . just the five righteous. . . . Besides,
even though Hawthorne didn't preach—well, hard *enough*;
even if *no* one reads him, we can't blame Dickens—we've no
right to do that. *Surely I*' I had grown quite eloquent—
and scarlet.

He waved me blandly aside. 'I blame nobody, my dear
young lady. Mine are merely old-fashioned opinions; and I
have no wish to enforce them. Nor even to share them. My
views, I mean '—he whisked me a generous little bow—'not these
few sunny minutes. They indeed are a rare privilege. No,
I loved old things when I was a child; I love them now. I
despise nothing simply because the Almighty has concealed its
uses. I see no virtue in mere size, or in mere rapidity of motion.
Nor can I detect any particular preciousness in time "saved,"
as you call it, merely to be wasted.'

The gay handkerchief flicked these sentiments to the heavens
as if in contemptuous challenge of the complete Railway Com-
panies of the Solar System, and dismayed with the burden of
my responsibility, I gazed out once more into the bird-enchanted,
shadowy greenland—whispering its decoy to us immediately
on the other side of its low stone wall.

A brief silence fell. There seemed suddenly to be nothing
left to talk about. The old gentleman peered sidelong at me
an instant, then thrust out a cramped-up hand, and lightly
touched my sleeve.

'I see you don't much affect my old-fashioned tune, ma'am.
But such things will not pester you for long. Most of my school
have years since set out on the long vacation. Soon they'll be
packing me off too; and not a soul left to write my epitaph. . . .

'Here lies old bones;
Sam Gilpin once.

'How'll that do, heh?' He rocked gently on his gingham.
'"Sam Gilpin once. . . ."' But that's gone too,' he added, as
if he were over-familiar with the thought.

'But I *do* understand, perfectly,' I managed to blurt out at
last. 'And I agree. And it's hateful. But we can't help

ourselves! You see we *must* go on. It 's the—the momentum;
the sheer impetus.'

He openly smiled on me. 'Well, well, well!' he said. '*Must*
go on, eh? And soon, too, must I. So we 're both of a mind
at last. And that being so, I wish I could admit you into my
museum over yonder. It is my last resource. I spend a
peaceful hour in it whenever I can. Hardly a day passes just
now but I make my pilgrimage there—between (to be precise,
my dear young lady)—between the 7.23 *up* and the 8.44 *down*.'

'And there are epitaphs?' I cried gaily, with that peculiar
little bell-peal in the voice, I 'm afraid, which one simply cannot
avoid when trying to placate infants, the ailing, and the
aged.

'Ay, Epitaphs,' he repeated. 'But very few of *this* headlong
century. The art is lost; the spirit 's changed. Once the living
and the dead were in a good honest humour with one another.
You could chisel the truth in, even over a lifelong crony's clay.
You could still share a jest together; one on this side of the grave,
one on that. But now the custom's gone with the mind. We
are too mortal solemn or too mortal hasty and shallow.

'Why, over there, mark ye '—he pointed the great fat-ferruled
stump of his umbrella towards the half-buried tombstones once
more—'over *there*, such things are as common as buttercups.
And I know most of 'em by heart. My father, ma'am, was the
last human creature laid to rest in that graveyard. He was a
scholar of a still older school than I—and that 's next quietest
to being in one's grave. I remember his tree there when it
sighed no louder than a meadow brook. Shut your eyes now
of a windy evening, and it might be the Atlantic. There they
lie. And I 'll crawl in somewhere yet, like the cat in the adage
—out of this noisy polluted world!' A little angry cloud began
to settle on his old face once more.

'And there 's two things else make it an uncommon pleasant
place to rest in—a little brawling stream, that courses along
upon its southern boundary, and the bees and butterflies and
birds. There 's rare plantage there, and it attracts rare visitors
—though not, I am grateful to say, the human biped. No.'

Yet again a swallow swooped in from the noonday blue in
a flight serene and lovely as a resting moonbeam. Somewhere
behind the peculiar fretwork with which all railway directors
embellish their hostels it deposited its tiny bundle of flies in

squawking mouths out of sight though not out of hearing, and, with a flicker of pinion, was out, off, away again, into the air.

My old gentleman had not noticed it. He was still gently fuming over the murdered past: still wagging his head in dudgeon in his antique high hat.

'But I had no idea,' I ventured to insinuate at last, 'there were ever many really original epi——'

'I am not expectant of "ideas" nowadays, ma'am,' he retaliated. 'We don't think: we plot. We don't live: we huddle. We deafen ourselves by shouting. "There is no *peace*, saith my God . . ." and I'll eat my hat, if He did not mean for the blind worms as well as "for the wicked."'

He stooped forward to look into my face. 'Smile you may, ma'am,' he went on a little petulantly, patting his emphasis once more on the yellowed ivory handle of his umbrella, 'you know there is *not*. But there, they too had their little faults. They were often flints to the poor; merciless to the humble:

'No Voice to scold;
     No face to frown;
No hand to smite
     The helpless down:
Ay, Stranger, here
     An Infant lies,
With worms for
     Welcome Paradise.

'*That's* there, I grant ye; to commemorate what they called a charity brat; that's there, and it was true to the times.'

His voice had completely changed in his old-fashioned recitation of the little verses; he declaimed them with oval mouth, without gesture, and yet with a kind of half-timid enthusiasm.

'And then,' he continued, 'there's little Ann Hards:

'They took me in Death dim,
     And signed me with God's Cross;
Now am I Cherub praising Him
     Who but an infant was.

And not many yards distant is a spinster lady who used to live in that old Tudor house whose chimney-stacks you can see there above the trees. She was a little "childish," poor creature, but a gentle loving soul—Alice Hew:

'Sleep sound, Mistress Hew!
     Birds sing over you;

> The sweet flowers flourish
> Your own hands did nourish;
> And many 's the child
> By their beauty beguiled.
> They prattle and play
> Till night call them away;
> In shadow and dew:
> Sleep sound, Mistress Hew!'

I leant forward in the warm ambrosial air. It seemed I could almost read the distant stones myself in its honey-laden clearness. 'Please, please go on—if it does not tire you. How I wish I could venture in! But there goes the station master— the "Station Master"! Isn't *that* medieval enough? And I *suppose* there 'll be no time!'

'Right once more: the bull's-eye once more,' he retorted in triumph. 'No time; and less eternity. Think of it: I must have been fifty years on this world before those young eyes of yours were even opened. And was the spirit within *you* in a worse place then than this, think ye? And for the fifty years that you, perhaps, have yet to endure, shall I be in a worse, think ye?' A queer zestful look had spread over his features; and once again he lifted his voice, decanting the next lines as if in praise of some old vintage port:

> 'All men are mortal, and I know 't;
> As soon as man 's up he 's down;
> Here lies the ashes of Thomas Groat,
> Gone for to seek his Crown.

I knew Groat's nephews. "Old Tom" he used to be called: and by the wags, "Unsweetened." In three years they drank down the money that he had taken fifty to amass. He died of a stroke the night before my father was born—with a lighted candle and a key in his hand. Going to bed, ma'am.

'Then there 's old Sammie Gurdon's. Another character —twenty stone to the ounce; redder than his own Christmas baron of beef; with a good lady to match. But the inn 's pulled down now, and a chocolate-coloured jail has been erected over its ruins they call an hotel. And his son 's dead too:

> 'Maybe, my friend, thou 'rt main athirst,
> Hungry and tired, maybe:
> Then turn thy face by yon vane, due west;
> Trudge country miles but three;
> I 'll warrant my son, of the "Golden Swan,"
> Will warmly welcome thee.

"Golden Swan"! You should see it to-day, ma'am. "Ugly Duckling" would be nearer the mark! And now, if you'll take advantage of this elegant bench a moment'—he proffered a trembling and gallant hand—'you may just espy the sisters. See, now' — he had climbed up beside me — 'there's their cypresses, and, in the shade beneath, you should catch sight of the urns. Terra-cotta, ma'am; three. Do you see 'em? Three.'

I gazed and I gazed. And at last nodded violently.

'Good!' he cried. 'And thus it runs.' He traced with his umbrella in the air, over the inscription, as it were:

> 'Three sisters rest beneath
>   This cypress shade,
> Sprightly Rebecca, Anne,
>   And Adelaide.
> Gentle their hearts to all
>   On earth, save Man;
> In Him, they said, all Grief,
>   All Wo began.
> Spinsters they lived, and spinsters
>   Here are laid;
> Sprightly Rebecca, Anne,
>   And Adelaide.

And their nieces and grandnieces have gone on saying it—with worse manners—until one's ashamed to look one's own cat in the face. But that's neither here nor there. To judge from their portraits, mind ye, they were a rather masculine trio. And Nature prefers happy mediums. I'm not condemning them, dear young lady. God forbid; I'm no Puritan. But——'

'That reminds me,' I interposed hastily, 'of an epitaph in my own little churchyard—in Gloucestershire: it's on a wife:

> 'Here lies my wife,
>   Susannah Prout;
> She was a shrew
>   I don't misdoubt:
> Yet all I have
>   I'd give, could she
> But for one hour
>   Come back to me.'

'A gem! a gem! my dear young lady,' cried my old gentleman—as if he had himself remained a bachelor solely by accident; 'and that reminds me of one my dear Mother never tired of repeating:

> 'Ye say: We sleep.
>   But nay, We wake.
> Life was that strange and chequered dream
>   For the waking's sake.

And *that* reminds me of yet another which I chanced on—if
memory does not deceive me—in one of the old city churches
—of London: ah, twenty years gone or more:

> 'Here lieth Nat Vole,
> Asleep now, poor Soul!
> 'Twas one of his whims
> To be telling his dreams,
> Of the Lands therein seen
> And the Journeys he 'd been!
> La, if now he could speak,
> He 'd not listeners seek!'

'And who wrote *that*, I wonder?'

'Ah,' he echoed slyly, '"Who killed Cock Robin?" Dickie
Doggerel, maybe—his mark! But what I was going to tell
you concerns yet another spinster; also of this parish. Names
are no matter. She was a wild, dark-eyed solitary creature, and
in the wisdom of the Lord had a tyrant for a father. Even in
the nursery—generally a quiet enough little mite—when once
she had made up her mind, there was no gainsaying her. And
she had a peculiar habit—a rooted instinct—my dear young lady,
when she was crossed, of flinging herself flat on her face on the
floor. Quite silent, mind ye—like one of those corpse-mimick-
ing insects. Nothing would move her, while she could claw
tight to anything at hand.

'However trivial the cause—perhaps a mere riband in her
hair—that was the result. In a word, as we used to say when
we were boys, she shammed dead. Of course, as the years
went by, these fits of stubborn obstinacy were less frequent.
All went pretty well for a time, until her very wedding-day—
bells ringing, guests swarming, almond-blossom sprouting,
bridesmaids blooming—all of a zest. And then and there, fresh
from her maid, she flung herself flat on her face once more.
Refused to speak, refused to stir. Her father stormed; her
aunts cajoled; her old nurse turned on the watering-cart.'
My old gentleman grimly chuckled. 'No mortal use at all.
The lass was adamant.

'And fippety-foppety Mr Bridegroom, whom I never cared
much for sight or scent of, must needs smile and smile and return
home to think it over. From that moment her father too fell
mum. They shared the same house, the same rooms, the
same table—but mute as fish. And either for want of liberty
or want of company, the poor young thing fell into what

they used to call a decline. And then she died. And the old despot buried her, laying her north to south, and face downward in her coffin.'

'Face downward!' I exclaimed.

'Face downward,' he echoed, 'as by rights our sprightly three over yonder should have been buried, being all old maids. And she, poor soul, scarce in her twenties. . . . And for text: '*Thou art thy mother's daughter.*''

'Autres temps, autres mœurs,' I ventured, but feeling uncommonly like a piping wren meanwhile.

'Ah, ah, ah!' laughed my old gentleman; 'I have noticed it! . . . And now, perhaps you may be able to detect with those young eyes of yours a little old tombstone set under that cypress yonder. . . . Too far? Too "dark," eh? . . . Well, that's a sailor's; found wellnigh entirely fish-eaten in the Cove yonder —under Cheppelstoke Cliff. And pretty much to the point it is. Let—me—see. Ay, thus it goes.' He argued it out with his gloved forefinger for me:

> 'If thou, Stranger, be John Virgin, then the
>   Corse withinunder is nameless, for the Sea
>   so disfigured thy Face, none could tell
>   whether thou were John Virgin or no:
>   Ay, and whatever name I bore
>   I thank the Lord I be
>   Six foot in English earth, and not
>   Six fathom in the sea.

'Good English sense, that, with a bay-leaf of Greek and a pinch of Irish to keep it sweet. He was the ne'er-do-well son of an old miller, so they say, who ground for nothing for the poor. So that's once upon a time too! But there, ma'am, I'm fatiguing you. . . .'

'Please, please go on,' I pleaded hurriedly. 'What's that curious rounded stone rather apart from the others, with the ivy, a little up the hill?' We had resumed our seats on the hard varnished bench, as happy as lovebirds on a perch. My old gentleman evidently enjoyed being questioned.

'What, Fanny's? That's Fanny Meadows's, died of a consumption, poor lass, 1762—May 1762:

> '"One, two three"——
>   O, it was a ring
>   Where all did play
>   The hours away,

> Did laugh and sing
> Still, "One, two, three,"
> Ay, even me
> They made go round
> To our voices' sound:
> 'Twas life's bright game
> And Death was "he."
> We laughed and ran
> Oh, breathlessly!
> And I, why, I
> But a maid was then,
> Pretty and winsome,
> And scarce nineteen;
> But 'twas "One—two—three;
> And—out goes she!"'

His aged, faded eyes, blue as a raven's, narrowed at me an instant; and the queerest glimpse, almost one of anxiety, came into his face. He raised his head, as if to smile the reminder away, and busily continued. 'Now come back a little, along this side. A few paces beyond, under the hornbeam, lies Ned Gunn, a notorious poacher in these parts—though the ingrate's forgotten his dog:

> 'Where be Sam Potter now?
> *Dead as King Solomon.*
> Where Harry Airte I knew?
> *Gone, my friend, gone.*
> Where Dick, the pugilist?
> *Dead calm—due East and West.*
> Toby and Rob and Jack?
> *Dust every one.*
> Sure, they'll no more come back?
> *No: nor Ned Gunn.*

Not that there would be many to welcome him if he did. And next him lies a curmudgeonly old fellow of the name of Simpson, who lived in that old yellow stone house you may have seen beyond the meadows. He was a kind of caretaker. Many's the time he chased me when I was a lad for trespassing there:

> '"Is that John Simpson?"
> "Ay, it be."
> "What was thy age, John?"
> "Eighty-three."
> "Was 't happy in life, John?"
> "Life is vain."
> "What then of death, friend?"
> "Ask again."

And that, my dear young lady, is wisdom at any age; though
Simpson himself, mind ye, couldn't mumble at last a word you
could understand, having no teeth in his head.   And yet another
stranger is rotting away under an oblong of oak a pace or two
beyond Simpson.   I don't mean he was strange to the locality'—
he gazed full at me over his spectacles—'not at all—I knew him
well; though by habit he was a silent close-mouthed man, with
a queer dark eye.   I mean he was strange to this World.   And *he*
wrote his own epitaph:

> 'Dig not my grave o'er deep
>   Lest in my sleep
>   I strive with sudden fear
>   Toward the sweet air.
>
> 'Alas! Lest my shut eyes
>   Should open clear
>   To the depth and the narrowness——
>   Pity my fear!
>
> 'Friends, I have such wild fear
>   Of depth, weight, space;
>   God give ye cover me
>   In easy place!

Not that they favoured him much on that account! It's
a hard soil.   And next *him,* with snapdragons shutting their
mocking mouths at you out of every crumbling cranny, is Tom
Head.   A renowned bell-ringer in his day:

> 'I rang yon bells a score of years:
>   Never a corse went by
> But they all said—bid old Tom Head
>   Knoll the bell dolesomely:
> Ay, and I had a skill with the rope
>   As made it seem to sigh.

'Now I must tell you there was an old gentleman lived here
before my time—and his name is of no consequence—who had
a fancy for commemorating those who would otherwise have
left scanty remembrances enough behind them.   Some I have
already made mention of.   Here's another.   Nearly every
village, you must know, my dear young lady, has its half-wit,
but not every village graveyard.   And where this one's bush
is, they call Magpie Corner.   Let me see now. . . .' My old

gentleman made two or three false starts here; but at last it
ran 'free.

> 'Here lieth a poor Natural:
> The Lord who understandeth all
> Hath opened now his witless eyes
> On the Green Fields of Paradise.

> 'Sunshine or rain, he grinning sat:
> But none could say at who or what.
> And all misshapen as he were,
> What wonder folk would stand and stare?

> 'He'd whistle shrill to the passing birds,
> Having small stock of human words;
> And all his company belike
> Was one small hungry mongrel Tyke.

> 'Not his the wits ev'n joyed to be
> When Death approached to set him free——
> Bearing th' equality of all,
> Wherein to attire a Natural

'But there goes the signal! And we've scarce time for the
midget.'

A strange old green porter shuffled out from his den into the
sunshine. A distant screech, like the crow of a ghostly pheasant,
shrilled faintly out of the distance. I had suddenly grown a
little tired; and hated the thought of the journey before me.
But my arbitrary old gentleman cared for none of these things.

He gave me his 'midget' leisurely, academically, tenderly:

> 'Just a span and half a span
> From head to heel was this little man.
> Scarcely a capful of small bones
> Raised up erect this Midget once.
> Yet not a knuckle was askew;
> Inches for feet God made him true;
> And something handsome put between
> His coal-black hair and beardless chin.
> But now, forsooth, with mole and mouse,
> He keeps his own small darkened house.'

He paused an instant, and laid lightly two gloved, mysterious
fingers on my arm.

'She's coming,' he almost whispered. 'There's her white
wool against the blue.' He nodded towards the centipede-like
creature creeping over the greenness towards us. 'We are all

mythologists—and Goddesses! We can't avoid it and—and'—
he leaned closer and clucked the words under the very brim
of my hat—'it's called Progress. Veil then those dark eyes
just once of a morning, ma'am; and have a passing thought for
Sam Gilpin. We shall meet again; the unlikeliest like with
like. And this must be *quite* the last. Just beside a little stone
sill of water in that corner'—once more the iron-ferruled stump
was pointed towards the tombs—'where the birds come to
drink, is the figure of a boy standing there, in cold stone, listening. How many times, I wonder, have I scurried like a rabbit
at twilight past his shrine? And yet, no bones there; only a
passing reminder:

> 'Finger on lip I ever stand;
>   Ay, stranger, quiet be;
> This air is dim with whispering shades
>   Stooping to speak to thee.

What do we make of that, eh?'

He sprang up, his round glasses blazing in the sun. 'Well,
well! smiles be *our* finis, ma'am. And God bless you for your
grace and courtesy. . . . Drat the clumsy fellow!'

But it was I who 'passed on'—into the security of a 'compartment' filled with two fat commercial-looking gentlemen asleep;
a young lady in goggles smoking a cigarette; a haggard mother
with a baby and a little boy in velveteen trouserettes and a pale
blue bow who was sucking a stick of chocolate, and a schoolboy
swinging his shoes, learning geography, and munching apples.
A happy human family enough.

I joined them as amiably as the heat allowed. And my last
gliding glimpse of the tranquil little country station—burning
sweet-william, rioting rose—descried my old gentleman still on
his bench; still in his tall hat; still leaning on his gingham; a
kind of King Canute by the sad sea waves of Progress, tapping
out his expostulations and anathemas, though now to his own
soul alone.

From *Ding Dong Bell*.

POEMS

CHILDHOOD AND AGE

THE CHILDREN OF STARE

WINTER is fallen early
On the house of Stare;
Birds in reverberating flocks
Haunt its ancestral box;
Bright are the plenteous berries
In clusters in the air.

Still is the fountain's music,
The dark pool icy still,
Whereon a small and sanguine sun
Floats in a mirror on,
Into a West of crimson,
From a South of daffodil.

'Tis strange to see young children
In such a wintry house;
Like rabbits' on the frozen snow
Their tell-tale footprints go;
Their laughter rings like timbrels
'Neath evening ominous:

Their small and heightened faces
Like wine-red winter buds;
Their frolic bodies gentle as
Flakes in the air that pass,
Frail as the twirling petal
From the brier of the woods.

Above them silence lours,
Still as an arctic sea;
Light fails; night falls; the wintry moon
Glitters; the crocus soon
Will ope grey and distracted
On earth's austerity:

Thick mystery, wild peril,
Law like an iron rod:—
Yet sport they on in Spring's attire,
Each with his tiny fire
Blown to a core of ardour
By the awful breath of God.

WINTER

GREEN Mistletoe!
Oh, I remember now
A dell of snow,
Frost on the bough;
None there but I:
Snow, snow, and a wintry sky.

None there but I,
And footprints one by one,
Zigzaggedly,
Where I had run;
Where shrill and powdery
A robin sat in the tree.

And he whistled sweet;
And I in the crusted snow
With snow-clubbed feet
Jigged to and fro,
Till, from the day,
The rose-light ebbed away.

And the robin flew
Into the air, the air,
The white mist through;
And small and rare
The night-frost fell
Into the calm and misty dell.

And the dusk gathered low,
And the silver moon and stars
On the frozen snow
Drew taper bars,
Kindled winking fires
In the hooded briers.

And the sprawling Bear
Growled deep in the sky;
And Orion's hair
Streamed sparkling by:
But the North sighed low,
'Snow, snow, more snow!'

TOM'S ANGEL

No one was in the fields
But me and Polly Flint,
When, like a giant across the grass,
The flaming angel went.

It was budding time in May,
And green as green could be,
And all in his height he went along
Past Polly Flint and me.

We'd been playing in the woods,
And Polly up, and ran,
And hid her face, and said,
'Tom! Tom! The Man! The Man!'

And I up-turned; and there,
Like flames across the sky,
With wings all bristling, came
The Angel striding by.

And a chaffinch overhead
Kept whistling in the tree
While the Angel, blue as fire, came on
Past Polly Flint and me.

And I saw his hair, and all
The ruffling of his hem,
As over the clovers his bare feet
Trod without stirring them.

Polly—she cried; and, oh!
We ran, until the lane
Turned by the miller's roaring wheel,
And we were safe again.

THE SLEEPER

As Ann came in one summer's day,
  She felt that she must creep,
So silent was the clear cool house,
  It seemed a house of sleep,
And sure, when she pushed open the door,
  Rapt in the stillness there,
Her mother sat, with stooping head,
  Asleep upon a chair;
Fast—fast asleep: her two hands laid
  Loose-folded on her knee,
So that her small unconscious face
  Looked half unreal to be:
So calmly lit with sleep's pale light
  Each feature was; so fair
Her forehead—every trouble was
  Smoothed out beneath her hair.
But though her mind in dream now moved,
  Still seemed her gaze to rest—
From out beneath her fast-sealed lids,
  Above her moving breast—
On Ann; as quite, quite still she stood;
  Yet slumber lay so deep
Even her hands upon her lap
  Seemed saturate with sleep.
And as Ann peeped, a cloudlike dread
  Stole over her, and then,
On stealthy, mouselike feet she trod,
  And tiptoed out again.

AGE

This ugly old crone—
Every beauty she had
When a maid, when a maid.
Her beautiful eyes,
Too youthful, too wise,
Seemed ever to come
To so lightless a home,
Cold and dull as a stone.

And her cheeks—who would guess
Cheeks cadaverous as this
Once with colours were gay
As the flower on its spray?
Who would ever believe
Aught could bring one to grieve
So much as to make
Lips bent for love's sake
So thin and so grey?
O Youth, come away!
All she asks is her lone,
This old, desolate crone.
She loves us no more;
She is too old to care
For the charms that of yore
Made her body so fair.
Past repining, past care,
She lives but to bear
One or two fleeting years
Earth's indifference: her tears
Have lost now their heat;
Her hands and her feet
Now shake but to be
Shed as leaves from a tree;
And her poor heart beats on
Like a sea—the storm gone.

ENVOY

CHILD, do you love the flower
   Ashine with colour and dew
Lighting its transient hour?
     So I love you.

The lambs in the mead are at play,
   'Neath a hurdle the shepherd's asleep:
From height to height of the day
     The sunbeams sweep.

Evening will come. And alone
  The dreamer the dark will beguile;
All the world will be gone
  For a dream's brief while.

Then I shall be old; and away:
  And you, with sad joy in your eyes,
Will brood over children at play
  With as loveful surmise.

DREAM AND VISION

ARABIA

FAR are the shades of Arabia,
  Where the Princes ride at noon,
'Mid the verdurous vales and thickets,
  Under the ghost of the moon;
And so dark is that vaulted purple
  Flowers in the forest rise
And toss into blossom 'gainst the phantom stars
  Pale in the noonday skies.

Sweet is the music of Arabia
  In my heart, when out of dreams
I still in the thin clear mirk of dawn
  Descry her gliding streams;
Hear her strange lutes on the green banks
  Ring loud with the grief and delight
Of the dim-silked, dark-haired Musicians
  In the brooding silence of night.

They haunt me—her lutes and her forests;
  No beauty on earth I see
But shadowed with that dream recalls
  Her loveliness to me:
Still eyes look coldly upon me,
  Cold voices whisper and say—
'He is crazed with the spell of far Arabia,
  They have stolen his wits away.'

NOD

SOFTLY along the road of evening,
  In a twilight dim with rose,
Wrinkled with age, and drenched with dew,
  Old Nod, the shepherd, goes.

His drowsy flock streams on before him,
   Their fleeces charged with gold,
To where the sun's last beam leans low
   On Nod the shepherd's fold.

The hedge is quick and green with brier,
   From their sand the conies creep;
And all the birds that fly in heaven
   Flock singing home to sleep.

His lambs outnumber a noon's roses,
   Yet, when night's shadows fall,
His blind old sheep-dog, Slumber-soon,
   Misses not one of all.

His are the quiet steeps of dreamland,
   The waters of no more pain,
His ram's bell rings 'neath an arch of stars,
   'Rest, rest, and rest again.'

THE LISTENERS

'Is there anybody there?' said the Traveller,
   Knocking on the moonlit door;
And his horse in the silence champed the grasses
   Of the forest's ferny floor:
And a bird flew up out of the turret,
   Above the Traveller's head:
And he smote upon the door again a second time;
   'Is there anybody there?' he said.
But no one descended to the Traveller;
   No head from the leaf-fringed sill
Leaned over and looked into his grey eyes,
   Where he stood perplexed and still.
But only a host of phantom listeners
   That dwelt in the lone house then
Stood listening in the quiet of the moonlight
   To that voice from the world of men:
Stood thronging the faint moonbeams on the dark stair,
   That goes down to the empty hall,

Hearkening in an air stirred and shaken
   By the lonely Traveller's call.
And he felt in his heart their strangeness,
   Their stillness answering his cry,
While his horse moved, cropping the dark turf,
   'Neath the starred and leafy sky;
For he suddenly smote on the door, even
   Louder, and lifted his head:—
'Tell them I came, and no one answered,
   That I kept my word,' he said,
Never the least stir made the listeners,
   Though every word he spake
Fell echoing through the shadowiness of the still house
   From the one man left awake:
Ay, they heard his foot upon the stirrup,
   And the sound of iron on stone,
And how the silence surged softly backward,
   When the plunging hoofs were gone.

MAERCHEN

SOUNDLESS the moth-flit, crisp the death-watch tick;
Crazed in her shaken arbour bird did sing;
Slow wreathed the grease adown from soot-clogged wick:
   The Cat looked long and softly at the King.

Mouse frisked and scampered, leapt, gnawed, squeaked;
Small at the window looped cowled bat a-wing;
The dim-lit rafters with the night-mist reeked:
   The Cat looked long and softly at the King.

O wondrous robe enstarred, in night dyed deep:
O air scarce-stirred with the Court's far junketing:
O stagnant Royalty—A-swoon? Asleep?
   The Cat looked long and softly at the King.

FLOTSAM

SCREAMED the far sea-mew. On the mirroring sands
Bell-shrill the oyster-catchers. Burned the sky.
Couching my cheeks upon my sun-scorched hands,
Down from bare rock I gazed. The sea swung by.

Dazzling dark blue and verdurous, quiet with snow,
Empty with loveliness, with music a-roar,
Her billowing summits heaving noon-aglow—
Crashed the Atlantic on the cliff-ringed shore.

Drowsed by the tumult of that moving deep,
Sense into outer silence fainted, fled;
And rising softly, from the fields of sleep,
Stole to my eyes a lover from the dead;

Crying an incantation—learned, Where? When? . . .
White swirled the foam, a fount, a blinding gleam
Of ice-cold breast, cruel eyes, wild mouth—and then
A still dirge echoing on from dream to dream.

ALL THAT'S PAST

VERY old are the woods;
    And the buds that break
Out of the brier's boughs,
    When March winds wake,
So old with their beauty are—
    Oh, no man knows
Through what wild centuries
    Roves back the rose.

Very old are the brooks;
    And the rills that rise
Where snow sleeps cold beneath
    The azure skies
Sing such a history
    Of come and gone,
Their every drop is as wise
    As Solomon.

Very old are we men;
    Our dreams are tales
Told in dim Eden
    By Eve's nightingales;
We wake and whisper awhile,
    But, the day gone by,
Silence and sleep like fields
    Of amaranth lie.

CREATURES

NICHOLAS NYE

THISTLE and darnel and dock grew there,
    And a bush, in the corner, of may,
On the orchard wall I used to sprawl
    In the blazing heat of the day;
Half asleep and half awake,
    While the birds went twittering by,
And nobody there my lone to share
    But Nicholas Nye.

Nicholas Nye was lean and grey,
    Lame of a leg and old,
More than a score of donkey's years
    He had seen since he was foaled;
He munched the thistles, purple and spiked,
    Would sometimes stoop and sigh,
And turn to his head, as if he said,
    'Poor Nicholas Nye!'

Alone with his shadow he 'd drowse in the meadow,
    Lazily swinging his tail,
At break of day he used to bray,—
    Not much too hearty and hale;
But a wonderful gumption was under his skin,
    And a clear calm light in his eye,
And once in a while he would smile a smile—
    Would Nicholas Nye.

Seem to be smiling at me, he would,
    From his bush in the corner, of may—
Bony and ownerless, widowed and worn,
    Knobble-kneed, lonely and grey;
And over the grass would seem to pass
    'Neath the deep dark blue of the sky,
Something much better than words between me
    And Nicholas Nye.

But dusk would come in the apple boughs,
   The green of the glow-worm shine,
The birds in nest would crouch to rest,
   And home I'd trudge to mine;
And there, in the moonlight, dark with dew,
   Asking not wherefore nor why,
Would brood like a ghost, and as still as a post,
   Old Nicholas Nye.

MASTER RABBIT

As I was walking,
Thyme sweet to my nose,
Green grasshoppers talking,
Rose rivalling rose:

And wings, like amber,
Outspread in light,
As from bush to bush
The linnets took flight:

Master Rabbit I saw
In the shadow-rimmed mouth
Of his sandy cavern
Looking out to the South.

'Twas dew-tide coming,
The turf was sweet
To nostril, curved tooth,
And wool-soft feet.

Sun was in West:
Like crystal in beam
Of its golden shower
Did his round eye gleam.

Lank horror was I,
And a foe, poor soul!—
Snowy flit of a scut,
He was into his hole:

And—*Stamp, stamp, stamp!*
Through dim labyrinths clear;
The whole world darkened,
A Human near!

A ROBIN

GHOST-GREY the fall of night,
    Ice-bound the lane,
Lone in the dying light
    Flits he again;
Lurking where shadows steal,
Perched in his coat of blood,
Man's homestead at his heel,
    Death-still the wood.

Odd restless child; it's dark;
    All wings are flown
But this one wizard's—hark!—
    Stone clapped on stone!
Changeling and solitary,
Secret and sharp and small,
Flits he from tree to tree,
    Calling on all.

THE HOLLY

THE sturdiest of forest-trees
With acorns is inset;
Wan white blossoms the elder brings
To fruit as black as jet;
But O, in all green English woods
Is aught so fair to view
As the sleek, sharp, dark-leaved holly tree
And its berries burning through?

Towers the ash; and dazzling green
The larch her tassels wears;
Wondrous sweet are the clots of may
The tangled hawthorn bears;
But O, in heath or meadow or wold
Springs aught beneath the blue
As brisk and trim as a holly-tree bole
With its berries burning through?

When hither, thither, falls the snow,
And blazes small the frost,
Naked amid the winter stars
The elm's vast boughs are tossed;
But O, of all that summer showed,
What now to winter's true
As the prickle-beribbed dark holly tree,
With berries burning through!

THE MOTH

ISLED in the midnight air,
Musked with the dark's faint bloom,
Out into glooming and secret haunts
　　The flame cries, 'Come!'

Lovely in dye and fan,
A-tremble in shimmering grace,
A moth from her winter swoon
　　Uplifts her face:

Stares from her glamorous eyes;
Wafts her on plumes like mist;
In ecstasy swirls and sways
　　To her strange tryst.

THE SCRIBE

WHAT lovely things
　　Thy hand hath made:
The smooth-plumed bird
　　In its emerald shade,
The seed of the grass,
　　The speck of stone
Which the wayfaring ant
　　Stirs—and hastes on!

Though I should sit
　　By some tarn in thy hills,
Using its ink
　　As the spirit wills
To write of Earth's wonders,
　　Its live, willed, things

Flit would the ages
  On soundless wings
Ere unto Z
  My pen drew nigh;
Leviathan told,
  And the honey-fly:

And still would remain
  My wit to try—
My worn reeds broken,
  The dark tarn dry,
All words forgotten—
  Thou, Lord, and I.

DIRGE AND GHOST

THE GHOST

'WHO knocks?' 'I, who was beautiful,
  Beyond all dreams to restore,
I, from the roots of the dark thorn am hither.
  And knock on the door.'

'Who speaks?' 'I—once was my speech
  Sweet as the bird's on the air.
When echo lurks by the waters to heed;
  'Tis I speak thee fair.'

'Dark is the hour!' 'Ay, and cold.'
  'Lone is my house.' 'Ah, but mine?'
'Sight, touch, lips, eyes yearned in vain.'
  'Long dead these to thine . . .'

Silence. Still faint on the porch
  Brake the flames of the stars.
In gloom groped a hope-wearied hand
  Over keys, bolts, and bars.

A face peered. All the grey night
  In chaos of vacancy shone;
Nought but vast sorrow was there—
  The sweet cheat gone.

AUTUMN

THERE is a wind where the rose was;
Cold rain where sweet grass was;
  And clouds like sheep
  Stream o'er the steep
Grey skies where the lark was.

Nought gold where your hair was;
Nought warm where your hand was;
  But phantom, forlorn,
  Beneath the thorn,
Your ghost where your face was.

Sad winds where your voice was;
Tears, tears where my heart was;
  And ever with me,
  Child, ever with me,
Silence where hope was.

THE HOUSE

'MOTHER, it's such a lonely house,'
The child cried; and the wind sighed.
'A narrow but a lovely house,'
  The mother replied.

'Child, it is such a narrow house,'
The ghost cried; and the wind sighed.
'A narrow and a lonely house,'
The withering grass replied.

THE GHOST

  PEACE in thy hands,
  Peace in thine eyes,
  Peace on thy brow;
Flower of a moment in the eternal hour,
  Peace with me now.

  Not a wave breaks,
  Not a bird calls,
  My heart, like a sea,
Silent after a storm that hath died,
  Sleeps within me.

  All the night's dews,
  All the world's leaves,
  All winter's snow
Seem with their quiet to have stilled in life's dream
  All sorrowing now.

THE THORN

O THOU who pausest here,
With naught but some thorned wilding near
To tell of beauty; be not sad.
For he who in this grave is laid
Would give the all on earth he had
One moment but by thee to stand
And with warm hand touch hand.

THE FAMILIAR

'ARE you far away?'
'Yea, I am far—far;
Where the green wave shelves to the sand,
And the rainbows are;
And an ageless sun beats fierce
From an empty sky:
There, O thou Shadow forlorn,
Is the wraith of thee, I.'

'Are you happy, most Lone?'
'Happy, forsooth!
Who am eyes of the air; voice of the foam;
Ah, happy in truth.
My hair is astream, this cheek
Glistens like silver, and see,
As the gold to the dross, the ghost in the mirk,
I am calling to thee.'

'Nay, I am bound,
And your cry faints out in my mind.
Peace not on earth have I found,
Yet to earth am resigned.
Cease thy shrill mockery, Voice,
Nor answer again.'
'O Master, thick cloud shuts thee out
And cold tempests of rain.'

FARE WELL

WHEN I lie where shades of darkness
Shall no more assail mine eyes,
Nor the rain make lamentation
    When the wind sighs;
How will fare the world whose wonder
Was the very proof of me?
Memory fades, must the remembered
    Perishing be?

Oh, when this my dust surrenders
Hand, foot, lip, to dust again,
May these loved and loving faces
    Please other men!
May the rusting harvest hedgerow
Still the Traveller's Joy entwine,
And as happy children gather
    Posies once mine.

Look thy last on all things lovely,
Every hour. Let no night
Seal thy sense in deathly slumber
    Till to delight
Thou have paid thy utmost blessing;
Since that all things thou wouldst praise
Beauty took from those who loved them
    In other days.

HERE AND HEREAFTER

THE EXILE

I AM that Adam who, with Snake for guest,
Hid anguished eyes upon Eve's piteous breast.
I am that Adam who, with broken wings,
Fled from the Seraph's brazen trumpetings.
Betrayed and fugitive, I still must roam
A world where sin, and beauty, whisper of Home.

Oh, from wide circuit, shall at length I see
Pure daybreak lighten again on Eden's tree?
Loosed from remorse and hope and love's distress,
Enrobe me again in my lost nakedness?
No more with wordless grief a loved one grieve,
But to Heaven's nothingness re-welcome Eve?

THE BOTTLE

Of green and hexagonal glass,
    With sharp, fluted sides—
Vaguely transparent these walls,
    Wherein motionless hides
A simple so potent it can
    To oblivion lull
The weary, the racked, the bereaved,
    The miserable.

Flowers in silent desire
    Their life-breath exhale—
Self-heal, hellebore, aconite,
    Chamomile, dwale:
Sharing the same gentle heavens,
    The sun's heat and light,
And, in the dust at their roots,
    The same shallow night.

Each its own livelihood hath,
　　Shape, pattern, hue;
Age on to age unto these
　　Keeping steadfastly true;
And, musing amid them, there moves
　　A stranger, named Man,
Who of their ichor distils
　　What virtue he can;

Plucks them ere seed-time to blazon
His house with their radiant dyes;
Prisons their attar in wax;
Candies their petals; denies
Them freedom to breed in their wont;
Buds, fecundates, grafts them at will;
And with cunningest leechcraft compels
　　Their good to his ill.

Intrigue fantastic as this
　　Where shall we find?
Mute in their beauty they serve him,
　　Body and mind.
And one—but a weed in his wheat—
Is the poppy—frail, pallid, whose juice
With its saplike and opiate fume
Strange dreams will induce

Of wonder and horror. And none
　　Can silence the soul,
Wearied of self and of life,
　　Earth's darkness and dole,
More secretly, deeply. But finally?—
　　Waste not thy breath;
The words that are scrawled on this phial
　　Have for synonym, *death*—

Wicket out into the dark
　　That swings but one way;
Infinite hush in an ocean of silence
　　Aeons away—

Thou forsaken!—even thou!—
 The dread good-bye;
The abandoned, the thronged, the watched,
 the unshared—
 Awaiting me—I!

VAIN QUESTIONING

WHAT needest thou?—a few brief hours of rest
Wherein to seek thyself in thine own breast;
A transient silence wherein truth could say
Such was thy constant hope, and this thy way?—
 O burden of life that is
 A livelong tangle of perplexities!

What seekest thou?—a truce from that thou art;
Some steadfast refuge from a fickle heart;
Still to be thou, and yet no thing of scorn,
To find no stay here, and yet not forlorn?—
 O riddle of life that is
 An endless war 'twixt contrarieties.

Leave this vain questioning. Is not sweet the rose?
Sings not the wild bird ere to rest he goes?
Hath not in miracle brave June returned?
Burns not her beauty as of old it burned?
 O foolish one to roam
 So far in thine own mind away from home!

Where blooms the flower when her petals fade,
Where sleepeth echo by earth's music made,
Where all things transient to the changeless win,
There waits the peace thy spirit dwelleth in.

THE IMAGINATION'S PRIDE

BE not too wildly amorous of the far,
 Nor lure thy fantasy to its utmost scope.
Read by a taper when the needling star
 Burns red with menace in heaven's midnight cope.
Friendly thy body: guard its solitude.
 Sure shelter is thy heart. It once had rest
Where founts miraculous thy lips endewed,
 Yet nought loomed further than thy mother's breast.

O brave adventure! Ay, at danger slake
　　Thy thirst, lest life in thee should, sickening, quail;
But not toward nightmare goad a mind awake,
　　Nor to forbidden horizons bend thy sail—
Seductive outskirts whence in trance prolonged
　　Thy gaze, at stretch of what is sane-secure,
Dreams out on steeps by shapes demoniac thronged
　　And vales wherein alone the dead endure.

Nectarous those flowers, yet with venom sweet.
　　Thick-juiced with poison hang those fruits that shine
Where sick phantasmal moonbeams brood and beat,
　　And dark imaginations ripe the vine.
Bethink thee: every enticing league thou wend
　　Beyond the mark where life its bound hath set
Will lead thee at length where human pathways end
　　And the dark enemy spreads his maddening net.

Comfort thee, comfort thee. Thy Father knows
　　How wild man's ardent spirit, fainting, yearns
For mortal glimpse of death's immortal rose,
　　The garden where the invisible blossom burns.
Humble thy trembling knees; confess thy pride;
　　Be weary. O, whithersoever thy vaunting rove,
His deepest wisdom harbours in thy side,
　　In thine own bosom hides His utmost love.

I SIT ALONE

I sit alone,
And clear thoughts move in me,
Pictures, now near, now far,
Of transient fantasy.
Happy I am, at peace
In my own company.

Yet life is a dread thing, too,
Dark with horror and fear.
Beauty's fingers grow cold,
Sad cries I hear,
Death with a stony gaze
Is ever near.

Lost in myself I hide
From the cold unknown:
Lost, like a world cast forth
Into space star-sown:
And the songs of the morning are stilled,
And delight in them flown.

So even the tender and dear
Like phantoms through memory stray—
Creations of sweet desire,
That faith can alone bid stay:
They cast off the cloak of the real
And vanish away.

Only love can redeem
This truth, that delight;
Bring morning to blossom again
Out of plague-ridden night;
Restore to the lost the found,
To the blinded, **sight.**

MUSIC

WHEN music sounds, gone is the earth I know,
And all her lovely things even lovelier grow;
Her flowers in vision flame, her forest trees,
Lift burdened branches, stilled with ecstasies.

When music sounds, out of the water rise
Naiads whose beauty dims my waking eyes,
Rapt in strange dream burns each enchanted face,
With solemn echoing stirs their dwelling-place.

When music sounds, all that I was I am
Ere to this haunt of brooding dust I came;
While from Time's woods break into distant song
The swift-winged hours, as I hasten along.

SHADOW

EVEN the beauty of the rose doth cast,
When its bright, fervid noon is past,
A still and lengthening shadow in the dust,
　　Till darkness come
　　And take its strange dream home.

The transient bubbles of the water paint
'Neath their frail arch a shadow faint;
The golden nimbus of the windowed saint,
  Till shine the stars,
  Casts pale and trembling bars.

The loveliest thing earth hath, a shadow hath,
A dark and livelong hint of death,
Haunting it ever till its last faint breath.
  Who, then, may tell
The beauty of heaven's shadowless asphodel?

ESSAYS

ON A BOOK OF WORDS[1]

[1922]

THERE are lovers of books—undeserving perhaps of the more elegant term bibliophile—who confess to an almost panic dread of libraries. It is a strange imbecility of mind, though perhaps the fumes of perishing calf and morocco, the hue of fading gilt, the inaudible channerin' of the worm in the folio, or the spectral lamentations of forgotten authors aid in their undoing. Repetition of the experience seems only to intensify their unease. What to the elect is an earthly paradise is for these simpletons a form of purgatory both of the body and the spirit. Their only tolerable excuse is a sort of modesty. Are they not, they may plead, in the presence of that with which not even the diuturnity of an Old Parr would suffice to familiarize them? How can they, then, but be conscious that nine-tenths at least of the living waters in reservoir around them must, so far as their own thirsty souls are concerned, remain for ever stagnant?

For such poor shrinking creatures a multitude of books is no company. They would far rather share the tittle-tattle of the loved-one in the wilderness, sans even verses, jug, and bread. And yet every volume, even the dingiest pamphlet in those lifeless vaults, once held the attention of a living eye and brain. It must, it surely must, contain humanity in some detectable degree of solution? It fulfilled an obligation or an office, an ambition or an ideal. It was well-intended—maybe to instruct, to edify, to proselytize, or to explain; honourable privileges all. It may even have supplied a long-felt want. But alas, it is books of this very kind that are apt to wear so badly. Likely enough, it is their mute presence in congregation that so afflicts the over-sensitive. Their existence is little but a perennial mouldering. They are fated to serve no posterity however patiently upon their shelves they stand and wait.

With this in mind, one is tempted—though it might be dangerous—to maintain that the best books in the world were

[1] A Glossary of Words, Phrases, Names, and Allusions in the Works of English Authors, particularly of Shakespeare and his Contemporaries, by Robert Nares.

written chiefly for pleasure and with an after-hope to please. For if, in the words of the *Familiar Letters*, love not only sets the imagination in a strange fit of working, but also 'amuses the understanding,' so too should a labour of love. Its incitement comes from within; its source is in the hidden uplands of the heart. Not that it can be a labour without effort. The cost of it may be extreme. For it is nothing but a fallacy to suppose that what men do of their own choice and affection is less exhausting than a task against the grain. Self-imposed burdens are burdens none the less; but we carry them with a serener spirit, and with an inward happiness which shows itself in a grace and persuasiveness otherwise all but unattainable.

Better yet, what in the making—given the material, means, and craftsmanship—pleases the maker of a thing has pleasure in its gift. It will charm as well as interest; may in proving useful prove delightful. How this mere state of mind and mood reveals itself in a book it may be extremely difficult to detect and to specify. The influence is as elusive as the dream in happy eyes, or playing rainbows on the sea. But nothing by comparison, no motive, no zeal, no skill is so effective, or so stealthy. For it may haunt the most unlikely places, and play odd antics. It thrusts out its tongue at us from the corbels and gargoyles of an old church, dances in a picture of the stillest life, calls beauty into the darkest of Thomas Hardy's lyrics, bandies snatches of song under the thunders of *Lear*, and *may* even peep out of the crannies of a *Critique of Pure Reason*.

Probably the last personage and place in which we should expect to discover this incentive, this reward are a lexicographer and his dictionary. When Walter Pater prescribed the literary novice a daily dose of Johnson, he certainly intended it rather as a tonic than as a cordial. Under *flea*, it is true, under *patriot*, under *lexicographer* itself, the Great Bear deposited a rare honey. Doubtless the tomes of the *New English Dictionary* secretly scintillate with intellectual gaiety and glee and verve. But who, at the name of Richardson, happily recalls, not Samuel, but Charles? The vision of what kind of Ark arises in the fancy at mention of Noah Webster? What porridge had Dr Peter Mark Roget? The term dictionary remains austere, and, no more than either lexicon, concordance, or thesaurus, suggests a paradise of dainty delights.

For this reason, his own work in this kind completed, Robert

Nares avoided the title. He preferred the more modest 'glossary.' For his book, his preface tells us, represents not 'the labours of the anvil or the mine,' but the avocation of a studious leisure. He confesses without shame or caution that its compilation 'amused' him; and he gave it to the world in the hope that it would entertain its 'reader.' In a similar happy condition of mind Bunyan began and finished his *Progress :* setting 'pen to paper with delight.' So, too, Montaigne:

Reader, loe here a well-meaning Booke. It dothe at the first entrance forewarne thee, that in contriving the same I have proposed unto myselfe no other than a familiar and private end: I have no respect or consideration at all, either to thy service, or to my glory: my forces are not capable of any such desseigne.

Not that Nares, any more than Bunyan or Montaigne, slighted anvil and mine. His life was a full and various one. Son (as a lexicographer should be) of a celebrated musician, he was born in 1753, and attained the satisfactory age of seventy-five. Apart from his *Elements in Orthoëpy* (a less ingratiating title), he wrote 'light pieces,' essays, and pamphlets. In 1782 he was presented with the small living of Easton Maudit, and in 1800 became archdeacon of Stafford. He earned respect, we are told, not only as a gentleman and scholar, but as a sound divine. He launched the *British Critic* and steered it in triumph to its forty-second volume. For twelve years he was librarian in the Manuscript Department of the British Museum. He helped to found the Royal Society of Literature. He was thrice married.

Such industry and enterprise might well have satisfied an ordinary man. But these activities were his occupations, his 'more serious occupations.' His *Glossary* illustrates the scholarly joys in between. It grew and spread slowly in the interstices of his workaday life, like a blossoming bine on the walls of an old house. Take an instance:

WOODBINE, or WOODBIND. The common name, ancient and modern, for the wild honeysuckle.

See Johnson's Gerard, p. 891, etc.; but there is reason to think that Shakespeare employed it instead of *bindweed* for the convolvulus, in the following lines:

So does the woodbine the sweet honeysuckle
Gently entwine; the female ivy so
Enrings the barky fingers of the elm.
Mid. N. Dr., iv., i.

Two parallel similes must be here intended, or we lose the best effect of the poetry; and the former comparison seems quite parallel to one of Ben Jonson:

> Behold,
> How the blue *bind-weed* doth itself infold
> With honey-suckle.
>
> *Masq., Vision of Delight.*

Now the blue *bind-weed* is the blue convolvulus (Gerard, 864), but the calling it *wood-bine* has naturally puzzled both readers and commentators; as it seems to say that the honeysuckle entwines the honeysuckle. Supposing convolvulus to be meant, all is easy, and a beautiful passage preserved. Another mode of construction makes . . .

This is a fragment representative of Nares's method and his style. Let the blue bindweed be his scholarly interest, the honeysuckle his mind's delight, and we realize what keeps his *Glossary* sweet. As occasion allowed, he took it up; as duty dictated, he set it aside. The slightest acquaintance with its pages reveals both the range and the felicity of the literary journeyings it represents. Not only are its contents honey in the hive, but they admit us, if only in glimpses, to the wild stretches of valley, wood, and meadow whence their nectar was gathered.

The *Glossary*, moreover, was not only the reward of a peculiar species of delectation; its incentive was one of the best man can have, either in this world or in view of the next—admiration. Nares's primary aim was to enable every reader of 'our admirable Shakespeare' 'to enjoy the unencumbered productions of the poet.' He found his idol—above a century ago!—almost overwhelmed by his commentators. Armed with the sharp billhook of erudition and good sense, he attacked their female ivies. All his long life he had played Tom Tiddler, his 'ground' the Elizabethan play-books and the like, and the specimens in his *Glossary*—obsolete even in his own day—are his shining 'gold and silver.'

At need and with justice he can rebuke and correct even his master Shakespeare. Far oftener he sighs his 'exquisite' and 'beautiful.' His unwearying joy both as a man and as a lexicographer is in the creative literature of his chosen period. He entranced his eye with its poetry, bringing to its illustration a mind and memory filled full of 'life.' He etymologized, if ever man did, with his eye not only on the word but on the object.

In general his criticism of a commentator is as urbane as it appears to be final: 'Spital or Spittle. An abbreviation or corruption of hospital. . . . Mr Gifford has attempted to establish a distinction between *spital* and *spittle*; thus giving our ancestors credit for a nicety they never reached or intended.' And so on for a full column of instances. Or again, respecting *bases* and petticoats: 'Thus it will be seen that Mr Gifford's conjecture on the subject (Massinger, vol. iii, p. 141) was nearly right.'

His common sense is twice blest:

To *draw dryfoot* was, according to Dr Johnson, to trace the marks of the *dry foot*, without the scent. Dr Grey would have it to follow by the scent; but a dry foot can have no scent. Who shall decide when doctors disagree? In this case, perhaps, sportsmen, to whom I refer it. A *drawn fox* is a hunted fox: 'When we beat the bushes, etc., after the fox we call it *drawing*.'—*Gent. Recr., Hunting*, p. 17, 8vo.

Again:

Eyes, kissing of. The commentators on Shakespeare have very sagaciously told us that: 'It was formerly *the fashion to kiss the eyes*, as a mark of extraordinary tenderness.' . . . Say rather, that it was the natural impulse of affection in all ages. . . .

On occasion, Nares will draw even more openly on his personal experience:

Tuttle, the maze in; that is, the maze in Tothill Fields. Of these fields, let me speak with the respect which Dr Johnson, in the first edition of his Dictionary, paid to Grub Street. They were the Gymnasium of my youth. . . .

But—and 'commentators' are not a timid or over-sensitive folk —Nares can also be pungent and severe: 'A droil . . . Mr Lemon deduces it from τρίβω, tero, but his etymologies are often made as if for sport, to try the patience of his readers.' 'This is mere stuff' is another tartish reference to Mr Lemon. 'How rash conjectural criticism is, when the language of the author criticized is very imperfectly understood.'

But such little tournaments as these are only a subsidiary form of entertainment. To the expert they no doubt prove as provocative as was the fanfare of distant trumpets to the war-horse in the Book of Job. The novice may enjoy them in the same way as any amateur of a game of skill enjoys the practice of a professional. For Nares is always easy, never specialistic or dry. His desire is not to humiliate an adversary, never merely to exhibit his own erudition or ingenuity, but to elucidate, retrieve, disencumber. As criticism of his fellow-craftsmen, therefore, his *Glossary* is not only a lesson in method but also in manners. A drawn donkey is doubtless a hunted donkey. But

Nares is out not to bait but for sport, to entertain himself and his reader. His aim is to free his beloved originals from mere artificial difficulties. He believes that what they wrote they wrote with deliberation and intention. He simplifies.

One use of Nares, then, is as an occasional aid to lovers of the literature of the sixteenth and seventeenth centuries. It illustrates what is obsolete, not only in the language, but in the manners and customs of that period. Its author rarely ventures beyond Elizabeth, and left the compilation of similar dictionaries for the works of Chaucer's age, and for what preceded it, to his successors. For this reason his Glossary is usually to be found, concealing its gems of purest ray serene, among 'works of reference.' It is a sad reflection on our own times that the 1905 reprint of his book, edited by J. O. Halliwell and Thomas Wright, has lately been 'remaindered'—though this may bring it within easier reach of the true enthusiast.

Merely to visit it is to make a sad waste of its abundant hospitality, to ignore the very virtues that differentiate it from its fellows. For Nares not only gives information, he gives himself. His book is reading in the real sense, not for the snatched minute but for the solid hour; and reading so various and condensed that even a repeated exploration of any one page fails to exhaust it. Such is the natural resilience of the ordinary mind that certain sorts of information slip as easily out of it as they slip into it; but not without friction, it may be hoped, and not without the vestiges of a deposit.

The book is instantly entertaining. What decent curiosity could resist, say, such a succession of enigmas as *pes*, *pestle* (*not* the mortar variety), *peter-man*, *peter-sa-meene*, *petrel* (not the 'stormy'), *pew-fellow*, *to pheeze*, *pheuterer*, *Philip*? Because it is instantaneously entertaining, while not exciting, it is an excellent bed-book; heavy only in a material sense. What more dream-exciting lullabies for an adult head could be found than such citations as 'You shall (in this *New World*) as commonly see legges of men hang up, as here with us you shall find *pestels* of porke, or legges of veale'; or, 'Being one day at church she made mone to her *pew-fellow*'; or:

> *Peter-see-me* shall wash thy nowl
> And Malligo glasses fox thee.

or:

> To whit, to whoo, the owle does cry,
> *Phip, phip*, the sparrowes as they fly.

The unconscious, surely, whatever and wherever it be, requires constant nourishment.   A nightly platter of *hors-d'œuvres* should not come amiss.   And Nares' is crammed from cover to cover with these seductions.   Yet it is no mere collection of gauds, toys, trinkets, gewgaws, pieces of festive finery.   Its aggregate is the mirror of a time, of a state of the imagination, of a complete continent of human interest.   It is English in bouquet to the minutest bubble of its foam.   It is the work of a man's mind, masculine, substantial, sound, various.   One may speculate whether in the natural order of things it could ever be even the delectation of a woman's.

Its one requisite in a reader is simply a delight in words—words as words, and for their own sweet sake: the words beloved by Edward Thomas:

> Out of us all
> That make rhymes,
> Will you choose
> Sometimes—
> As the winds use
> A crack in a wall
> Or a drain,
> Their joy or their pain
> To whistle through—
> Choose me,
> You English words?
> I know you:
> You are light as dreams,
> Tough as oak,
> Precious as gold,
> As poppies and corn,
> Or an old cloak;
> Sweet as our birds
> To the ear,
> As the burnet rose. . . .
> But though older far
> Than oldest yew,—
> As our hills are, old,—
> Worn new
> Again and again:
> Young as our streams
> After rain:
> And as dear
> As the earth which you prove
> That we love. . . .

Such delight is not perhaps the plant of a season's raising. Yet its seed seems to be innate in the human mind.   While facts to the youthful digestion may prove as distasteful to it as fat, from his first birthday onwards a child hungers for words almost as instinctively at least as he pines for lollipops. His mother tongue is as natural a nutriment as his mother's milk. And a lively interest and joy in a word as often as not precede the acquisition of its exact meaning.

Indeed the finer shades of signification in the larger part of a mature vocabulary — woefully limited as such a vocabulary usually is — have rather been divined from a series of contexts than ascertained from a precise definition. For the lasting vivification of a word, the presence of the object to which it applies is of course indispensable. Yet word may come first, its object later. The virgin senses, the quick apprehension, and the tenacious memory of childhood and youth alone perhaps are capable of their indissoluble welding together. Of name and thing our most valuable knowledge consists. In later life, thank heaven, the desire for knowledge may sharpen; but our powers of assimilation are then desperately poorer. The prevalent weakness, too, of many minds — the radical deficiency of mediocre books — is not only the possession of a scanty vocabulary, but also of a vocabulary nebulous, unattached, inexact, inert. On the other hand, the weakness of a copious over-latinized vocabulary usually consists in its feeble relationship to the senses, to actuality. Thomas Brownes are few. A *little* intellect adrift amid abstractions is a spectacle far less entertaining than a balloon. If we fully animated in our minds all that we said, how much we should be saying!

Alas, then, Robert Nares's *Glossary*, since it is not a child's book, and treats of the obsolete, can only indirectly enrich one's verbal treasury. To put his treasures to actual use to any pronounced extent would be but to parley Euphuism. Perhaps even the notion that a word which has once fallen into disuse can be reinsinuated into the common speech is nothing but a mumpsimus. Certainly to patch and purfle out a style even with the Philip and Cheyney once the common wear would make it conspicuous, but scarcely admirable.

None the less our modern English, whether in speech or in writing, needs renovations of the kind that farces this old *Glossary*. A language stales. Not only new terms for new-found needs — and the imagination to coin them — are required to give it freshness, colour, and vivacity, but an abundance of approximate synonyms. The tendency to make one word enough when two or more would be a feast is a curmudgeonly one when carried to an extreme. Writers nowadays are apt to lead rather sequestered lives—a little vacant of event, out of the world's pomp and pride and vehemence. Between the classes and between the professions gulfs are fixed that in Shakespeare's day were easily bridged. And though thoughts and ideas are excellent company, they are the wholesomer and much the happier for a close alliance with the seven senses. Unless the memory is stored with easily retrieved words and phrases, racy, resonant and idiomatic, and, above all, with such as instantly evoke objects and qualities, and set echoing near and far the secret heights and recesses of the imagination, the mind starves, and the tongue falters for the means to express itself. Nares is a museum of words that once so served our animated forbears; and even if they have earned, as now they possess, a lasting privacy, they and their illustrations will dance the eye, titillate nose and ear, and strengthen the wits.

After all, whatever its chances and changes, however mummified and fossilized it may appear to be, a word is never dead. Like its maker, it awaits reanimation. Ours the trump. Isolated, it may be a meaningless (though according to some philosophers it can never be an impotent) symbol. In the company of a few of its kin and kind its discovery may be as exciting an experience as that of finding a strange animal taking its ease in a familiar barn. A pleasant-sounding old term even in isolation may act on the fancy like a charm. In collusion with its fellows it resembles an incantation. Up and down these pages these strange and irresistible decoys are sounding—if only we will give them ear.

If, moreover, we indulge a peculiar taste for antiquated words, as for antiquated porcelain, gems, curios, or postage stamps, Nares again is our priceless repository. For like such objects, words gather with age a curious flavour, look, mien, and reference. The bloom—if only a mildew—of sentiment creeps over them. The process is obvious. The neologism subsides into the colloquial, the colloquial may attain to the literary (the Promised Land), or to the poetic (a sort of Nirvana), or it may lapse into disuse. In the last resort it becomes first *passé*, then old-fashioned, then antique, then archaic, then a mere relic. But since, unlike flowers and insects, words are man-made, a certain respect should be theirs even when they are in the sere, and a more curious appearance of hidden energy may be manifest the older they grow. There the old thing lies in its shroud—a verbal Methuselah: yet but one instant's imaginative use of it may restore its voice, its character, its energy, and its personality. It is, too, seldom the words of infrequent and nice and rare usage that utterly perish; only the miserably and heedlessly over-worked. For words antique, on which Time has scattered her poppy, lulling them merely to an agelong sleep, awaiting merely their Prince Charming, Nares again is the lively hostel.

Or if, once more, stray fragmentary remembrances and mementoes of a wild and copious and full-charged day that long since rang to its evensong attract and entice us, then Nares yet again is our lure. Share but his comments on *mandrake* or *iniquity*; *owle-glass*, *gorbellied*, *Pimlico*, or *ivy-bush*; *elements* and *humour*; *gib-cat* and *Judas-coloured*; *knives*, *neck-verse*, *starch*, *primavista*, *Nicholas*, or *kneeling*; *musk*, *hell*, *gloves*, *cock-shut*, or *golden plaister*, you may not thereby become a full man, you may not even join the ranks of the well-informed, but you may deserve to be his devotee. If—and in these slippery times it may any day prove a serviceable one—if the faculty is ours to enjoy a dainty, obsolete or obsolescent, even though its in-gredients consist solely of inscrutable reactions excited by the alphabet, then *jumball*, *manchet*, *marchpane*, *Florentine*, and *lumber pie* are ours for the calling—and *lambswool* and like pota-tions wherewith to wash them down. Otherwise:

Let the cooke bee thy physition, and the shambles thy apothe-caries shop: hee that for every qualme will take a receipt, and cannot make two meales, unless Galen bee his Gods good, shall bee sure to make the physition rich and himselfe a begger: his bodie will never bee without diseases, and his purse ever without money.

Nares was a man of taste, and a scholar; he was also quite evidently a man of wholesome and full-blooded appetites. His book radiates the zeal and zest of his literary coursings and questings and lyings-in-wait. Games of all kinds—parlour, grass, and otherwise, fabrics and clothes, 'characters,' actors, streets, taverns, and the more romantic type of rogue are all after his fancy.

The mere suggestion that his *Glossary* may feast the idle and ignorant, given only a liking for the Elizabethan vernacular and habits, may appear to cast a shadow on its learning and science, its seriousness. Far from it: his book is a godsend to the dunce. He leaves the obscure illuminated. He thoroughly knows, and can hospitably share, his knowledge. Guide he set out to be; philosopher he proves himself to be—a critic of mankind neither harsh, nor fastidious, nor aloof, yet, one we feel, with unflinching principles and standards. And at last and at best, Nares becomes a friend, pleased with and modestly proud of his collection, and anxious only to share it with a fellow fanatic.

To abandon one's own time and environment, even when it wears so uninviting an exterior as may now and then to-day's —to flee away into the past and be at rest—is not only an impracticable feat. It would be a poor show of insight and courage. Contrariwise, to live only in to-day is to be the slave of the clock, let alone the newspapers. An occasional rapid and light-hearted excursion into the imaginable regions of another century, the century of England's greatest literature, of her loveliest music, her most romantic enterprise, to which mere distance no doubt lends a large and deceptive fraction of its enchantment—this surely is the pleasantest of mental stimulants. As a cursory reading book Nares's *Glossary* consists, it may be granted, of tidbits and snippets. As a whole, it is a gallimaufry, though one neither confused nor heterogeneous. It may be reserved, and no doubt the undeserving will continue to reserve it, for the noonday's need, not for the midnight's luxury. Still, first and foremost, its amused author hoped and intended to 'entertain' his reader. He succeeds in so doing, with *words*; and what better claim on our attention can novelist, historian, or poet prefer?

ON 'THE CRICKET ON THE HEARTH'

INTRODUCTION

'THE kettle began it': and such is the strange power of words that merely this quartet of them if they were chanced on at the beginning of any story, anywhere, would infallibly suggest to the lover of David, Carker, Mrs Gamp, and Barnaby, two others —Charles Dickens. And if they were in French or German, we should realize instantly that Fritz and Froggie had gone a-borrowing. But in Dickens's vocabulary the word *began* in such a connection actually means, Wait if you please in perfect patience and delight until I am completely ready to go on!

The consequence is that we read steadily for four pages—i.e. for precisely five minutes by the cuckoo clock in Mrs Peery-bingle's cheerful and elastic kitchen—with its Father Time, its mowing Haymaker, and its Moorish palace, one and all indelibly and tinily stamped with the same C. D.—before we discover what precisely that 'it' is—'a song of invitation and welcome.' In fact, a lyric! And though at emotional crises a line or two of blank verse fell from Dickens's pen as naturally as dew upon a primrose; though he could hardly say *Bo* to a goose, and particularly to a Christmas goose, without becoming lyrical; though 'no man ever talked poetry 'cept a beadle on boxin' day'; though Sam Weller indulged in a song and Mr Curdle knew all about the 'unities'; the Cricket, like one of the Chimes, expatiates in positive *rhyme*.

Its rhymes, it is true, are disguised as innocent prose—a literary device naïvely amusing perhaps for the first time, and a plague in excess. It resembles the trick played by Red Riding Hood's Wolf when he called on her grandmother—but that call was never repeated! Bereft of it, the lines run merrily enough:

It 's a dark night, and the rotten leaves are lying by the way;
And, above, all is mist and darkness, and, below, all is mire and
    clay;
And there 's only one relief in all the sad and murky air;
And I don't know that it is one, for it 's nothing but a glare. . . .

There is little in them or in the rest of them to hint that Dickens
would have proved a different kind of poet from the poet that
he so richly was in prose if he had indulged more frequently in
verse. But they do hint that verse (with a little more elbow-
grease) would have come pretty easily to him, and that he might
in due season have proved a dangerous rival to the author of
The Ingoldsby Legends.

What the lines declaim to be 'coming, coming, coming' is of
course the Cricket. And it is a pity that Dickens leaves unde-
scribed this queer little sing-song skeletal creature—*one* of the
commonest of the Victorian domestic animals, and much scarcer
nowadays—at least in his London. It would be a peculiar
pleasure to compare his vignette of it in words with Dürer's
drawing of a rhinoceros and with William Blake's flea.

The Kettle, however, is less described than *is*—not only in so
many words, but in so many of Dickens's words. And though it
may be taken as a symbol of his continuously simmering 'sub-
consciousness' which boiled over in 1845 into this queer, thronged
shapeless, helter-skelter, and even hugger-mugger story, it was
Father Time's gentle reminder or menace in October of the same
year which warned him that yet another Yuletide was at hand,
that it would be a poor specimen without a story, and so compelled him to put that kettle on the hob.

As material for *fiction* the 'Cricket,' or rather the first hint of
it, came from the proposed title for an 'abandoned little weekly'
which Dickens had been for a while debating and had finally
discarded. He thought 'it would be a delicate and beautiful
fancy for a Christmas book, making the Cricket a little household
god—silent in the wrong and sorrow of the tale, and loud again
when all went well and happy.' It was at any rate a pretty
fancy, but it gave him much trouble. In a letter to John Forster
on 31st October, having announced the death of a beloved
raven that had perished of a diet of putty and paint—'he kept
his eye to the last upon the meat as it roasted, and suddenly
turned over on his back with a sepulchral cry of *Cuckoo*!'—he
confessed that he was 'sick, bothered and depressed' and never
in such 'bad writing cue' in all his life—then thirty-three years
gone. 'My life is one demd horrid grind,' remarked Mr Mantalini; and Mr Mantalini was not of the same order of parasites
as an author.

In Dickens's case, it was a condition of mind due in part, no doubt, to the anxieties and misgivings connected with his editorship of the forthcoming *Daily News*—an office which he actually held for less than three weeks—21st January to 9th February of the new year. It left him 'tired to death and quite worn out.' In spite of the journalistic triumphs of a different kind which came after, he failed in this, in Mr Chesterton's view, not because he was careless, but, rather, because he was too conscientious: 'It was not that he had the irresponsibility of genius; rather it was that he had the irritating responsibility of genius; he wanted everybody to see things as he saw them'— a wise comment that it is as well to keep in mind, and even in relation to *The Cricket on the Hearth*.

It is 'A Fairy Tale of Home.' What wonder then that it reached its tenth edition in less than a year, that it was even twice as successful as his two previous Christmas stories had been; the degree of that success being measurable by the fact that he had been bitterly disappointed at receiving rather less than half of the 'cool thousand' which he had expected from the sales of the *Christmas Carol* three years before. 'Money talks' —much too loudly and intermittently at times. Mention of it here is a tribute not only to his popularity, but to the intelligence of the reading public of his day, far less numerous than that of our own, which in spite—or possibly because—of universal 'education' seems to be less discriminating. It is a tribute that may be compared with the welcome lavished on the Plays by the 'general' in 1600. Transpose the authors; what would have been the outcome?

Not that *The Cricket* is by any means a masterpiece. A moment's comparison of it with the *Carol* is enough, I think, to show that while every page of it is manifestly Dickens, the tale as a whole is no less manifestly less excellent Dickens. However heedfully he may have worked at his fiction, his supreme faculty of course was that of improvisation. No other English writer, not even Defoe, so easily out-warbles the Tennysonian brook. And though we may rejoice that his godmother never whispered in his infant ear any urgent warning of the dangers of this seducer, it does at times lead him astray, and it often leads him far abroad. He revels, he insists, he expatiates, he embroiders, he pokes fun—precious beads, no doubt, though we may continue to pine for the string. That in spite, however, of all this apparent ease and abandon he must frequently have paused, is amusingly suggested by a page of his manuscript produced in facsimile in the *Life*—the first page of the *Carol*. A few lines towards the end of it have been deleted, and in the right-hand lower corner a number of dots are discernible in a little haphazard diagram. The diagram, an irregular ring round the dots, may well have been added afterwards. The dots themselves tell, surely, as plainly as dots can, that for a minute or two the magician had been pausing for 'ideas.' At the next, out these ideas came with the abundance of buttercups in June.

But so vivid, self-contained, and definite is the theme of the *Carol* that the tale itself far more closely resembles a rich formal garden than a luxuriant meadow. This is not so with *The Cricket*. Here too is abundance—but abundance in excess; an abundance ample enough to have sufficed the most lovable of his disciples for yet another and by no means the shortest of his interminable novels; and it may seem nothing but curmudgeonly to quarrel with it. Still, excess is much easier than economy; Dickens might well have given a thought to his imitators; and, after all, the story remains 'the thing.' This one contains, for example, on the positive side, no fewer than four characters, each one of whom might have served for a full-length portrait in a full-sized novel.

Dot, whom in the first few pages we are somehow led to assume to be not only middle-aged but eccentric (and certainly not the possessor of chubby little hands), as soon as she becomes her real, round, dimpled and blooming self is as apples to wax compared with Dora. The blind girl, Caleb's daughter, with perhaps the rather oddly inappropriate name of Bertha, is little more than a latent wraith of sentiment, though one can imagine what Dickens might have done with her if he had had the opportunity of first talking her over with Wilkie Collins—whom he was not to meet until 1850. Gruff Tackleton, again, prior at least to his abrupt conversion, is obviously pining for the post of leading villain in a complete piece; and Caleb is even better—a definite and delicate creation. Compare him in mere physical substance with his son, come home so oddly, with his 'great brown club' from the 'golden South Americas,' 'where parrots, mines and Mexicans come from.' Even when this odd young wanderer discards his long white beard, he is never less artificial than the beard he discards. With the beard *in situ* Edward Lear could best have finished him off. As for Tilly Slowboy (and her baby—borrowed on the father's side, so to speak, from Mr Punch), she is midway between a lay figure and one of the not less lively than comic reliefs in another *Nicholas Nickleby*.

In every direction the story is equally lavish. Where else in a small space shall we enjoy such a harvest of youth and beauty? And as for the baby (yet again)—well, on the mother's side, 'It *is* a baby.' So densely thronged indeed is Caleb's tiny room on the evening of the Feast that we can hardly see the walls for the company.

So much for the humans—apart, even now, from the Carrier, and from the dismal-minded gummidgean Mrs Fielding. But what of Boxer, with his 'knob of a tail,' what of the Cricket and Mr Peerybingle's admirable horse? What of the appurten- ances? We may, it is true, ponder a little dubiously on the fairies. But though Dickens at times failed to permit some of his creatures to come or to keep *quite* alive, this is never so with his inanimates. There is as much *life* in the equilateral triangular impressions of Dot's pattens in the Carrier's backyard as there is in the two (quite remarkably small) feet which they have the privilege of keeping out of its slush. While the Kettle, not to mention the Cricket, apart from its being the most metallic, in- fallible and unmitigated cast iron, is no less of a 'personality' than Dot herself or any other creature of flesh and blood in the story.

With what generosity too do these creations of genius—and not a syllable of a paean has yet been sung to Tackleton's dramatic Wedding Cake or Dot's Veal and Ham Pie—even if some of them are inadequately vitalized, indulge in the highly improbable in order to remain unmistakably Dickensian. At some vague point in the story, for example, we realize that what we supposed was to be Dot's story is really and truly May's story, and, at that, little more than a meagre sketch. For it is only with a con- siderable gulp, surely, that even the enthusiast can swallow the Carrier's jealousy concerning his demure and darling Dot. And is it even remotely credible (not in actuality indeed but in the story itself) that Bertha could be so grossly deceived even by so real and so loving a father? Did Dickens at this particular juncture indeed care two pins either way? Why too have we been condemned to the end of January—and a thaw? Had *The Cricket* preceded the *Carol* can we doubt that it would have been accompanied by volleys of holly, by pale-green cascades of mistletoe?

And since Dickens all but invented, or at any rate re-discovered the English Christmas—the Christmas of Everyman under his own snug roof, with a blazing fire in the chimney, a goose in the larder, ample capacity for punch and plum-pudding and mincemeat, a hospitable heart, nimble toes, and a positive passion for kiss-in-the-ring and moonshine, no one could deny him the right to as many Christmases as the muses might permit. But even though his *Cricket* is not concerned with his own specific Feast, the upshot of it is yet another of his judgment days—with all the good people made better, and the bad at peace with the best. It is the more remarkable, then, that with its very last page and with one waft of his wand, he should have shattered its complete 'illusion'; and in a sorrowful word or two have transported the reader into the very presence of the magician himself. But, *why*, apart from obvious reasons, Dot was 'a little figure very pleasant to me'; and *who* precisely was the owner of the 'broken child's-toy' lying abandoned on the ground, are questions which may beguile the curious, but not necessarily the devotee.

That Dickens himself delighted in his own blissful exuberance cannot be doubted, though we may imagine Miss Austen's quiet glance at such proceedings. He could not help it. He was indefatigably willin'. He was born and made that way: he poured out everything he had at the moment's behest, on and on. He was in his own field as prolific as Nature herself, and (though it is unwise to be too sure of Nature) as apparently heedless. How far then in its sentimentality, in its formlessness and exaggeration, with its improbabilities and complications, the *Cricket* is the result of trying too much, or of trying too little, is a doubtful question.

But no purely literary criticism of Dickens either at his best or worst is ever likely to be anything but a little wide of the mark. Even when his characters are mere puppets they amused him. And that alone ensures, or should ensure, their amusing us; unless of course 'we are *not* amused.' They have too one very peculiar gift. When the play is over and when the curtain is down, we may discover that they have not only thrown off all extravagance, but have also shed their sawdust and are proving themselves to have been not only alive but natural.

For what remains in the memory after reading a book—apart perhaps from definite fragments—is a sort of sublimation of it as a whole and in all its parts. The writer of it may himself have been unaware of this sublimation since it need not necessarily coincide with his intention and conception. So with Charles Dickens: though he could not refrain his heart and keep it low, though his head often followed his nose, it was his genius that had the largest share in his stories. And that being so, their too-much may thin off like a vapour, and the residue deposit itself in the mind at last as a curious essence. So, *pace* the Cricket, a miniature if angular Charles Dickens himself, the Kettle may be compared entirely to its own advantage with any other kettle either in fact or fiction. Indeed, it could take on a complete ironmonger's shopful of kettles, spout in air, and 'lick the lot.' But in the event it is much more than merely that. It is a sort of composite Platonic idea of all the kettles of every one's childhood—since all Dickens's life on earth (apart from jars) was a kind of childhood—and as such we may lovingly admire it in the company, say, of Chardin's bottle, Dürer's bunch of violets, Hardy's Tess's shoes, and even of Macbeth's dagger.

ON DESERT ISLANDS

THE mere cadence of the six syllables, a Tale of Adventure, instantly conjures up in the mind a jumbled and motley host of memories. Memories not only personal but, as we may well suspect, racial; and not only racial but primeval. Ages before history learned its letters, there being no letters to learn; ages before the children of men built the city and the tower called Babel and their language was confounded and they were scattered, the rudiments of this kind of oral narrative must have begun to flourish. Indeed the greater part of even the largest of dictionaries, with every page in the most comprehensive of atlases, consists of relics and records in the concisest shorthand from bygone chapters in the tale whereof we know neither the beginning nor the end—that of Man's supreme venture into the world without, and into the world within.

The mountains, the oceans, the stars bear witness to it—at least in name; though many such names are now but gibberish and may strive in vain to find their once 'belouèd tong' again. Whether, too, it has been passed on from mouth to mouth or from hand to hand, not only has this order of fiction proved by far the most prolific, but it bids fair to continue to stuff our remotest descendants with rapture, envy, aspiration, and nightmare, until humanity and the planet it occupies are no more.

Within its kind its range is almost illimitable. It ascends by steady gradations from the anecdote to the epic. It includes not only the penny plain and the twopence coloured, broadside and chapbook, but such masterpieces as the *Odyssey*, the *Golden Ass*, *Don Quixote*, *Simplicissimus*, and the Scottish Ballads. Sweeney Todd and Sinbad the Sailor are as welcome in its vast hostelry as the Knights of the Round Table, Baron Munchausen and the hunters of the Snark; and some of the best of the 'flickers' or 'movies'—though their medium of expression is solely the play of light on a game of Let's Pretend, with what could not be too meagre a commentary in words—are still after the same pattern.

Its place in literature varies with its quality, its equivalent on the stage being melodrama, from *The Tragedy of Dr Faustus* at one extreme to that of poor gay Mr Punch and his dog Toby at the other.   In its relation to poetry and belles-lettres it is usually pretty much what earthenware is by comparison with porcelain, or the brass in an orchestra with the strings.   In marrow and matter it appeals straight to whatever vestiges of the boy we have left in us rather than to what faint memorials we may still treasure of the child.   Its chief concern is with the activities of the body; far less with the workings of the mind or the state of the soul.   Yet its order of morals is rigid if primitive.   The bad man abounds in it, and less frequently the bad female also, but its hero invariably has 'his principles' to steer by, however crazy a helmsman he may be.   Apart from this, the author's attention is fixed not on what in humanity is a little lower than the angels but on what is akin to the higher animals.   And if he preach at all, it is usually by way of wholesome practice rather than of precept; while the virtues he instils are those of the ready hand, the nimble tongue, and quick wits.

Hunger and thirst, danger and difficulty, the strange, the far-fetched, the outlandish, these are its chief incentives.   And its reward, the adventure over, something not only of a material but of a solid order—a few sacks, say, of moidores, doubloons, and precious stones; and for makeweight, a ravishingly beautiful señorita from some castle in Spain, who was wooed perhaps in the first chapter, and thereafter only dreamed of until she is won in the last.   All but all her joys, however, should await an untold epilogue.   As positive cargo she is supererogatory.

Though not exactly hostile to them, the tale of adventure is for the most part indifferent to social or domestic interests. These are at best but its background and its foil, and even at that, it much prefers their primary colours to their finer shades. For in this blood-and-thunder type of fiction anything may happen at any moment.   In the novel of manners, or of the ichor-and-Psyche type, very little (and to some tastes even that little may be too much), happens at all.   In the one, character is of supreme importance; in the other *a* character, and that character need be nothing more complicated than merely a man—raw *homo*, that is, with little admixture of *sapiens*. Such a tale, then, is apt to be rather coarse fare for the truly sophisticated.

Yet in its latest variant, the detective story, even philosophers have found a way of 'escape,' and of one great divine at least it is recorded that he was kept up most of the small hours one night in 1883 in pursuit of a young person named Jim Hawkins. What wonder, indeed, if out of a continual twilight of abstractions and formulae (even though it may be suddenly irradiated at last with sunrise), the metaphysically minded should pine at times for the grosser actualities; what wonder if many such tales have been the work of 'dreamers' who have been prevented from, or are by nature averse to seeking adventure in three dimensions; or of wanderers who having gone to and fro in the world have at length returned home, yet still pine on for the wild and far.

The rapid narrowing in, alas, of our earthly area effected by modern invention suggests that there will soon be no wild and far for which to pine. A world measured by flying is a very much smaller place than a world measured by walking; and out of sight was once out of hearing. This is not so—and for humane reasons, one must suppress a natural sigh—now. Changes of circumstance such as our new facilities provide—inveterate foes of those who prefer travel with travail—affect not only the fancy but the imagination, and it is *distance* that lends enchantment to the view.

Definite statistics are not available, but it seems probable not only that adventures in the usual meaning of the term were more frequent in less crowded, secure, and gregarious ages than our own, but also that, per head of the population, they are at present on a richer scale than they are likely to be in the future. Once upon a time almost any journey by land or sea was at least an invitation to hazard, and a hazard strange, not familiar. Nowadays, though we are most of us more habitually in motion than our ancestors, the enfeebling slogan is 'safety first.' Otherwise we stay at home (more or less at ease), and dabble in physical extremes at second hand. Chiefly—dingy and dubious though most of such records are — in our newspapers. Our adventurings are less, that is, of the body than of the mind and imagination, though few of us even faintly realize the potential scope of the latter.

Still, even in the dullest of existences, this spicy flavour of adventuring cannot be entirely absent. It is the salt that keeps life sweet, it is the savour that preserves it from putrefaction; and we welcome every fleeting taste of it. Contrast is much;

novelty is more; the unforeseen, if it refrain from the tragic, is seldom without its charm; and a gay heart is hospitable even when its giddiest up or its dismallest down verges on an ordeal. A crooked sixpence on a crooked stile, a noise in the night, a new hat, a kiss under the mistletoe, a forty-to-one chance, to fall asleep in the wrong train, to break one's leg, to lose one's heart—or one's head, to drink two bottles of wine where one would serve, to be a worm—and turn: all such little experiences may be tinged with the adventurous. And a tinge is enough.

The most disconcerting of little *mis*adventures, too, may wear the prettiest colours in retrospect; for the wounds of vanity leave amusing scars. And to have made a preternatural fool of oneself for half an hour is apt to wear better in memory than months and months of undiluted self-respect.

While there is still any life left in our bones we most of us at least desire to live vividly and variously, if not dangerously. It is only the tepid who idolize the happy medium; only the too-safe who never risk anything; only the over-complicated who pine after what is nowadays called—and apparently with no intention of irony — the simple life. And though the very derivation of the word proves that 'adventures' come not for the seeking but are the gift of Fortune, it is none the less true that they are the reward of the adventurous. The open eye and heart and mind may enjoy them daily—a sunshine morning, a moonlight night, snow at daybreak, a baby in the cradle, honey for tea; to cite only the less evidently intellectual. Merely to be alive, indeed, is adventure enough in a world like this, so erratic and disjointed; so lovely and so odd and mysterious and profound. It is, at any rate, a pity to remain in it half dead.

Yet another ingredient either in essence or in tincture is seldom absent from the tale of adventure—the romantic. And whatever else this battered term may signify, romance is invariably flavoured with the extreme. It flowers in the mind when life is being lived not merely at an uncustomary but at a hazardous poise. It must come of itself, yet is so much sought after that we talk of the romance of Commerce and of Big Business, though for the most part such talk is only flattery. One hears less of the romance of slow failure, the romance of growing old, the romance of disease and death.

The sudden attainment of wealth, or of power, or of fame may be romantic; an abrupt unforeseen fall from high estate is hardly less so. Rare beauty, human or natural or supernatural, is romantic. So too may be a unique ugliness. The romantic is also not far distant from the tragic on the one side, and on the other from the sentimental. Lay it on too thick and it is as insipid as a wedding-cake consisting solely of sugar-icing. It is perhaps most effective when it is most unexpected; then a mere relish, a mere glint of it may redeem a situation which otherwise would be commonplace. And even wit may have that glint. Charles II knew it: 'I fear, gentlemen, I am an unconscionable time a-dying'; and Wilde: 'Alas, I am dying beyond my means.'

The romantic is a thing of moments rather than of hours. Repetition or monotony dulls the appropriate nerve. A novelty, then, may or may not be romantic, but singularity almost always is. In part for this reason perhaps, a piece of handicraft with all its defects is preferable to anything flawless turned out by a machine. What other charm, except indeed of the homely order, has the home-made? We dull life by a mechanical repetition and imitation. We dull it still more if we submit it to mere system and if we ourselves become machines. In the game of follow-my-leader little depends on the led.

So with science: its discoveries are romantic in kind and effect while they remain novelties, and chiefly when they are concerned with the outskirts of knowledge. There, romance may glitter like the dawn-lit crags of El Dorado, even though the man of science (until recently at any rate) has been a rather chilly friend to those who indulge in it. When the ignorant novice reads that a certain kind of oak tree has lately been discovered which is more sensitive to gradations of colour than the human eye; that an ant knows her queen is near even when cold steel a half-inch thick dissevers them one from the other; that Sirius has a companion sun whose mass, as compared with steel, is what that of steel is compared with oxygen—when such crumbs of fact as these come his way, he gapes for joy and wonderment. He loves them not for their truth's sake but for themselves. They are at least as seductive as the wildest extravaganzas of fiction. Since facts are but facts, however, it is we of course who must supply the charm, and for this reason alone a little learning—just as much as one can treasure—may be no less fascinating than it is dangerous.

We boast, on the other hand, of the stupefaction of our grand-fathers if they could be roused from their graveyard slumbers to marvel at our automobiles and our gramophones, our sub-marines and aeroplanes, our wireless, our poison gases. They might — for an hour or two. And then perhaps they would begin to marvel at our smoke and our smells, our nerves and our newspapers. For singularity soon wears off, and mere novelty soon stales. And after that sad mutation things must wait awhile—and not always in vain—for the most beguiling change of all, since it is Time itself that sheds on all things human, even on the velocipede, the antimacassar, the bustle, and the Picca-dilly weeper, the last and loveliest iridescence—that of romance.

For an object which is not of a perishing nature becomes first old, then old-fashioned, then antique, then antiquated, then archaic, then ancient; and at last may be drenched with a romanticalness of which its original owner had not the faintest inkling—Noah's gangway, Absalom's hair, Cleopatra's looking-glass, Tutankhamen's slippers, Caesar's sword. Our newest of novelties, our very last things out, even our youngest poets, are all on their way to this home of rest. We pine for the curious, the bizarre. We return to find our peace in the familiar and the near. For which reason—as Edward Thomas, faithful lover of all things old and English, realized—such simple ancient familiar things as a plough, a ship, or a farm-wagon continue to shed, for the eye that can see and dream together, a romance which is shared by the ruins of Babylon, the songs of the Sirens, and the roses of Damascus.

It may be observed, however, that what to a secure onlooker is a pleasingly romantic situation may be grim matter-of-fact to those actually engaged in it. To be besieged with Helen in Troy; to be congealed amid the icy wastes of the Arctic, or lost in the Sahara; to be a royal fugitive in an oak tree, a Colonel Lawrence in Mecca, a Charles Doughty in the sandy wilds of Arabia, a Mallory on the ultimate peak of Everest; all these are probably more *romantic* situations to contemplate than to share. And one of their chief conditions is that of the precarious and fleeting. The sword hangs suspended by a thread. That harlequin, Luck, is as capricious as genius. That siren, Fortune, sings sweetest among rocks.

Perhaps the chief charm of the *Thousand and One*, the *Arabian Nights*, for example—one of the very few books in the world, I suppose, of little account in the country of its origin and a classic abroad—is, first, the peculiar density of its romance, and, next, the extraordinary penalties bestowed on the characters who indulge in it. To have one's thumbs lopped off as a punishment for an innocent attachment to garlic; to be flayed alive for ogling a princess; to submit to such indignities as did Sinbad the Sailor—ordeals like these so related belong rather to the romantic than to the classic order of events and show a glint on their imaginative surface like the colours on a stagnant pool.

So too with life simplified and essentialized rather than distorted. Barren must be the mind incapable of being enchanted by the limpid and unadorned romance enshrined in the Old Testament. Are not the first chapters of Genesis, with their history of the Creation and their tale of the Garden, entirely apart from their spiritual truth and their imaginative sufficiency, one of the most romantic stories in the world? Are not the histories of Jacob, of Joseph, of Absalom, of Daniel, of Naaman, of Jonah, and even of Job—whatever other inexhaustible riches of spirit or symbol or 'meaning' are theirs—coloured through and through with this strange dye?

Strangely enough, too, gregarious by instinct though we humans are, and though two in a garden may make a paradise of the everywhere: a complete solitude, also, may be saturated with the romantic.

Is not this great globe itself a celestial solitary?

> Hope, fear, false joy and trouble—
> These the four winds which daily toss this Bubble.
> His breath a vapour, and his life a span,
> 'Tis glorious misery to be born a man.

That bubble floats on in the severing ether, voyaging, as I have read somewhere, towards a remote (and somewhat inscrutable) goal in the void of space called *Mu* in Leo. And as with the world, so with the conscious beings that inhabit it—possibly the only beings of their specific nature, as our modern astronomers surmise, in the complete stellar and physical universe. Almost impassably cut off as we now are from the natural trust and fellowship of unhumanized beast and bird, so too in some degree we are severed even from our nearest and dearest. By means of those frail tentacles, our senses, we explore the outward semblance of our fellow-creatures; but flesh is flesh and bone is bone, and only by insight and by divination can we pierce inward to the citadel of the mind and soul. We can only translate their touch, their gestures, the words they use, the changing looks on their faces into terms of our own consciousness and spirit. We believe them to be in all essential things like ourselves—whatever their arresting and delightful differences. We trust them not to be mere deceiving automata. Nevertheless, the inmost occupant of each one of us is a lifelong recluse.

> Yes: in the sea of life enisled,
>   With echoing straits between us thrown,
> Dotting the shoreless watery wild,
>   We mortal millions live *alone*.
> The islands feel the enclasping flow,
> And then their endless bounds they know.
>
> But when the moon their hollows lights,
>   And they are swept by balms of spring,
> And in their glens, on starry nights,
>   The nightingales divinely sing;
> And lovely notes, from shore to shore;
> Across the sounds and channels pour;
>
> O then a longing like despair
>   Is to their farthest caverns sent!
> For surely once, they feel, we were
>   Parts of a single continent. . . .

The vivid and positive realization of this may come seldom, but, when it does, it is sharp and appalling. The moment falls, unforeseen, inexplicable and, as if at the insidious wave of an enchanter's wand, the faces, the voices of the believed-in and beloved seem to be nothing but the creation of our own fantasy, and we are 'enisled.' Even the 'echoes' then, like the language-less scream of sea-bird and the drumming of wave on rock, are nothing but a mockery. We may work or play away most of our lives in evading this realization, but in the end we shall become our own Showman's boy and know that as mortals we are alone.

And though, before that end come, and in spite of the ramifications of butcher, baker, postman, and tax-collector, the kind of solitude one may pine for is to be found even in the England of our own day, and that of the astronomer, the bookworm, the miser, the lover, and the king are not beyond imagining; of the extreme spiritual solitudes familiar to many of our fellow-creatures we can be but vaguely aware. What spectres share the small hours with a criminal hemmed in at every turn by the physical and moral forces of law and order—an animal rejected of its kind? The solitude of the lunatic, of the devil-haunted, the habitually drugged? One savours a taste of this world's romance indeed with the realization that the cold relics on the dissecting-tables and in the brine-tanks of our hospitals, of which there appears to be an unfailing supply, are the refuse of men and women abandoned by life to so desolate a loneliness that there is no one on earth who will spare the time or the few shillings necessary to secure them a *friendly* burial.

We may now and again, too, encounter in our walks abroad a fellow-creature touched with a certain cast of strangeness and aloofness. We scan the fleshly house, but the windows are darkened. He or she was born, we may assume, to at least a concerned mother, into some imitation of a home, and lived for a while in childhood and youth within call of humanity. But by slow and infinite degrees, whether because of eccentricities of mind and character, pride, grief, aversion, fear, weakness, poverty, or riches, that human being has gradually become more and more withdrawn and insulated, and lives on, enringed ever more and more inaccessibly with barriers that divide the living one within from the natural advances, the active fellowship, the compassion, even the mere interest of mankind.

There are some, like Katherine Mansfield's charwoman, who have no place quiet or solitary enough to cry in; there are some to whom the insect-like hosts of London seem nothing but the bodiless and hostile spectres of a nightmare; and but a moment's divining thought of them assures us that the whole world's fiction and autobiography can tell us only a fraction of what mortal life at such extremes may come to mean.

And some there are of a mind so self-secure it needs but little company; and some of a heart all-welcoming, all-hospitable, who, though never less alone than when alone, shed on the world around them a peace and loving-kindness of a source as fresh and sweet as it is inexhaustible.

But apart from the life of the actual, of life at first hand, there are few experiences which we can so easily share and enjoy, by proxy, as that of *physical* solitude. What other theme in fiction

is more deeply saturated with the romantic and the adventurous?
Stories of this kind abound; and particularly in English fiction.
What in general are their conditions?

First, the victim and the hero of such a fate must fight—not,
as we all do, for life—but for a bare existence. And unlike many
of his fellow-creatures in real life he must not fight in vain. His
one problem, his one craving and desire (however irrational it
may be), must be merely to continue to keep alive. He must,
then, have courage and enterprise. No mere dreamer, thinker,
or philosopher need apply.

Next, since he is to be—and for some time to remain—alone,
his place of exile should be remote from the thronging haunts
and highways of mankind and dangerous of access though not
quite inaccessible. A naked and waterless waste from which
no escape is possible would admit of but the briefest period of
physical torture and a morbid activity of the mind. His resort
then must offer *some* hospitality to its guest, though it should
be well this side of the luxurious, since he must spend in it a
quick and lively existence. And though the odds against his
survival must not be overwhelming, they should at least appear
to be long. He must indeed survive to tell us his tale; for of the
solitude of the grave, whether in St Innocent's churchyard or
beneath the sands of Egypt, we can retrieve no direct tidings,
or at best—tidings dubious, meagre, and unsatisfying.

Our solitary, too—if his record is to be moving—should be
more or less continually aware of his isolation. So much the
better if from some point of vantage amid his wild and barbarous
scenery he can keep watch on the horizon whence at length
rescue will come. Finally, he may effect his own rescue. But
to see him merely walk out of his trap is an eventuality not quite
romantic enough. A profoundly sundering yet traversable
medium must sever him, then, from his fellow-creatures.

The sands of the Sahara or of the Gobi desert would keep such
a secret, or, failing these, some green and peaceful oasis in a
region encircled by an unintermittent cyclone, or by a ring of
subterranean fire. Jules Verne, for example, may not have
completely explored the monster-haunted deeps in the centre
of the earth; and the practicability of voyaging into space seems
to be once more engaging the speculations not of mere visionaries
only but even of the matter-of-fact.

Short of the subterranean, the submarine, and the wild

vacancies of space, however, the conditions of an ideal retreat from the tumult and artificialities of man are fulfilled—solitude, danger, strangeness, the unknown, the discoverable, the eventual means of escape—if our hermitage is an island. An island volcanic or coralline, an island that out of the mists of daybreak, or in the cheating lights of evening, lifts itself from the snows of its surges, serene, strange, aloof in its forlorn beauty, dumb clock of countless ages, the haven of a few birds and roving brutes, the kindly nursery of seal and sea lion, and green with palm and tamarisk.

An island let it be, say, three or four hundred to a thousand miles or so from the nearest habitations of humanity and well out of the usual sea-trade routes, preferably uncharted, fairly commodious, say thirteen miles by four, of a climate whose extremes are not of a pitiless severity, an island which Nature's bounty has endowed with shade, fresh water, shelter, and food fit for human consumption. And there—our recluse.

Every seaman, every wanderer on the deep, has hearkened to the decoy of that ideal island; and where is the landsman with soul so dead—even though his eye has been lifted over no greater expanse of salt water than can be scanned from the steps of a bathing-machine—who in his homesick moments has never caught its enchanting echo? The English in particular are as a people naturally beguiled by the thought of the smallest strip or patch of land that is surrounded by water. How could it be otherwise, since theirs is that notorious little three-cornered island of 'a natural bravery . . . with rocks unscalable and roaring waters,' against whose western coasts for ever beats the prodigious Atlantic? The seas are in their blood. They have been scoffed at as a nation of shopkeepers; 'merchant adventurers' has a pleasanter sound. They have been eyed askance as a horde of money-hunting land-grabbers; freeborn crusading colonists is a pleasanter way of putting it. Again and again they have had to face the charge of insularity, but then was there ever a national shortcoming so inevitable? What wonder that, rather greedily maybe and not always with too nice a gesture, they have sucked 'of the abundance of the seas, and of treasures hid in the sand'? . . .

MADE AT THE
TEMPLE PRESS
LETCHWORTH
IN
GREAT BRITAIN

EVERYMAN'S LIBRARY
A CLASSIFIED LIST OF THE 961 VOLUMES

In each of the thirteen classifications in this list (except BIOGRAPHY) the volumes are arranged alphabetically under the *authors' names*, but Anthologies and works by various hands are listed under titles. Where authors appear in more than one section, a cross-reference is given, viz.: (*See also* FICTION). The number at the end of each item is the number of the volume in the series.

All the volumes are obtainable in the standard Cloth binding; selected volumes obtainable in Leather are marked L.

BIOGRAPHY

Audubon the Naturalist, Life and Adventures of. By R. Buchanan. 601
Baxter (Richard), Autobiography of. Ed. by Rev. J. M. Lloyd Thomas. 868
Beaconsfield (Lord), Life of. By J. A. Froude. 666
Berlioz (Hector), Life of. Translated by Katherine F. Boult. 602
Blackwell (Dr Elizabeth): Pioneer Work for Women. With an Introduction by Mrs Fawcett. 667
Brontë (Charlotte), Life of. By Mrs Gaskell. Intro. by May Sinclair. 318
    (*See also* FICTION)
Browning (Robert), Life of. By E. Dowden. 701
    (*See also* POETRY AND DRAMA)
Burney (Fanny), Diary. A selection edited by Lewis Gibbs. 960
Burns (Robert), Life of. By J. G. Lockhart. Intro. by E. Rhys. 156
    (*See also* POETRY AND DRAMA)
Buxton (Sir Thomas Fowell), Memoirs of. Ed. by Charles Buxton. 773
L Byron's Letters. Introduction by André Maurois. 931
    (*See also* POETRY AND DRAMA)
Carey (William), Life of: Shoemaker and Missionary. By George Smith. 395
Carlyle's Letters and Speeches of Cromwell. 3 vols. 266–8
  ,,   Reminiscences. 875   (*See also* ESSAYS *and* HISTORY)
Cellini's (Benvenuto) Autobiography. 51
Cibber's (Colley) An Apology for his Life. 668
Columbus, Life of. By Sir Arthur Helps. 332
Constable (John), Memoirs of. By C. R. Leslie, R.A. 563
Cowper (William), Selected Letters of. Intro. by W. Hadley, M.A. 774
    (*See also* POETRY AND DRAMA)
De Quincey's Reminiscences of the Lake Poets. Intro. by E. Rhys. 163
    (*See also* ESSAYS)
De Retz (Cardinal): Memoirs. By Himself. 2 vols. 735–6
Dickens (Charles), Life of. By John Forster. Introduction by G. K. Chesterton. 2 vols. 781–2   (*See also* FICTION)
Disraeli (Benjamin), Life of. By J. A. Froude. 666
Evelyn's Diary. 2 vols. Introduction by G. W. E. Russell. 220–1
Fox (George), Journal of. Text revised by Norman Penney. 754
Franklin's (Benjamin) Autobiography. 316
Gibbon (Edward), Autobiography of. 511   (*See also* HISTORY)
Gladstone, Life of. By G. W. E. Russell ('Onlooker'). 661
Goethe, Life of. By G. H. Lewes. Intro. by Havelock Ellis. 269
Hastings (Warren), Life of. By Capt. L. J. Trotter. 452
Hodson of Hodson's Horse. By Capt. L. J. Trotter. 401
Hudson (W. H.), Far Away and Long Ago. 956
Hutchinson (Col.), Memoirs of. Intro. Monograph by F. P. G. Guizot. 317
L Johnson (Dr Samuel), Life of. By James Boswell. 2 vols. 1–2
  ,,   ,, Lives of the Poets. 770–1 (*See also* TRAVEL)
Keats (John), Life and Letters of. By Lord Houghton. Introduction by R. Lynd. 801   (*See also* POETRY AND DRAMA)
Lamb (Charles), Letters of. 2 vols. 342–3
    (*See also* ESSAYS *and* FOR YOUNG PEOPLE)
Lincoln (Abraham), Life of. By Henry Bryan Binns. 783 (*See also* ORATORY)
Mahomet, Life of. By Washington Irving. Intro. Prof. E. V. Arnold. 513

I

BIOGRAPHY—*continued*

CLASSICAL

ESSAYS AND BELLES-LETTRES

Anthology of Prose. Compiled and Edited by Miss S. L. Edwards. 675
Arnold's (Matthew) Essays. Introduction by G. K. Chesterton. 115
     „   „   Study of Celtic Literature, and other Critical Essays,
                with Supplement by Lord Strangford, etc. 458
                    (See also POETRY)
Bacon's Essays. Introduction by Oliphant Smeaton. 10
          (See also PHILOSOPHY)
Bagehot's Literary Studies. 2 vols. Intro. by George Sampson. 520–1
Belloc's (Hilaire) Stories, Essays, and Poems. 948
Brown's Rab and his Friends, etc. 116
Burke's Reflections on the French Revolution and contingent Essays.
   Introduction by A. J. Grieve, M.A. 460
          (See also ORATORY)
Canton's (William) The Invisible Playmate, W. V., Her Book, and In
          (See also FOR YOUNG PEOPLE)   [Memory of W. V. 566
Carlyle's Essays. 2 vols. With Notes by J. Russell Lowell. 703–4
     „   Past and Present. Introduction by R. W. Emerson. 608
     „   Sartor Resartus and Heroes and Hero Worship. 278
          (See also BIOGRAPHY and HISTORY)
Castiglione's The Courtier. Translated by Sir Thomas Hoby. Intro-
   duction by W. H. D. Rouse. 807
L Century of Essays, A. An Anthology of English Essayists. 653
Chesterfield's (Lord) Letters to his Son. 823
L Chesterton's (G. K.) Stories, Essays, and Poems. 913
Coleridge's Biographia Literaria. Introduction by Arthur Symons. 11
     „   Essays and Lectures on Shakespeare, etc. 162
          (See also POETRY)
L De la Mare's (Walter) Stories, Essays, and Poems. 940
De Quincey's (Thomas) Opium Eater. Intro. by Sir G. Douglas. 223
     „   „   The English Mail Coach and Other Writings.
            Introduction by S. Hill Burton. 609
          (See also BIOGRAPHY)
Dryden's Dramatic Essays. With an Introduction by W. H. Hudson. 568
Elyot's Gouernour. Intro. and Glossary by Prof. Foster Watson. 227
L Emerson's Essays. First and Second Series. 12
L   „   Nature, Conduct of Life, Essays from the 'Dial.' 322
     „   Representative Men. Introduction by E. Rhys. 279
     „   Society and Solitude and Other Essays. 567
          (See also POETRY)
Florio's Montaigne. Introduction by A. R. Waller, M.A. 3 vols. 440–2
Froude's Short Studies. Vols. I and II. 13, 705
          (See also HISTORY and BIOGRAPHY)
Gilfillan's Literary Portraits. Intro. by Sir W. Robertson Nicoll. 348
Goethe's Conversations with Eckermann. Intro. by Havelock Ellis.
   851. (See also FICTION and POETRY)
Goldsmith's Citizen of the World and The Bee. Intro. by R. Church. 902
          (See also FICTION and POETRY)
Hamilton's The Federalist. 519
Hazlitt's Lectures on the English Comic Writers. 411
     „   The Round Table and Shakespeare's Characters. 65
     „   Spirit of the Age and Lectures on English Poets. 459
     „   Table Talk. 321
     „   Plain Speaker. Introduction by P. P. Howe. 814
Holmes's Autocrat of the Breakfast Table. 66
     „   Poet at the Breakfast Table. 68
     „   Professor at the Breakfast Table. 67
L Hudson's (W. H.) A Shepherd's Life. Introduction by Ernest Rhys. 926
Hunt's (Leigh) Selected Essays. Introduction by J. B. Priestley. 829
L Huxley's (Aldous) Stories, Essays, and Poems. 935
Irving's Sketch Book of Geoffrey Crayon. 117
          (See also BIOGRAPHY and HISTORY)
L Lamb's Essays of Elia. Introduction by Augustine Birrell. 14
          (See also BIOGRAPHY and FOR YOUNG PEOPLE)

ESSAYS AND BELLES-LETTRES—*continued*

Landor's Imaginary Conversations and Poems: A selection. Edited with Introduction by Havelock Ellis. 890

Lawrence (D. H.), Stories, Essays, and Poems. Edited by Desmond Hawkins. 958

Lowell's (James Russell) Among My Books. 607

Macaulay's Essays. 2 vols. Introduction by A. J. Grieve, M.A. 225–6
    „   Miscellaneous Essays and The Lays of Ancient Rome. 439
        (*See also* HISTORY *and* ORATORY)

Machiavelli's Prince. Special Trans. and Intro. by W. K. Marriott. 280
        (*See also* HISTORY)

Martinengo-Cesaresco (Countess): Essays in the Study of Folk-Songs. 673

Mazzini's Duties of Man, etc. Introduction by Thomas Jones, M.A. 224

Milton's Areopagitica, etc. Introduction by Professor C. E. Vaughan. 795
        (*See also* POETRY)

L Mitford's Our Village. Edited, with Intro., by Sir John Squire. 927

Montagu's (Lady) Letters. Introduction by R. Brimley Johnson. 69

Newman's On the Scope and Nature of University Education, and a paper on Christianity and Scientific Investigation. Introduction by Wilfred Ward. 723   (*See also* PHILOSOPHY)

Osborne's (Dorothy) Letters to Sir William Temple. Edited and connotated by Judge Parry. 674

Penn's The Peace of Europe. Some Fruits of Solitude, etc. 724

Prelude to Poetry, The. Edited by Ernest Rhys. 789

Reynold's Discourses. Introduction by L. March Phillipps. 118

Rhys's New Book of Sense and Nonsense. 813

Rousseau's Emile. Translated by Barbara Foxley. 518
        (*See also* PHILOSOPHY AND THEOLOGY)

Ruskin's Crown of Wild Olive and Cestus of Aglaia. 323
    „   Elements of Drawing and Perspective. 217
    „   Ethics of the Dust. Introduction by Grace Rhys. 282
    „   Modern Painters. 5 vols. Introduction by Lionel Cust. 208–12
    „   Pre-Raphaelitism. Lectures on Architecture and Painting, Academy Notes, 1855–9, and Notes on the Turner Gallery. Introduction by Laurence Binyon. 218
L   „   Sesame and Lilies, The Two Paths, and The King of the Golden River. Introduction by Sir Oliver Lodge. 219
    „   Seven Lamps of Architecture. Intro. by Selwyn Image. 207
    „   Stones of Venice. 3 vols. Intro. by L. March Phillipps. 213–15
    „   Time and Tide with other Essays. 450
    „   Unto This Last. The Political Economy of Art. 216
        (*See also* FOR YOUNG PEOPLE)

Spectator, The. 4 vols. Introduction by G. Gregory Smith. 164–7

Spencer's (Herbert) Essays on Education. Intro. by C. W. Eliot. 504

Sterne's Sentimental Journey and Journal and Letters to Eliza. Intro. by George Saintsbury. 796 (*See also* FICTION)

Stevenson's In the South Seas and Island Nights' Entertainments. 769
L   „   Virginibus Puerisque and Familiar Studies of Men and Books. 765
        (*See also* FICTION, POETRY, *and* TRAVEL)

Swift's Tale of a Tub, The Battle of the Books, etc. 347
        (*See also* BIOGRAPHY *and* FICTION)

Swinnerton's (Frank) The Georgian Literary Scene. 943

Table Talk. Edited by J. C. Thornton. 906

Taylor's (Isaac) Words and Places, or Etymological Illustrations of History, Ethnology, and Geography. Intro. by Edward Thomas. 517

Thackeray's (W. M.) The English Humorists and The Four Georges. Introduction by Walter Jerrold. 610
        (*See also* FICTION)

Thoreau's Walden. Introduction by Walter Raymond. 281

Trench's On the Study of Words and English Past and Present. Introduction by George Sampson. 788

Tytler's Essay on the Principles of Translation. 168

Walton's Compleat Angler. Introduction by Andrew Lang. 70

FICTION

Aimard's The Indian Scout. 428
Ainsworth's (Harrison) Old St Paul's. Intro. by W. E. A. Axon. 522
L   ,,   ,,   The Admirable Crichton. Intro. by E. Rhys. 804
L   ,,   ,,   The Tower of London. 400
      ,,   ,,   Windsor Castle. 709
      ,,   ,,   Rookwood. Intro. by Frank Swinnerton. 870
American Short Stories of the Nineteenth Century. Edited by John
    Cournos. 840
L Austen's (Jane) Emma. Introduction by R. B. Johnson. 24
    ,,   ,,   Mansfield Park. Introduction by R. B. Johnson. 23
    ,,   ,,   Northanger Abbey and Persuasion. Introduction by
       R. B. Johnson. 25
L   ,,   ,,   Pride and Prejudice. Introduction by R. B. Johnson. 22
L   ,,   ,,   Sense and Sensibility. Intro. by R. B. Johnson. 21
Balzac's (Honoré de) Atheist's Mass. Preface by George Saintsbury. 229
    ,,   ,,   Catherine de Médici. Introduction by George
       Saintsbury. 419
    ,,   ,,   Christ in Flanders. Introduction by George
       Saintsbury. 284
    ,,   ,,   Cousin Pons. Intro. by George Saintsbury. 463
    ,,   ,,   Eugénie Grandet. Intro. by George Saintsbury. 169
    ,,   ,,   Lost Illusions. Intro. by George Saintsbury. 656
    ,,   ,,   Old Goriot. Intro. by George Saintsbury. 170
    ,,   ,,   The Cat and Racket, and Other Stories. 349
    ,,   ,,   The Chouans. Intro. by George Saintsbury. 285
    ,,   ,,   The Country Doctor. Intro. George Saintsbury. 530
    ,,   ,,   The Country Parson. 686
    ,,   ,,   The Quest of the Absolute. Introduction by George
       Saintsbury. 286
    ,,   ,,   The Rise and Fall of César Birotteau. 596
    ,,   ,,   The Wild Ass's Skin. Intro. George Saintsbury. 26
    ,,   ,,   Ursule Mirouët. Intro. by George Saintsbury. 733
Barbusse's Under Fire. Translated by Fitzwater Wray. 798
L Bennett's (Arnold) The Old Wives' Tale. 919
L Blackmore's (R. D.) Lorna Doone. 304
L Borrow's Lavengro. Introduction by Thomas Seccombe. 119
    ,, Romany Rye. 120
      (See also TRAVEL)
Brontë's (Anne) The Tenant of Wildfell Hall and Agnes Grey. 685
L   ,, (Charlotte) Jane Eyre. Introduction by May Sinclair. 287
L   ,,   ,,   Shirley. Introduction by May Sinclair. 288
    ,,   ,,   The Professor. Introduction by May Sinclair. 417
    ,,   ,,   Villette. Introduction by May Sinclair. 351
L   ,, (Emily) Wuthering Heights. 243
Burney's (Fanny) Evelina. Introduction by R. B. Johnson. 352
Butler's (Samuel) Erewhon and Erewhon Revisited. Introduction by
       Desmond MacCarthy. 881
    ,,   ,,   The Way of All Flesh. Intro. by A. J. Hoppé. 895
Collins' (Wilkie) The Woman in White. 464
L Conrad's Lord Jim. Introduction by R. B. Cunninghame Grahame. 925
L Converse's (Florence) Long Will. 328
Dana's (Richard H.) Two Years before the Mast. 588
Daudet's Tartarin of Tarascon and Tartarin of the Alps. 423
Defoe's Fortunes and Misfortunes of Moll Flanders. Intro. by G. A. Aitken
    ,, Captain Singleton. Introduction by Edward Garnett. 74 [837
    ,, Journal of the Plague Year. Introduction by G. A. Aitken. 289
    ,, Memoirs of a Cavalier. Introduction by G. A. Aitken. 283
      (See also FOR YOUNG PEOPLE)
CHARLES DICKENS' WORKS. Each volume with an Intro. by G. K. Chesterton.
  American Notes. 290   L Christmas Stories. 414
L Barnaby Rudge. 76   L David Copperfield. 242
L Bleak House. 236   L Dombey and Son. 240
  Child's History of England. 291   Edwin Drood. 725
L Christmas Books. 239   L Great Expectations. 234

FICTION—*continued*

FICTION—continued

Galt's Annals of a Parish. Introduction by Baillie Macdonald. 427
Gaskell's (Mrs) Cousin Phillis, etc. Intro. by Thos. Seccombe. 615
L   „   Cranford. 83
      „   Mary Barton. Introduction by Thomas Seccombe. 598
      „   Sylvia's Lovers. Intro. by Mrs. Ellis Chadwick. 524
Ghost Stories. Edited by John Hampden. 952
      (See also POETRY AND DRAMA)
Gleig's (G. R.) The Subaltern. 708
Goethe's Wilhelm Meister. Carlyle's Translation. 2 vols. 599-600
      (See also ESSAYS and POETRY)
Gogol's (Nicol) Dead Souls. Translated by C. J. Hogarth. 726
      „   Taras Bulba and Other Tales. 740
L Goldsmith's Vicar of Wakefield. Introduction by J. M. D. 295
      (See also ESSAYS and POETRY)
Goncharov's Oblomov. Translated by Natalie Duddington. 878
Gorki's Through Russia. Translated by C. J. Hogarth. 741
Harte's (Bret) Luck of Roaring Camp and other Tales. 681
L Hawthorne's The House of the Seven Gables. Intro. Ernest Rhys. 176
      „   The Scarlet Letter. 122
      „   The Blithedale Romance. 592
      „   The Marble Faun. Intro. by Sir Leslie Stephen. 424
      „   Twice Told Tales. 531
      (See also FOR YOUNG PEOPLE)
L Hugo's (Victor) Les Misérables. Intro. by S. R. John. 2 vols. 363-4
L   „   „   Notre Dame. Introduction by A. C. Swinburne. 422
      „   „   Toilers of the Sea. Introduction by Ernest Rhys. 509
Italian Short Stories. Edited by D. Pettoello. 876
James's (G. P. R.) Richelieu. Introduction by Rudolf Dircks. 357
L James's (Henry), The Turn of the Screw and The Aspern Papers. 912
Jefferies's (Richard) After London and Amaryllis at the Fair. Intro. by
      David Garnett. 951
      (See also FOR YOUNG PEOPLE)
Kingsley's (Charles) Alton Locke. 462
L   „   „   Hereward the Wake. Intro. by Ernest Rhys. 296
      „   „   Hypatia. 230
L   „   „   Westward Ho! Introduction by A. G. Grieve. 20
      „   „   Yeast. 611
      (See also POETRY and FOR YOUNG PEOPLE)
      „   (Henry) Geoffrey Hamlyn. 416
      „   „   Ravenshoe. 28
L Lawrence's (D. H.) The White Peacock. 914
Lever's Harry Lorrequer. Introduction by Lewis Melville. 177
L Loti's (Pierre) Iceland Fisherman. Translated by W. P. Baines. 920
Lover's Handy Andy. Introduction by Ernest Rhys. 178
L Lytton's Harold. Introduction by Ernest Rhys. 15
L   „   Last Days of Pompeii. 80
      „   Last of the Barons. Introduction by R. G. Watkin. 18
      „   Rienzi. Introduction by E. H. Blakeney, M.A. 532
      (See also TRAVEL)
MacDonald's (George) Sir Gibbie. 678
      (See also ROMANCE)
Manning's Mary Powell and Deborah's Diary. Introduction by Katherine
      Tynan (Mrs Hinkson). 324
      „   Sir Thomas More. Introduction by Ernest Rhys. 19
Marryat's Jacob Faithful. 618
L   „   Mr Midshipman Easy. Introduction by R. B. Johnson. 82
      „   Percival Keene. Introduction by R. Brimley Johnson. 358
      „   Peter Simple. Introduction by R. Brimley Johnson. 232
      „   The King's Own. 580
      (See also FOR YOUNG PEOPLE)
L Maugham's (Somerset) Cakes and Ale. 932
Maupassant's Short Stories. Translated by Marjorie Laurie. Intro-
      duction by Gerald Gould. 907
Melville's (Herman) Moby Dick. Introduction by Ernest Rhys. 179

FICTION—*continued*

Melville's (Herman) Omoo. Introduction by Ernest Rhys. 297
L " " Typee. Introduction by Ernest Rhys. 180
L Meredith's (George) The Ordeal of Richard Feverel. 916
Mérimée's Carmen, with Prévost's Manon Lescaut. Intro. by Philip
Mickiewicz's (Adam) Pan Tadeusz. 842 [Henderson. 834
Modern Humour. Edited by Guy Pocock and M. M. Bozman. 957
Modern Short Stories. Edited by John Hadfield. 954
L Moore's (George) Esther Waters. 933
Mulock's John Halifax, Gentleman. Introduction by J. Shaylor. 123
Neale's (J. M.) The Fall of Constantinople. 655 [Bullen. 676
Paltock's (Robert) Peter Wilkins; or, The Flying Indians. Intro. by A. H.
Pater's Marius the Epicurean. Introduction by Osbert Burdett. 903
Peacock's Headlong Hall and Nightmare Abbey. 327
L Poe's Tales of Mystery and Imagination. Intro. by Padraic Colum. 336
(*See also* POETRY)
Prévost's Manon Lescaut, with Mérimée's Carmen. Introduction by
L Priestley's Angel Pavement. 938 [Philip Henderson. 834
Pushkin's (Alexander) The Captain's Daughter and Other Tales. Trans.
by Natalie Duddington. 898
Quiller-Couch's (Sir Arthur) Hetty Wesley. 864 [2 vols. 865–6
Radcliffe's (Ann) Mysteries of Udolpho. Intro. by R. Austin Freeman.
L Reade's (C.) The Cloister and the Hearth. Intro. by A. C. Swinburne. 29
" Peg Woffington and Christie Johnstone. 299
Richardson's (Samuel) Pamela. Intro. by G. Saintsbury. 2 vols. 683–4
" " Clarissa. Intro. by Prof.W. L. Phelps. 4 vols.882–5
Russian Authors, Short Stories from. Trans. by R. S. Townsend. 758
Sand's (George) The Devil's Pool and François the Waif. 534
Scheffel's Ekkehard: a Tale of the Tenth Century. 529
Scott's (Michael) Tom Cringle's Log. 710

SIR WALTER SCOTT'S WORKS:

Abbot, The. 124	L Ivanhoe. Intro. Ernest Rhys. 16
Anne of Geierstein. 125	L Kenilworth. 135
Antiquary, The. 126	Monastery, The. 136
Black Dwarf and Legend of	Old Mortality. 137
Montrose. 128	Peveril of the Peak. 138
Bride of Lammermoor. 129	Pirate, The. 139
Castle Dangerous and the Sur-	Quentin Durward. 140
geon's Daughter. 130	Redgauntlet. 141
Count Robert of Paris. 131	Rob Roy. 142
Fair Maid of Perth. 132	St. Ronan's Well. 143
Fortunes of Nigel. 71	Talisman, The. 144
Guy Mannering. 133	Waverley. 75
Heart of Midlothian, The. 134	Woodstock. Intro. by Edward
Highland Widow and Betrothed. 127	Garnett. 72

(*See also* BIOGRAPHY *and* POETRY)

Shchedrin's The Golovlyov Family. Translated by Natalie Duddington.
Introduction by Edward Garnett. 908
Shelley's (Mary Wollstonecraft) Frankenstein. 616
Sheppard's Charles Auchester. Intro. by Jessie M. Middleton. 505
Shorter Novels, Vol. I. Elizabethan and Jacobean. Edited by Philip
Henderson. 824
" " Vol. II. Jacobean and Restoration. Edited by Philip
Henderson. 841
" " Vol. III. Eighteenth Century (Beckford's Vathek,
Walpole's Castle of Otranto, and Dr. Johnson's
Rasselas). 856
Sienkiewicz (Henryk). Tales from. Edited by Monica M. Gardner. 871
Smollett's Peregrine Pickle. 2 vols. 838–9
" Roderick Random. Introduction by H. W. Hodges. 790
Stendhal's Scarlet and Black. Translated by C. K. Scott Moncrieff.
2 vols. 945–6
L Sterne's Tristram Shandy. Introduction by George Saintsbury. 617
(*See also* ESSAYS)

FICTION—*continued*

L Stevenson's Dr Jekyll and Mr Hyde. The Merry Men, and Other Tales.
L   ,,   The Master of Ballantrae and The Black Arrow. 764 [767
L   ,,   Treasure Island and Kidnapped. 763
       ,,   St. Ives. Introduction by Ernest Rhys. 904
          (*See also* ESSAYS, POETRY, *and* TRAVEL)
Surtees' Jorrocks' Jaunts and Jollities. 817
Swift's Gulliver's Travels. Unabridged Edition, with contemporary
   maps. Introduction by Harold Williams. 60
L Tales of Detection. Edited, with Introduction, by Dorothy L. Sayers. 928
Thackeray's Rose and the Ring and other stories. Intro. Walter Jerrold.
       ,,   Esmond. Introduction by Walter Jerrold. 73   [359
       ,,   Newcomes. Introduction by Walter Jerrold. 2 vols. 465–6
       ,,   Pendennis. Intro. by Walter Jerrold. 2 vols. 425–6
       ,,   Roundabout Papers. 687
L   ,,   Vanity Fair. Introduction by Hon. Whitelaw Reid. 298
       ,,   Virginians. Introduction by Walter Jerrold. 2 vols. 507–8
          (*See also* ESSAYS)
L Tolstoy's Anna Karenina. Trans. by Rochelle S. Townsend. 2 vols. 612–13
       ,,   Childhood, Boyhood, and Youth. Trans. by C. J. Hogarth. 591
       ,,   Master and Man, and other Parables and Tales. 469
       ,,   War and Peace. 3 vols. 525–7
Trollope's (Anthony) Barchester Towers. 30
       ,,   ,,   Dr. Thorne. 360
       ,,   ,,   Framley Parsonage. Intro. by Ernest Rhys. 181
       ,,   ,,   The Golden Lion of Granpère. Introduction by
               Sir Hugh Walpole. 761
       ,,   ,,   The Last Chronicles of Barset. 2 vols. 391–2
       ,,   ,,   Phineas Finn. Intro. by Sir Hugh Walpole. 2 vols.
       ,,   ,,   The Small House at Allington. 361   [832–3
       ,,   ,,   The Warden. Introduction by Ernest Rhys. 182
Turgenev's Fathers and Sons. Translated by C. J. Hogarth. 742
       ,,   Liza. Translated by W. R. S. Ralston. 677
       ,,   Virgin Soil. Translated by Rochelle S. Townsend. 528
L Voltaire's Candide and Other Tales. 936
L Walpole's (Hugh) Mr Perrin and Mr Traill. 918
L Well's (H. G.) The Time Machine and The Wheels of Chance. 915
Whyte-Melville's The Gladiators. Introduction by J. Mavrogordato. 523
Wood's (Mrs Henry) The Channings. 84
Woolf's (Virginia) To the Lighthouse. Intro. by D. M. Hoare. 949
Yonge's (Charlotte M.) The Dove in the Eagle's Nest. 329
       ,,   The Heir of Redclyffe. Intro. Mrs Meynell. 362
          (*See also* FOR YOUNG PEOPLE)
Zola's (Emile) Germinal. Translated by Havelock Ellis. 897

HISTORY

Anglo-Saxon Chronicle, The. Translated by James Ingram. 624
Bede's Ecclesiastical History, etc. Introduction by Vida D. Scudder. 479
Burnet's History of His Own Times. 85
L Carlyle's French Revolution. Introduction by H. Belloc. 2 vols. 31–2
       (*See also* BIOGRAPHY *and* ESSAYS)
Creasy's Decisive Battles of the World. Introduction by E. Rhys. 300
De Joinville (*See* Villehardouin)
Duruy's (Jean Victor) A History of France. 2 vols. 737–8
Finlay's Byzantine Empire. 33
       ,,   Greece under the Romans. 185
Froude's Henry VIII. Intro. by Llewellyn Williams, M.P. 3 vols. 372–4
       ,,   Edward VI. Intro. by Llewellyn Williams, M.P., B.C.L. 375
       ,,   Mary Tudor. Intro. by Llewellyn Williams, M.P., B.C.L. 477
       ,,   History of Queen Elizabeth's Reign. 5 vols. Completing
          Froude's 'History of England,' in 10 vols. 583–7
       (*See also* ESSAYS *and* BIOGRAPHY)
Gibbon's Decline and Fall of the Roman Empire. Edited, with Introduc-
   tion and Notes, by Oliphant Smeaton, M.A. 6 vols. 434–6, 474–6
       (*See also* BIOGRAPHY)

HISTORY—*continued*

Green's Short History of the English People. Edited and Revised by
L. Cecil Jane, with an Appendix by R. P. Farley, B.A. 2 vols. 727-8
Grote's History of Greece. Intro. by A. D. Lindsay. 12 vols. 186-97
Hallam's (Henry) Constitutional History of England. 3 vols. 621-3
Holinshed's Chronicle as used in Shakespeare's Plays. Introduction by
Professor Allardyce Nicoll. 800
Irving's (Washington) Conquest of Granada. 478
(*See also* ESSAYS *and* BIOGRAPHY)
Josephus' Wars of the Jews. Introduction by Dr Jacob Hart. 712
Lutzow's Bohemia: An Historical Sketch. Introduction by President
T. G. Masaryk. Revised edition. 432
Macaulay's History of England. 3 vols. 34-6
(*See also* ESSAYS *and* ORATORY)
Maine's (Sir Henry) Ancient Law. 734
Merivale's History of Rome. (An Introductory vol. to Gibbon.) 433
Mignet's (F. A. M.) The French Revolution. 713
Milman's History of the Jews. 2 vols. 377-8
Mommsen's History of Rome. Translated by W. P. Dickson, LL.D.
With a review of the work by E. A. Freeman. 4 vols. 542-5
Motley's Dutch Republic. 3 vols. 86-8
Parkman's Conspiracy of Pontiac. 2 vols. 302-3
Paston Letters, The. Based on edition of Knight. Introduction by
Mrs Archer-Hind, M.A. 2 vols. 752-3
Pilgrim Fathers, The. Introduction by John Masefield. 480
L Pinnow's History of Germany. Translated by M. R. Brailsford. 929
Political Liberty, The Growth of. A Source-Book of English History.
Arranged by Ernest Rhys. 745 [M.A. 2 vols. 397-8
Prescott's Conquest of Mexico. With Introduction by Thomas Seccombe.
Conquest of Peru. Intro. by Thomas Seccombe, M.A. 301
Sismondi's Italian Republics. 250
Stanley's Lectures on the Eastern Church. Intro. by A. J. Grieve. 251
Tacitus. Vol. I. Annals. Introduction by E. H. Blakeney. 273
" Vol. II. Agricola and Germania. Intro. E. H. Blakeney. 274
Thierry's Norman Conquest. Intro. by J. A. Price, B.A. 2 vols. 198-9
Villehardouin and De Joinville's Chronicles of the Crusades. Translated,
with Introduction, by Sir F. Marzials, C.B. 333
Voltaire's Age of Louis XIV. Translated by Martyn P. Pollack. 780

ORATORY

Anthology of British Historical Speeches and Orations. Compiled by
Ernest Rhys. 714
Bright's (John) Speeches. Selected with Intro. by Joseph Sturge. 252
Burke's American Speeches and Letters. 340. (*See also* ESSAYS)
Demosthenes: Select Orations. 546
Fox (Charles James): Speeches (French Revolutionary War Period).
Edited with Introduction by Irene Cooper Willis, M.A. 759
Lincoln's Speeches, etc. Intro. by the Rt Hon. James Bryce. 206
(*See also* BIOGRAPHY)
Macaulay's Speeches on Politics and Literature. 399
(*See also* ESSAYS *and* HISTORY)
Pitt's Orations on the War with France. 145

PHILOSOPHY AND THEOLOGY

L A Kempis' Imitation of Christ. 484
Ancient Hebrew Literature. Being the Old Testament and Apocrypha.
Arranged by the Rev. R. B. Taylor. 4 vols. 253-6
Aristotle, The Nicomachean Ethics of. Translated by D. P. Chase.
Introduction by Professor J. A. Smith. 547
(*See also* CLASSICAL)
Bacon's The Advancement of Learning. 719 (*See also* ESSAYS)
Berkeley's (Bishop) Principles of Human Knowledge, New Theory of
Vision. With Introduction by A. D. Lindsay. 483

PHILOSOPHY AND THEOLOGY—*continued*

Boehme's (Jacob) The Signature of All Things, with Other Writings. Introduction by Clifford Bax. 569

Browne's Religio Medici, etc. Intro. by Professor C. H. Herford. 92

Bunyan's Grace Abounding and Mr Badman. Introduction by G. B. Harrison. 815   *(See also* ROMANCE)

Burton's (Robert) Anatomy of Melancholy. Introduction by Holbrook Jackson. 3 vols. 886–8

Butler's Analogy of Religion. Introduction by Rev. Ronald Bayne. 90

Descartes' (René) A Discourse on Method. Translated by Professor John Veitch. Introduction by A. D. Lindsay. 570

L Ellis' (Havelock) Selected Essays. Introduction by J. S. Collis. 930

L Gore's (Charles) The Philosophy of the Good Life. 924

Hindu Scriptures. Edited by Dr Nicol Macnicol. Introduction by Rabindranath Tagore. 944

Hobbes' Leviathan. Edited, with Intro. by A. D. Lindsay, M.A. 691

Hooker's Ecclesiastical Polity. Intro. by Rev. H. Bayne. 2 vols. 201–2

Hume's Treatise of Human Nature, and other Philosophical Works. Introduction by A. D. Lindsay, M.A. 2 vols. 548–9

James (William): Selected Papers on Philosophy. 739

Kant's Critique of Pure Reason. Translated by J. M. D. Meiklejohn. Introduction by A. D. Lindsay, M.A. 909

Keble's The Christian Year. Introduction by J. C. Shairp. 690

King Edward VI. First and Second Prayer Books. Introduction by the Right Rev. Bishop of Gloucester. 448

L Koran, The. Rodwell's Translation. 380

Latimer's Sermons. Introduction by Canon Beeching. 40

Law's Serious Call to a Devout and Holy Life. 91

Leibniz's Philosophical Writings. Selected and trans. by Mary Morris. Introduction by C. R. Morris, M.A. 905

Locke's Two Treatises of Civil Government. Introduction by Professor William S. Carpenter. 751

Malthus on the Principles of Population. 2 vols. 692–3

Mill's (John Stuart) Utilitarianism, Liberty, Representative Government. With Introduction by A. D. Lindsay, M.A. 482

  ,,   Subjection of Women. *(See* Wollstonecraft, Mary, *under* SCIENCE)

More's Utopia. Introduction by Judge O'Hagan. 461

New Testament. Arranged in the order in which the books came to the Christians of the First Century. 93

Newman's Apologia pro Vita Sua. Intro. by Dr Charles Sarolea. 636   *(See also* ESSAYS)

Nietzsche's Thus Spake Zarathustra. Trans. by A. Tille and M. M. Bozman. 892

Paine's Rights of Man. Introduction by G. J. Holyoake. 718   [892

Pascal's Pensées. Translated by W. F. Trotter. Introduction by T. S. Eliot. 874   [C.I.E. 403

Ramayana and the Mahabharata, The. Translated by Romesh Dutt. 403

Renan's Life of Jesus. Introduction by Right Rev. Chas. Gore, D.D. 805

Robertson's (F. W.) Sermons on Christian Doctrine, and Bible Subjects. Each Volume with Introduction by Canon Burnett. 3 vols. 37–9 (*Note: No.* 37 *is out of print.*)

Robinson's (Wade) The Philosophy of Atonement and Other Sermons. Introduction by Rev. F. B. Meyer. 637

Rousseau's (J. J.) The Social Contract, etc. 660. *(See also* ESSAYS)

St Augustine's Confessions. Dr Pusey's Translation. 200

L St Francis: The Little Flowers, and The Life of St. Francis. 485

Seeley's Ecce Homo. Introduction by Sir Oliver Lodge. 305

Selection from St Thomas Aquinas. Edited by The Rev. Father M. C. D'Arcy. 953

Spinoza's Ethics, etc. Translated by Andrew J. Boyle. With Introduction by Professor Santayana. 481

Swedenborg's (Emmanuel) Heaven and Hell. 379

    ,,   ,,   The Divine Love and Wisdom. 635

    ,,   ,,   The Divine Providence. 658

L   ,,   ,,   The True Christian Religion. 893

POETRY AND DRAMA

POETRY AND DRAMA—*continued*

REFERENCE

ROMANCE

Aucassin and Nicolette, with other Medieval Romances. 497

Boccaccio's Decameron. (Unabridged.) Translated by J. M. Rigg. Introduction by Edward Hutton. 2 vols. 845–6

L Bunyan's Pilgrim's Progress. Introduction by Rev. H. E. Lewis. 204

Burnt Njal, The Story of. Translated by Sir George Dasent. 558

Cervantes' Don Quixote. Motteux's Translation. Lockhart's Introduction. 2 vols. 385–6

Chrétien de Troyes: Eric and Enid. Translated, with Introduction and Notes, by William Wistar Comfort. 698

French Medieval Romances. Translated by Eugene Mason. 557

Geoffrey of Monmouth's Histories of the Kings of Britain. 577

Grettir Saga, The. Newly Translated by G. Ainslie Hight. 699

Gudrun. Done into English by Margaret Armour. 880

Guest's (Lady) Mabinogion. Introduction by Rev. R. Williams. 97

Heimskringla: The Olaf Sagas. Translated by Samuel Laing. Introduction and Notes by John Beveridge. 717

      ,,   Sagas of the Norse Kings. Translated by Samuel Laing. Introduction and Notes by John Beveridge. 847

Holy Graal, The High History of the, 445

Kalevala. Introduction by W. F. Kirby, F.L.S., F.E.S. 2 vols. 259–60

Le Sage's The Adventures of Gil Blas. Intro. by Anatole Le Bras. 2 vols.

MacDonald's (George) Phantastes: A Faerie Romance. 732   [437–8 (*See also* FICTION)

Malory's Le Morte d'Arthur. Intro. by Professor Rhys. 2 vols. 45–6

L Morris (William): Early Romances. Introduction by Alfred Noyes. 261

   ,,   ,,   The Life and Death of Jason. 575

Morte d'Arthur Romances, Two. Introduction by Lucy A. Paton. 634

Nibelungs, The Fall of the. Translated by Margaret Armour. 312

Rabelais' The Heroic Deeds of Gargantua and Pantagruel. Introduction by D. B. Wyndham Lewis. 2 vols. 826–7

Wace's Arthurian Romance. Translated by Eugene Mason. Layamon's Brut. Introduction by Lucy A. Paton. 578

SCIENCE

Boyle's The Sceptical Chymist. 559

Darwin's The Origin of Species. Introduction by Sir Arthur Keith. 811 (*See also* TRAVEL)   ·   [E. F. Bozman. 922

L Eddington's (Sir Arthur) The Nature of the Physical World. Intro. by

Euclid: the Elements of. Todhunter's Edition. Introduction by Sir Thomas Heath, K.C.B. 891

Faraday's (Michael) Experimental Researches in Electricity. 576

Galton's Inquiries into Human Faculty. Revised by Author. 263

George's (Henry) Progress and Poverty. 560

Hahnemann's (Samuel) The Organon of the Rational Art of Healing. Introduction by C. E. Wheeler. 663

Harvey's Circulation of the Blood. Introduction by Ernest Parkyn. 262

Howard's State of the Prisons. Introduction by Kenneth Ruck. 835

Huxley's Essays. Introduction by Sir Oliver Lodge. 47

     ,,   Select Lectures and Lay Sermons. Intro. Sir Oliver Lodge. 498

Lyell's Antiquity of Man. With an introduction by R. H. Rastall. 700

Marx's (Karl) Capital. Translated by Eden and Cedar Paul. Introduction by G. D. H. Cole. 2 vols. 848–9

Miller's Old Red Sandstone. 103

Owen's (Robert) A New View of Society, etc. Intro. by G. D. H. Cole. 799

L Pearson's (Karl) The Grammar of Science. 939

Ricardo's Principles of Political Economy and Taxation. 590

Smith's (Adam) The Wealth of Nations. 2 vols. 412–13

Tyndall's Glaciers of the Alps and Mountaineering in 1861. 98

White's Selborne. Introduction by Principal Windle. 48

Wollstonecraft (Mary), The Rights of Woman, with John Stuart Mill's The Subjection of Women. 825

TRAVEL AND TOPOGRAPHY

FOR YOUNG PEOPLE

FOR YOUNG PEOPLE—*continued*

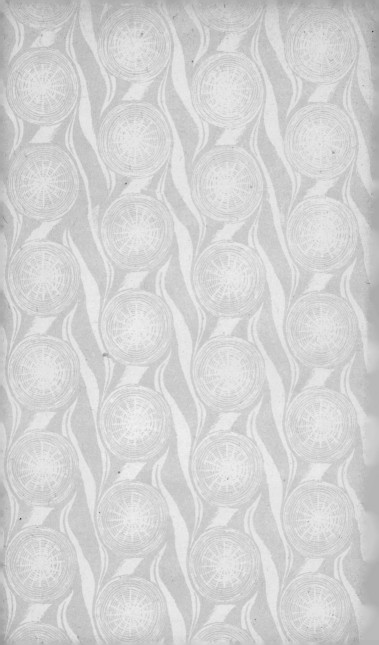